A Concise Guide to Technical Communication

SECOND CANADIAN EDITION

A Concise Guide to Technical Communication

Laura J. Gurak
University of Minnesota

John M. Lannon
University of Massachusetts–Dartmouth

Jana Seijts
University of Western Ontario

SECOND CANADIAN EDITION

PEARSON

Toronto

Vice-President, Editorial Director: Gary Bennett
Editor-in-Chief: Michelle Sartor
Acquisitions Editor: David S. Le Gallais
Marketing Manager: Jennifer Sutton
Developmental Editor: Karen Townsend
Project Manager: Ashley Patterson
Manufacturing Manager: Susan Johnson
Production Editor: Lila Campbell
Copy editor: Ruth Bradley-St-Cyr
Proofreaders: Julia Hubble, Lila Campbell
Compositor: Christine Velakis
Permissions Editor: Marnie Lamb
Art Director: Julia Hall
Cover and Interior Designer: Anthony Leung
Cover Image: ShutterStock Images

10 9 8 7 6 5 4 3 2 1 [EB]

Library and Archives Canada Cataloguing in Publication

Gurak, Laura J.
    A concise guide to technical communication / Laura J. Gurak, John M. Lannon, Jana Seijts. —2nd Canadian ed.

Includes bibliographical references and index.
ISBN 978-0-205-07512-6

    1. Communication of technical information—Textbooks.   2. Technical writing—Textbooks.   I. Lannon, John M   II. Seijts, Jana   III. Title.

T10.5.G87 2012   601'.4   C2011-906902-4

ISBN 978-0-205-07512-6

BRIEF CONTENTS

Contents   vii

Preface   xv

PART ONE   **Technical Communication Techniques
and Considerations   1**

CHAPTER 1   An Introduction to Technical Communication   3

CHAPTER 2   A World of People and Purposes   21

CHAPTER 3   Designing Usable Information   39

CHAPTER 4   Writing and Editing for Usability   49

CHAPTER 5   Conducting Research for Technical Communication   79

CHAPTER 6   Technical Communication in a Digital World   102

CHAPTER 7   Page Layout and Document Design   125

CHAPTER 8   Graphics and Visual Information   150

CHAPTER 9   Ethical Issues in Technical Communication   179

CHAPTER 10   Copyright and Privacy   196

PART TWO   **Technical Communication Situations
and Applications   215**

CHAPTER 11   Everyday Written Communication Situations   217

CHAPTER 12   Presentation Skills   253

CHAPTER 13   Product-Oriented Communication Situations   273

CHAPTER 14   Complex Communication Situations   304

APPENDIX A   Grammar   343

APPENDIX B   Documentation   359

References   395

Index   403

CONTENTS

Preface xv

**Part One
Technical Communication
Techniques and
Considerations** 1

CHAPTER 1
An Introduction to Technical
Communication 3

Communicating about Technology 4
Main Characteristics of Technical
    Communication 5
    Accessibility 5
    Usability 5
    Relevance 6
Types of Technical Communication 7
Technical Communication in the Workplace 10
    *The Importance of Employability
        Skills 11*
Teamwork, Virtual Teams, and Project
    Management 13
    *Teamwork: How to Manage a Collaborative
        Project 13*
    *Tools: How to Use Digital Technology in a
        Team 13*
Societal Dimensions of Technical
    Communication 16
Ethical Dimensions of Technical
    Communication 17

CHAPTER 2
A World of People and
Purposes 21

People, Purposes, and Communities 22
    Identify Discourse Communities 22
    *Provide Information that Your Audience
        Needs 24*
    *Define Your Primary and Secondary
        Purposes 24*
Analyzing Your Audience 26
Analyzing the Communication Purpose 29
Analyzing the Communication Context 30
    Conducting an Audience–Purpose
        Interview 30
More Tools for Understanding Audience 32
Using Information from Your Analysis 32
Recognizing that Audiences Are Not
    Passive 33
Typical Audiences and Purposes for Technical
    Communication 34

CHAPTER 3
Designing Usable Information 39

Usability and Technical Information 40
Usability During the Planning Stages 40
    *Perform an Audience and Purpose
        Analysis 40*
    Perform a Task Analysis 40
    Develop an Information Plan 42
    Research Your Topic 42

Usability During the Writing and Design
  Process   42
  Test Early Versions of Your Communication
    Product   42
  Revise Your Plan and Your Product   44
  Create Documentation That Is Context-
    Sensitive   45
Usability After the Information Is Released   45
  Provide Mechanisms for User
    Feedback   46
  Plan for the Next Version or Release   46

CHAPTER 4
Writing and Editing for
Usability   49

Writing Clearly and Correctly   50
Creating an Outline   51
Writing Clear Paragraphs   52
  Structure of a Paragraph   53
  A Closer Look at Paragraph Structure   53
  Paragraph Types   54
Creating Paragraph Coherence through the Use
  of Transition Devices   57
Building Clear Sentences   59
  Parallel Structure in Sentences   60
  Sentence Patterns   60
Editing for Grammar and Style   61
Document Layout and Usability   72
  Use White Space and Effective Page
    Design   72
  Create an Overview   72
  Chunk Information   74
  Create Headings   74
  Use the Margins for Commentary   75
Proofreading Your Final Draft   75

CHAPTER 5
Conducting Research for Technical
Communication   79

Thinking Critically About Research   80
Primary Research   80

  Informative Interviews   80
  Surveys and Questionnaires   81
  Public Records and Organizational
    Publications   83
  Personal Observation and Experiments   83
Internet and Digital Research   84
  Online News Sites and Magazines   84
  Government Research Sites and Other
    Government Documents   85
  Community Discussion Groups and
    Bulletin Boards   85
  Blogs and Wikis   85
  Email Lists   86
  Online Videos and Streaming   87
  Internet-Searchable Library
    Databases   87
  Other Websites   87
  Evaluating Sources from the Web   87
  Managing Your Information   89
C.A.R.S. Method for Evaluating Online
  Sources   90
  Credibility   91
  Accuracy   91
  Reasonableness   91
  Support   91
Other Electronic Research Tools   91
  Google Scholar   91
  Compact Discs (CD-ROMs)   92
  Online Retrieval Services   92
  Library Catalogues   93
Hard Copy Research   93
  Bibliographies   93
  Encyclopedias   93
  Dictionaries   94
  Handbooks   94
  Almanacs   94
  Directories   94
  Guides to Literature   94
  Indexes   94
  Abstracts   95
  Access Tools for Government
    Publications   96

CHAPTER 6
Technical Communication in a Digital World   102

Communicating in Digital Space   103
Designing Information   103
   Writing Issues   103
   Design Issues   105
   Technical Issues   108
Online Documentation and Interface
   Design   109
   Online Documentation   110
   Interface Design   110
Corresponding over the Wires: Email,
   Smartphones, Blogs, and Instant
   Messaging   111
   Email   111
   Smartphones 115
   Tablet Personal Computers
      (Tablet PC)   115
   Workplace Blogs   116
   Instant Messaging   116
Social Media   117
   Facebook   117
   Twitter   117
   Digg   118
   Tumblr   118
   Foursquare   118
   A Caution When Using Social Networking
      Sites   119
Telecommuting and Virtual Teams   120
Presentation Software   120

CHAPTER 7
Page Layout and Document Design   125

Creating Visually Effective Documents   126
   How Page Design Transforms a
      Document   126
   How Readers View a Page   126

   Electronic Pages   128
Formatting the Page Effectively   128
   Using a Grid Structure   130
   Creating Areas of Emphasis Using White
      Space   130
   Using Lists   132
   Using Headings   133
Using Typography Effectively   136
   Selecting Fonts   136
   Combining Fonts   137
   Choosing Fonts for Readability   138
Providing Effective Search Options   139
   Table of Contents and Index   139
   Running Heads and Feet   140
   Electronic Searching   140
Designing Electronic Documents   142
   Webpages   142
   Online Help   143
   PDF Files   144
   CDs and Other Media   144
Creating and Using Style Sheets and Tools   145
   Organizational Style Guides and Style
      Sheets   146
   Style Tools Using Word-Processing and
      Layout Software   146
   Style Tools Using CSS and HTML for
      Webpages   146

CHAPTER 8
Graphics and Visual Information   150

The Power of the Picture   151
When to Use Visuals   152
Different Visuals for Different Audiences   152
Text into Tables   153
Numbers into Images   155
   Graphs   155
   Charts   160
Illustrations   165
Diagrams   165
   Exploded Diagrams   166

Cutaway Diagrams 167
Symbols and Icons 167
Wordless Instruction 168
Photographs 168
Maps 168
Visualization and Medical Imaging 171
Software and Web-Based Images 171
Using Colour 172
Avoiding Visual Noise 174
Visuals and Ethics 174
Cultural Considerations 175

CHAPTER 9
Ethical Issues in Technical
Communication 179

Ethics, Technology, and Communication 180
Examples of Ethical Issues in Technical
   Communication 180
   The Walkerton Tragedy 180
   The Tainted Blood Scandal 181
Types of Ethical Choices 182
Legal versus Ethical 183
   Copyright 184
   Plagiarism 184
   Privacy 185
Additional Ways in Which Actions Can Be
   Unethical 185
   Yielding to Social Pressure 185
   Mistaking Groupthink for Teamwork 186
   *Suppressing Knowledge the Public
      Needs* 187
   *Exaggerating Claims About
      Technology* 187
   Exploiting Cultural Differences 187
Types of Technical Communication Affected by
   Ethical Issues 188
   Graphics 188
   Webpages and the Internet 188
   Memos and Emails 189
   Instructions 190

Reports 190
Proposals 190
Oral Presentations 190
Responding to Ethical Situations 191

CHAPTER 10
Copyright and Privacy 196

Why Technical Communicators Need to
   Understand Copyright and Privacy 197
Copyright—An Overview 197
   *How Copyright Infringement Differs from
      Plagiarism* 198
   *How Copyright Law Differs from Patent or
      Trademark Law* 198
   *How Individuals and Companies Establish
      Copyright* 199
   *What Rights a Copyright Holder Can
      Claim* 199
   *When You Can and Cannot Use
      Copyrighted Material* 199
   *When Your Company Owns the
      Material* 202
Documenting Your Sources 203
Electronic Technologies and Copyright 203
   Photocopiers and Scanners 203
   *The Web as a Marketplace of Ideas and
      Information* 204
   Using Material from the Internet 204
   Locating Copyright-Free Art 205
   Email and Electronic Messages 205
   CD-ROMs and Multimedia 205
Privacy—An Overview 206
Computer Technologies, Privacy, and Technical
   Communication 206
   Privacy in Cyberspace 208
   Shopping Online 208
   Global Privacy Issues 210
   Privacy and Documentation 212
   Privacy and Videotapes 212

**Part Two
Technical Communication
Situations
and Applications   215**

Chapter 11
Everyday Written Communication
Situations   217

Email   218
   Audience and Purpose Analysis   218
   Types of Email   218
   Typical Components of Email   219
   *Style and Netiquette of Workplace
      Email   220*
   Usability Considerations   220
Memos   224
   Audience and Purpose Analysis   224
   Types of Memos   225
   Typical Components of a Memo   225
   Usability Considerations   227
Letters   227
   Audience and Purpose Analysis   228
   Types of Letters   229
   Typical Components of a Letter   231
   Specialized Components of a Letter   233
   Usability Considerations   235
Résumés   238
   Audience and Purpose Analysis   238
   Typical Components of a Résumé   241
   Organization of a Résumé   241
   Online Résumé Services   241
   New Types of Résumés   242
Short Reports   243
   Audience and Purpose Analysis   243
   Types of Short Reports   243
   Typical Components of Short Reports   246
   Usability Considerations   246

CHAPTER 12
Presentation Skills   253

Effective Presentations   254
Analyzing Audience and Purpose   254
Types of Presentations   255
   Informative Presentations   255
   Training Sessions   255
   Persuasive Presentations   255
   Action Plans   255
   Sales Presentations   255
Typical Components of Presentations   256
   Introduction   256
   Body   256
   Conclusion   257
   Time Constraints   257
   Sample Outline for a Presentation   257
Skills for Effective Presentations   258
   Plan Your Presentation   258
   Work in a Group   258
   Follow a Presentation Sequence   258
   Learn to Manage Your Nerves   259
   Keep the Audience's Attention   259
   *Be Prepared to Deal with Difficult
      Questions   260*
   *Work on Your Presentation Look and
      Style   260*
Using Visuals   261
   Computer Projection Software   261
   *PowerPoint, Keynote, and Similar
      Presentation Software   261*
   The Presentation Software Debate   262
   Other Visual Aids   263
   Presenting the Visuals   264
Meetings   264
   Prepare for the Meeting   265
   Organize the Meeting   265
   Follow a Plan   265
   On Meeting Day   266
Persuasive Presentations   266

Ethics   266

Emotion   266

Reason   267

Non-Verbal Communication   268

Facial Expression   268

Tone of Voice   268

Posture   268

Usability Considerations   269

CHAPTER 13
Product-Oriented Communication
Situations   273

Specifications   274

Audience and Purpose Analysis   274

Types of Specifications   277

Typical Components of Specifications   277

Usability Considerations   279

Brief Instructions   280

Audience and Purpose Analysis   280

Types of Brief Instructions   282

Typical Components of Instructions   282

Usability Considerations   283

Procedures   284

Audience and Purpose Analysis   285

Types of Procedures   285

Typical Components of Procedures   286

Usability Considerations   289

Documentation and Manuals   290

Audience and Purpose Analysis   290

Types of Manuals   291

Typical Components of Manuals   291

Usability Considerations   293

Technical Marketing Material   296

Audience and Purpose Analysis   296

*Types of Technical Marketing
Material   297*

*Typical Components of Technical
Marketing Material   298*

Usability Considerations   298

CHAPTER 14
Complex Communication
Situations   304

Definitions and Descriptions   305

Audience and Purpose Analysis   305

Types of Definitions and Descriptions   305

*Typical Components of Expanded
Definitions and Descriptions   312*

Usability Considerations   313

Long Reports   316

Audience and Purpose Analysis   317

Types of Long Reports   317

A General Model for Long Reports   320

*Front Matter and End Matter in Long
Reports   321*

Usability Considerations   329

Proposals   331

Audience and Purpose Analysis   331

Types of Proposals   331

Typical Components of Proposals   332

Usability Considerations   338

APPENDIX A
Grammar   343

Punctuation   343

Lists   345

Embedded Lists   345

Vertical Lists   345

Sentence Fragments and Run-On
Sentences   347

Avoiding Sentence Fragments   347

Avoiding Run-On Sentences   349

Usage (Commonly Misused Words)   350

Subject–Verb and Pronoun–Antecedent
Agreement   351

Subject–Verb Agreement   351

Pronoun–Antecedent Agreement   352

Faulty Modification   352

Parallel Structure   353
Transitions Within and Between
    Paragraphs   354
Mechanics   355
    Abbreviations   356
    Hyphenation   356
    Capitalization   357
    Use of Numbers   357
    Spelling   358

APPENDIX B
Documentation   359

Quoting the Words of Others   359
    Paraphrasing the Words of Others   359
    What You Should Document   359
Documenting Sources   360

Using MLA Documentation Style   361
    MLA Parenthetical References   361
    MLA Works Cited Entries   363
    MLA Works Cited Page   373
Using APA Documentation Style   373
    APA Parenthetical References   374
    APA References Entries   375
    APA References List   384
Using CSE and Other Numbered Documentation
    Styles   384
    CSE Numbered Citations   385
    References   385
    CSE References Entries   385
IEEE Style   387

References   395
Index   403

Preface

Even the most casual observer can see the powerful, compelling relationships between technology and communication. The growing number and complexity of new technologies, from personal computers to medical devices to internet applications, require accurate information on how to operate and maintain these devices. The use of technologies—HTML coding, web applications, online help screens—to communicate information across global boundaries means that every professional needs to understand technology.

To meet this need, institutions offer technical communication degrees or certificates through a combination of face-to-face, interactive television, and web-based classes. Some students major or minor in technical communication, while others take technical writing and communication courses to fulfill humanities requirements and enhance their skills as engineers, scientists, or other specialists. In addition, writing-intensive programs, especially in engineering or science institutions, often focus on technical writing. Even high schools are now adding technical writing to their list of elective classes.

Whatever its context, technical communication is rarely a value-neutral exercise in "information transfer." It is a rhetorical, social transaction comprising interpersonal, cultural, ethical, legal, and technological components. In today's global environment, a one-size-fits-all approach simply does not work. Effective technical communication must be clear, accurate, and organized, and must be tailored for specific audiences and purposes.

With those requirements in mind, we have created the second Canadian edition of *A Concise Guide to Technical Communication*. This book draws on the strengths of John M. Lannon's best-selling *Technical Communication* (now in its twelfth edition)—its accessible style, clear examples, and time-tested approaches—but in a more streamlined version focusing on critical topics such as copyright, document design, usability, information technologies (including the internet), and online communications. The book retains key qualities of the larger text but in a smaller, more concise, technology-centred volume. Students and faculty alike will appreciate its trim size, content, and direct access to information.

The Audience for This Book

Most technical communication texts have dual audiences. One audience is instructors, who use textbooks to plan a syllabus, design assignments, and create lectures and discussions. This *Concise Guide* is suitable for a range of instructors, from experienced to novice. All instructors will find this text easy to digest, streamlined in its use of features, and relevant to current technology topics. Novice instructors will find useful examples, exercises, and checklists. In addition, MyCanadianTechCommLab offers online quizzes, further exercises, and other teaching resources. Experienced instructors will find that the concise format allows for enhancements within their classrooms without restricting them to one perspective or set of examples.

The student audience for this text is also varied. Students in introductory technical communication will find that the text and MyCanadianTechCommLab contain fundamental concepts, situational strategies, and other supporting features. Advanced students will be able to move quickly into issues of audience, purpose, and design. All students will appreciate the emphasis on the internet, visual communication, and usability. Examples throughout this text reflect a variety of majors. Students from engineering, science, health care, and other disciplines will find this book useful and relevant, whether in a traditional technical writing class or in a writing-intensive section of their major.

How This Book Is Organized

This book is organized into two parts. Part One, Technical Communication Techniques and Considerations, covers issues of central importance to today's technical communicator: audience, purpose, usability, research, the internet, ethics, copyright, document design, and graphics. Part Two, Technical Communication Situations and Applications, incorporates the considerations from Part One in treating various types of workplace communication (email, memos, reports, specifications, oral reports, websites, and the like).

Hallmarks of the Canadian Edition

Layered approach. Instructors can use this *Concise Guide* alone or in combination with their own materials. Instructors may wish to teach the chapters in order, which allows for a logical teaching sequence, especially for an introductory course with students from mixed disciplines. Yet the chapters, and the modules within each chapter, can be taught in virtually any sequence.

Range of skill levels. Students in technical communication courses often span a wide range of writing skills. Although this book contains a solid section on grammar and style (Chapter 4), certain features of MyCanadianTechCommLab will be particularly useful for students who need help in this area.

Compact format. For instructors and students alike, a shorter, more compact text is extremely appealing. Instructors will appreciate the small size, because it allows them to use supplementary material without overloading the student. Students will value a concise text, because material is easy to look up, access, and carry in a backpack.

In addition to its compact size, the *Concise Guide* offers a unique combination of features:

* real examples taken from Canadian industry, government, and high technology, reproduced to look like the originals
* chapter vignettes detailing the careers of Canadian technical communicators
* sections on Canadian copyright, privacy, ethics, and social issues
* sections on usability, document design, and page layout from a human factors perspective
* a thorough chapter on visual communication
* a thorough chapter on presentation skills
* a cutting-edge chapter on technical communication in the digital world
* end-of-chapter items, including Checklists and Exercises, some with a Focus on Writing or a Focus on Research
* end-of-chapter exercises that encourage collaborative work, The Collaboration Window, and a global perspective, The Global Window.

New to the Second Canadian Edition

In developing the second Canadian edition of *A Concise Guide to Technical Communication*, we have included Canadian examples throughout the text. Special emphasis has been placed on providing readers with the most up-to-date information on the Canadian laws that are most relevant to technical communicators and providing web addresses for readers to seek out more detailed information on specific legislation. Each chapter in this edition emphasizes usability, with revised examples, discussions, and guidelines.

A sampling of new material:

* A new sample of a long report is featured in Chapter 14. The new report contains the cover, introduction, body text, headings, and conclusion.
* Chapter 5 provides coverage of internet research methods, including Wikipedia and Google Scholar. The chapter includes effective research strategies, and teaches students how to recognize reliable sources. The pitfalls of internet research are also presented.

- Chapter 6 is updated to include coverage of social media (including Facebook and Twitter) and the uses of social media in business.
- Chapter 6 contains coverage of new technologies. For this edition, the information is expanded to include information about smartphones, tablet PCs, and video conferencing, and their uses in business.
- Chapter 11 is updated to focus on electronic communication, such as memos via email, and includes a new discussion on email etiquette.
- Appendix B: Documentation is updated to reflect the changes made to MLA in 2009, as well as the new APA standards.

Supplements

The following ancillary materials are available to accompany *A Concise Guide to Technical Communication*, Second Canadian Edition:

- An *Instructor's Manual* and *PowerPoint Presentation* are available for download from a password-protected section of Pearson Canada's online catalogue (vig.pearsoned.ca). Navigate to your book's catalogue page to view a list of the supplements that are available. See your local sales representative for details and access.
- *MyCanadianTechCommLab* (www.mycanadiantechcommlab.ca). This state-of-the-art, interactive, and instructive solution for technical communication is designed to be used as a supplement to a traditional lecture course or to completely administer an online course. Throughout the text, icons highlight material where related activities or samples are available on MyCanadianTechCommLab:

  - *Explore* dozens of **writing samples**, from letters to emails to reports, that model effective communication.
  - *Practise* correcting ineffective communication using interactive **document makeovers.** Feedback guides you to understand problems and find solutions.
  - *Watch* **videos** of professionals from various fields talking about how their writing and speaking are vital components of their success in business and industry.

  MyCanadianTechCommLab also includes a Pearson eText that gives students access to the text whenever and wherever they have access to the internet. eText pages look exactly like the printed text, offering powerful new functionality for students and instructors. Users can create notes, highlight text in different colours, create bookmarks, zoom, click hyperlinked words and phrases to view definitions, and view in single-page or two-page view. Pearson eText allows for quick navigation to key parts of the eText using a table of contents and provides a full-text search. The eText may also offer links to associated media files, enabling users to access videos, animations, or other activities as they read. A student access card for MyCanadianTechCommLab is packaged with every new copy of the text. Access codes can also be purchased through campus bookstores or through the website.

- *CourseSmart* goes beyond traditional expectations—providing instant, online access to the textbooks and course materials you need at a lower cost for students. And even as students save money, you can save time and hassle with a digital eTextbook that allows you to search for the most relevant content at the very moment you need it. Whether it's evaluating textbooks or creating lecture notes to help students with difficult concepts, CourseSmart can make life a little easier. See how when you visit www.coursesmart.com/instructors.
- Pearson's *Technology Specialists* work with faculty and campus course designers to ensure that Pearson technology products, assessment tools, and online course materials are tailored to meet your specific needs. This highly qualified team is dedicated to helping schools take full advantage of a wide range of educational resources, by assisting in the integration of a variety of instructional materials and media formats. Your local Pearson Canada sales representative can provide you with more details on this service program.

Acknowledgments

Special words of thanks to David Le Gallais, Carolin Sweig, Karen Townsend, Lila Campbell, Ashley Patterson, and Ruth Bradley St-Cyr of Pearson Canada for their work in overseeing the publication of this second Canadian edition of *A Concise Guide to Technical Communication*. Thanks also go to my colleagues at the Richard Ivey School of Business at the University of Western Ontario who supported and encouraged me throughout the writing of this book. Shannon Mighton, my amazing research assistant, I am especially indebted to you for all your long hours and hard work searching for source material, and for your computer expertise!

I would also like to acknowledge the many reviewers of this textbook for their detailed and helpful comments: Dave Banninga, Niagara College; Heather Barfoot, Niagara College; Grant Coleman, Mohawk College; Mary Ellen Coxworth, Durham College; Sandi Mills, Centennial College; B. Lynn Paul, Mohawk College; Sarah O'Rourke, Humber College; Linda Reiche, Algonquin College in the Ottawa Valley; and Shelley Zwicker, Lunenburg Campus, Nova Scotia Community College.

Over the years, I have had the good fortune of teaching hundreds of students both at the University of Western Ontario and the University of Manitoba. A special thanks to the students of the Richard Ivey School of Business and the Faculty of Engineering, University of Western Ontario. To all of you, I owe a debt of gratitude for motivating me to write a book focused on the principles of good technical communications.

Thank you to my mom and dad for encouraging me to pursue my passion for writing. Last but not least, I dedicate this book to Gerard, Aiden, and Arianna. Thank you for your love, support, and, above all, your patience as I spent many hours glued to my computer. I'm sure you are all happy that this book is finally completed!

Technical Communication Techniques and Considerations

CHAPTER 1
An Introduction to Technical Communication   3

CHAPTER 2
A World of People and Purposes   21

CHAPTER 3
Designing Usable Information 39

CHAPTER 4
Writing and Editing for Usability   49

CHAPTER 5
Conducting Research for Technical Communication 79

CHAPTER 6
Technical Communication in a Digital World   102

CHAPTER 7
Page Layout and Document Design   125

CHAPTER 8
Graphics and Visual Information   150

CHAPTER 9
Ethical Issues in Technical Communication   179

CHAPTER 10
Copyright and Privacy   196

CHAPTER **1**

An Introduction to Technical Communication

Chapter Objectives

By the end of this chapter you will:

1. Be familiar with the principle characteristics of effective technical communication.

2. Know the different types of documents that technical communicators produce.

3. Be aware of the importance of teamwork in technical communication.

4. Know how to manage a collaborative project.

Nico Leenders, Chatham, Ontario

After finishing a degree in Fine Arts from Concordia University, Nico Leenders enrolled in a two-year Motive Power Technician program at Fanshawe College. With graduation looming, his job hunt led him to RM Restorations. Upon discovery that he was a university graduate, the classic car restoration company redirected Nico to its sister company, RM Auctions, North America's leading classic car auction house, where he was hired to write automobile descriptions in auction catalogues. There was just one problem: Nico Leenders was a terrible writer.

"I was held back one year from Concordia because I failed my mandatory English competency exam. Later, aptitude testing scores placed my writing in the 40th percentile, and my worst class at Fanshawe was Technical Writing!" Despite a sinking feeling that he was in over his head, Nico dusted off his old technical writing textbook and focused on the basics. "I have always been able to formulate clear, concise, and logical ideas, but I lacked the fundamental writing skills to express myself properly on paper. I studied those books as if my life depended on it."

Determined not to fail, Nico ensured that his writing improved dramatically in a very short time. During the following three years, he wrote thousands of pages for auction catalogues, becoming the auction house's best in-house writer. Moreover, he was recently promoted to the position of editor of RM Magazine. In the end, writing became a newfound passion. "I can't believe it, but I come into work each day looking forward to the challenges of writing."

Communicating about Technology

Communication is a two-way process of transmitting information (messages) between two or more people using any of the five senses. As humans, we have an innate ability to communicate with one another in a variety of ways. We can write, speak, or use non-verbal communication to share information with one another. Moreover, as a social behaviour, good communication requires both the sender and receiver to use a common system of symbols, signs, behaviour, speech, writing, or signals to create shared understanding.

Today, we live in a world in which many of our everyday actions depend on complex but important technical information. When you purchase a wallet-sized calculator, for example, the instruction manual is often larger than the calculator itself. When you install any new device, from a DVD player to a microwave oven, from a cable modem to a new computer, it's the set-up information that you look for as soon as you open the box. Household appliances, banking systems, online courses, business negotiations, government correspondence and affairs, and almost every other aspect of your daily life are affected by technologies and technical information.

Technical communication has existed since the very earliest examples of human writing. In 3200 BCE, the Sumerians used a stylus and a block of wet clay to record information (Wilford, 1999). Most people trace the rise of the profession of modern technical communication to the period following World War II. The rapid development of new technologies during this time created a need for accompanying technical information, such as instructions, manuals, and documentation. In the 1970s, when the personal computer was invented, well-designed technical communication became vital as more and more non-technical people began using computers, software, and related devices. Today, with a large percentage of the population using the internet, banking via the telephone or the computer, and interacting with technology in many other ways, well-designed technical information has become even more important.

Main Characteristics of Technical Communication

Technical communication is the art and science of making complex technical information accessible, usable, and relevant to most people in most settings. Effective technical communication is an art because it requires an instinct for clear writing and good visual design. But technical communication is also a science, because it is a systematic process based on key principles and guidelines. The following principles characterize effective technical communication.

Accessibility

Information is accessible if people can obtain it and understand it. For example, if documentation for a help system is included on a CD-ROM, the people using this information must have access to a CD-ROM drive in order to read it. In addition, if a set of instructions is being distributed around the world, these instructions must be written in many languages in order to be accessible to international users.

A group of technical editors at IBM has developed a list of "quality characteristics" that help them determine if their technical documents meet high standards and are of superior quality. These characteristics suggest specific ways writers can make their communication accessible (Hargis, Hernandez, Hughes, & Ramaker, 1997, p. 2):

- Accuracy—has no mistakes or errors
- Clarity—avoids ambiguity
- Completeness—includes all necessary information
- Concreteness—uses concrete examples and language
- Organization—follows sequences that make sense for the situation
- Visual effectiveness—uses layout, screen design, colour, and other graphical elements effectively

Usability

To be usable, information must be efficient: it must allow people to perform tasks or retrieve information as quickly and easily as possible. To assess usability, examine the design of the table of contents, index, headings, and page layout; as well, determine if the language is written at the appropriate technical level. When technical communicators assess a document's usability, they often try to find out how long it takes a typical user to find specific information in the document and whether that person locates this information using the index or table of contents. For instance, if a manager consults the company's employee handbook for information about vacation time and cannot find this information (or cannot find it quickly), then the document is not usable and should be revised.

Relevance

Relevant information maintains a focus on the specific audience—the readers, listeners, or viewers. These users need answers to their immediate questions and needs; they do not need piles of data. Information is relevant if the audience can apply it to the task at hand. According to David W. Norton, "technical communicators serve their companies best when they understand how to use and convey their knowledge strategically" (Norton, 2000, p. 89). For instance, if a person is interested in how to use an internet service provider's (ISP) software to connect their computer to the internet, then the documentation should explain how to install the software and dial up the ISP; it should not digress into a history of how the internet developed. Similarly, language must be relevant to the intended audience. For an audience of general computer users who want to install a sound card, overly technical language would be inappropriate. To be relevant, information must also focus on the purpose of the communication. Although the history of sound cards might seem interesting to engineers, the writer has to determine whether this information is relevant to the purpose of the document. If it is an instruction manual (how to install a sound card), then this purpose dictates that historical information is not relevant.

Often technical communication is thought of in relation to the documents and technologies we have just described; that is, technical communication is designed to teach a general audience how to perform a specific task involving a common sort of technology (how to set up a DVD player, install a new sound card in a PC, or attach a mulching blade to a lawn mower). But technical information is also used by technical specialists, managers, and others. A surgeon performing heart surgery must have clear information about how to install a pacemaker. A government research scientist must have accurate instructions about how to write a grant proposal or how to perform a particular experiment. An engineer must have access to the right specifications for designing a bridge or configuring an application. In all settings in which people must understand complex information, there is a need for technical communication.

Consider the following example, which illustrates how technical information can be made accessible by using consistent terminology. Unlike creative forms of writing, in which writers vary their choice of words, technical communication uses consistent terminology when referring to the same item or task.

Assume that you have just purchased a new children's toy that needs assembling. The writer of the instructions decided to vary the terminology in these instructions. Here is her first draft:

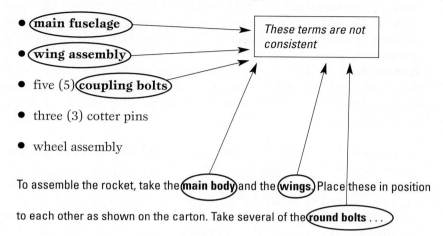

The list of parts mentions "main fuselage" and "wing assembly," but the instructions refer to "main body" and "wings." Likewise for "coupling bolts" versus "round bolts." Are these the same pieces? Can you picture the tired parent holding the instructions, looking in confusion at the welter of parts? If you don't use the same terms, how will your reader know for sure what is what?

No list of technical communication characteristics can address all possible situations and decisions that you will encounter. Wherever you work, you will face challenges that ultimately require your best analytical and social skills. For instance, clarity is a common goal in technical communication. But sometimes being crystal clear is impossible, because not enough information is available, or the sheer quantity of information makes the document confusing. In other situations, clarity and directness may strike some readers as overly blunt and offensive. As you read this book, remember that communication ultimately exists in a context, and that context may be full of personalities, preferences, stresses, budget pressures, and timelines—all of which can change overnight. Your documents must cut through these contexts to communicate with your target audience, no matter what else is going on.

Types of Technical Communication

Some common forms of technical communication are listed here. Although these categories can overlap considerably, reading this list should give you a feel for the kinds of documents technical communicators produce.

- **Manuals.** Almost every technology product or service has an accompanying manual. Manuals provide information on how to use a product, along with background information, such as technical specifications or lists of materials. You have certainly used such manuals—to connect the components of your sound system, to do routine maintenance on your bicycle or inline skates, or to set up your answering machine. Most manuals are also available in electronic form: as help files, CDs, or PDF documents on the company website.

- **Procedures.** Procedures are an important form of technical communication. Procedures explain how to perform a task or how a particular process happens. Many companies maintain standard operating procedures (SOPs) for tasks such as how to test soil samples or how to access corporate databases.

- **Instructions.** Instructions resemble manuals and procedures in that they explain how to do something. However, instructions are often very specific systematic lists of the actual steps involved in using a product or performing a procedure. For instance, if you purchase a memory upgrade for your computer, you will probably receive a list of instructions on how to install this upgrade. This list may be a separate document or part of a manual or larger set of instructions.

- **Quick reference cards.** In some situations, a long list of procedures or instructions is inappropriate, because the user is already familiar with the "big picture." For instance, you may regularly call home to access your voice mail, and you may have the primary commands memorized. But there are certain tasks you may perform infrequently, such as changing your outgoing message from another phone. For tasks that users perform on a limited basis, a short summary of the keypad commands may be all that is needed. These commands can often fit on a quick reference card designed to fit into a wallet or the actual device (beside the telephone keypad, for instance).

- **Reports.** There are many types of reports, including recommendation reports and analytical reports. Reports generally focus on a specific problem, issue, or topic. They may recommend a course of action or analyze a particular technology or situation. For example, a task force in your community may be studying plans for highway expansion or a new shopping centre. After completing an initial study, task forces often present reports to the city council or other decision-makers, and written copies of these reports are available for public review. Reports can be made available in hard copy or on the web.

- **Proposals.** Proposals make specific recommendations and propose solutions to technical problems. A proposal's purpose is usually to persuade readers to improve conditions, accept a service or product, or otherwise support a plan of action. Proposals are sometimes written in response to calls for proposals (CFPs) or requests for proposals (RFPs). For example, a non-profit childcare facility may need safer playground equipment, or a pharmaceutical company may wish to develop a new web-based education program for its employees. These organizations would issue RFPs, and each interested vendor would prepare a proposal that assesses the problem, presents a solution, and defines the process and fees associated with implementing the solution.

- **Memos.** A vital form of technical communication, memos serve various purposes: to inform, to persuade, to document, or to encourage discussion. Memos are usually brief and follow a format that includes a header (To, From, Date, Re:) and a page or two of body text. An employee might write a memo to his manager requesting a pay raise; an engineer might write a memo to her design team explaining a technical problem and offering a solution; a team of students might write a memo to their instructor explaining their progress on a class project.

- **Email.** Email is essentially the electronic version of a memo. In fact, most email is patterned after the memo, with a header containing fields for To, From, Date, and Re: already built in. Yet email messages are more common than paper memos. In most work settings, people use email to relay scheduling, policy, procedure, and miscellaneous information. They communicate via email with clients, customers, and suppliers, as well as with associates worldwide. People are more inclined to forward email messages and they tend to be more casual and hasty with email than with paper memos.

- **Blogs.** Weblogs or blogs have become very popular in today's electronic information world. A blog is an online journal. It is frequently updated by the blogger, who uses the electronic space to chronicle his or her thoughts, feelings, and opinions on a wide variety of topics. Individuals and organizations use blogs and online journals to communicate with those who share similar interests. Blogs tend to be user-friendly because they include several useful components. For example, most blogs include archives, which allow readers to search past blog postings for specific information. Many blogs allow readers to post comments, thus giving blogs an interactive quality and providing a greater depth of information. Moreover, while many blogs are text-based, they can also include music, videos, and photos.

- **Vlogs.** A videolog, or vlog, is a blog that contains video content. Vloggers make entries into these video journals, which viewers can then download or transfer to a portable player. Many organizations have found that vlogs are effective tools for developing brand loyalty: they provide information about products and services and educational information to a wide range of interested viewers.

- **Podcasts.** A podcast is a digital audio file created using an XML-based technology called Really Simple Syndication (RSS). Listeners can download recorded content to a personal computer or mobile device. What makes podcasts innovative is that individuals or groups have the ability to record their own broadcasts and upload them to the web.

- **Wikis.** A wiki is server software that allows users to collaborate with each other to create, edit, delete, or modify webpage content quickly and easily using any web browser. Wiki websites can either be public (anyone surfing the site can assess its content) or private (only those who have been invited by the wiki owner (administrator) can have access to the site content). The best-known example of a public wiki is Wikipedia.org. In many companies and organizations, wikis have become an affordable and effective intranet (private computer network) and knowledge management system for the sharing and archiving of information for employees and members.

Although these document types are the most common kinds of technical communication, many others exist, depending on the company or profession. For example, nursing requires specific forms for documenting a patient's medical condition, and engineering has its own types of technical communication. In addition, the specific audience and purpose in each situation determines the appropriate type of communication.

Technical communication documents can also be formatted and packaged in various media:

- CD-ROM
- Internet webpages (the entire worldwide internet)
- Intranet webpages (an internal network)
- Electronic text, including email or attachments
- Online help
- Printed matter, including books, paper memos, bound reports, and brochures
- Training sessions or oral presentations

Technical Communication in the Workplace

People who make technical information accessible to different audiences are called "technical communicators." In more and more organizations, this position is a full-time job, with titles including the following:

- Technical writer or editor
- User experience engineer
- Web designer
- Online documentation specialist
- Information developer
- Instructional developer

Technical communicators write and design documentation, online information, software interfaces, and other documents and materials for users of high technology. Technical communicators also write technical memos, reports, grant applications, and other specialized documents.

Virtually all technical professionals, at one time or another, function as part-time technical communicators. These technical experts are often required to present their knowledge to non-expert audiences. For instance, a nuclear engineer testifying before a parliamentary committee would need to explain nuclear science to non-scientists and to address the concerns of policy-makers. People from many other occupations (lawyers, health care professionals, historians, managers, and so on) communicate specialized information to non-expert audiences:

- Medical professionals discuss health matters with patients.
- Attorneys interpret the law for clients.
- Historians describe complex historical events for people who did not experience those events.
- Managers interpret business objectives for the people they supervise.

The Importance of Employability Skills

As a technical communicator, you will need to possess a wide range of skills in order to be successful in the workplace. These skills are commonly known as "employability skills" and refer to the foundation, "soft," or process skills needed to ensure the support of a respectful and efficient workplace. According to the Conference Board of Canada's "Employability Skills 2000+," Canadian employers are looking for employees who possess the following traits:

- People who can communicate, think, and continue to learn throughout their lives.
- People who can demonstrate positive attitudes and behaviour, responsibility, and adaptability.
- People who can work independently and in teams.

Additionally, the importance of post-secondary education should not be overlooked. According to Statistics Canada, in 2008, the employment rate for those who had not attended college or university was 58%; for those who attended and completed some level of post-secondary education, the employment rate was 83%. Moreover, post-secondary graduates earn upwards of 60% more than those without post-secondary education (Statistics Canada, 2010). As demonstrated by the Society for Technical Communication, gaining expertise in technical writing can be done by following various educational paths, such as obtaining a Bachelor of Arts degree, or a Master of Science degree (STC, 2011). Technical communicators work within the larger field of business communication and specialize in designing and developing communication products that transfer the technical knowledge of experts to a wider audience. Because the task of the technical communicator involves working with people in order to learn and communicate information that is relevant, useful, and accessible, he or she will need to develop a strong skill set. It's important to remember that these skills do not develop overnight; rather, they develop throughout your education and career. Figure 1.1 shows the employability skills that you need to be competitive in the Canadian workplace.

Employability Skills 2000+

The skills you need to enter, stay in, and progress in the world of work—whether you work on your own or as a part of a team.

These skills can also be applied and used beyond the workplace in a range of daily activities.

Fundamental Skills
The skills needed as a base for further development

You will be better prepared to progress in the world of work when you can:

Communicate
- read and understand information presented in a variety of forms (e.g., words, graphs, charts, diagrams)
- write and speak so others pay attention and understand
- listen and ask questions to understand and appreciate the points of view of others
- share information using a range of information and communications technologies (e.g., voice, e-mail, computers)
- use relevant scientific, technological and mathematical knowledge and skills to explain or clarify ideas

Manage Information
- locate, gather and organize information using appropriate technology and information systems
- access, analyze and apply knowledge and skills from various disciplines (e.g., the arts, languages, science, technology, mathematics, social sciences, and the humanities)

Use Numbers
- decide what needs to be measured or calculated
- observe and record data using appropriate methods, tools and technology
- make estimates and verify calculations

Think & Solve Problems
- assess situations and identify problems
- seek different points of view and evaluate them based on facts
- recognize the human, interpersonal, technical, scientific and mathematical dimensions of a problem
- identify the root cause of a problem
- be creative and innovative in exploring possible solutions
- readily use science, technology and mathematics as ways to think, gain and share knowledge, solve problems and make decisions
- evaluate solutions to make recommendations or decisions
- implement solutions
- check to see if a solution works, and act on opportunities for improvement

Personal Management Skills
The personal skills, attitudes and behaviours that drive one's potential for growth

You will be able to offer yourself greater possibilities for achievement when you can:

Demonstrate Positive Attitudes & Behaviours
- feel good about yourself and be confident
- deal with people, problems and situations with honesty, integrity and personal ethics
- recognize your own and other people's good efforts
- take care of your personal health
- show interest, initiative and effort

Be Responsible
- set goals and priorities balancing work and personal life
- plan and manage time, money and other resources to achieve goals
- assess, weigh and manage risk
- be accountable for your actions and the actions of your group
- be socially responsible and contribute to your community

Be Adaptable
- work independently or as a part of a team
- carry out multiple tasks or projects
- be innovative and resourceful: identify and suggest alternative ways to achieve goals and get the job done
- be open and respond constructively to change
- learn from your mistakes and accept feedback
- cope with uncertainty

Learn Continuously
- be willing to continuously learn and grow
- assess personal strengths and areas for development
- set your own learning goals
- identify and access learning sources and opportunities
- plan for and achieve your learning goals

Work Safely
- be aware of personal and group health and safety practices and procedures, and act in accordance with these

Teamwork Skills
The skills and attributes needed to contribute productively

You will be better prepared to add value to the outcomes of a task, project or team when you can:

Work with Others
- understand and work within the dynamics of a group
- ensure that a team's purpose and objectives are clear
- be flexible: respect, be open to and supportive of the thoughts, opinions and contributions of others in a group
- recognize and respect people's diversity, individual differences and perspectives
- accept and provide feedback in a constructive and considerate manner
- contribute to a team by sharing information and expertise
- lead or support when appropriate, motivating a group for high performance
- understand the role of conflict in a group to reach solutions
- manage and resolve conflict when appropriate

Participate in Projects & Tasks
- plan, design or carry out a project or task from start to finish with well-defined objectives and outcomes
- develop a plan, seek feedback, test, revise and implement
- work to agreed quality standards and specifications
- select and use appropriate tools and technology for a task or project
- adapt to changing requirements and information
- continuously monitor the success of a project or task and identify ways to improve

The Conference Board of Canada

255 Smyth Road, Ottawa
ON K1H 8M7 Canada
Tel. (613) 526-3280
Fax (613) 526-4857
Internet: www.conferenceboard.ca/education

Figure 1.1 Critical Skills Required for the Canadian Workforce.
Source: Employability Skills 2000+ Brochure 2000 E/F (Ottawa: The Conference Board of Canada, 2000).

Teamwork, Virtual Teams, and Project Management

Technical communication in workplace settings is rarely done by one lone writer or editor; instead, most projects are done in project teams of writers, web designers, engineers or scientists, managers, legal or regulations experts, and other members of the organization. Teams may be made up of people from one site or location, but increasingly, teams are distributed across different job sites, time zones, and countries. The internet—via email, streamed video, instant messaging, blogs, and other digital communication tools—provides the primary means for these distributed (or virtual) teams to do their work. In addition, tools such as computer-supported co-operative work (CSCW) software and project management software (such as Microsoft Project) allow complex projects to be discussed, planned, and implemented among virtual teams. In the end, whether entirely on-site or entirely distributed, teams are made up of people and personalities. Thus, team members need to be able to work together, and the digital tools they use should support their communication, collaborations, and key tasks to help them complete the project successfully.

There are two important considerations in technical communication team projects: *teamwork* and *tools*.

Teamwork: How to Manage a Collaborative Project

Teamwork is successful only when there is strong co-operation, a recognized team structure, and clear communication. The TIPS box on the next page provides some guidelines for managing a team project—on-site, virtual, or combination.

Tools: How to Use Digital Technology in a Team

Digital technology is a key support of teamwork. The following tools are commonly used in most workplace settings:

- **Email and attachments.** Probably the most commonly used tool, email is great for short messages and as a way to include many people and to keep track of what was agreed to. The attachment feature allows team members to share and discuss entire documents.
- **Project management software.** Most large organizations use some type of software, such as Microsoft Project for PC users or Merlin for Mac users, to manage large, complex team projects.
- **Virtual project teams.** In an increasingly global and collaborative marketplace, work teams can span borders as well as companies. For example, eRoom.net's Pam Sullivan (2001) cites the example of Hewlett-Packard.

The company uses "contract manufacturers" working in different locations and countries to source the various parts needed to build their printers. This requires HP "to manage multiple suppliers and inventories" in order to make this complex system work. As a result, "virtual workspaces," developed by companies such as IBM with its Lotus QuickPlace, provide free or low cost electronic workspaces to address the challenges involved in keeping project teams, especially international or intercompany teams, in touch. Virtual workspaces provide a password-protected website with services ranging from email to information storage to chat rooms. These sites usually offer tools that allow team members to chat live or work independently and store their work for other teammates to review later.

TIPS FOR MANAGING A TEAM PROJECT

- **Appoint a group manager.** The manager assigns tasks, enforces deadlines, chairs meetings, consults with supervisors, and generally "runs the show."
- **Define a clear and definite goal.** Spell out the project's goal and the group's plan for achieving it.
- **Identify the type of document required.** Is this a report, a proposal, a manual, a brochure, or a pamphlet? Are graphics and supplements (abstract, appendixes, and so on) needed? Will the document be in hard copy, digital form, or both?
- **Divide the tasks.** Who will be responsible for which parts of the document or which phases of the project? Who is best at doing what (writing early or final drafts, editing, layout, design and graphics, oral presentation)? Which tasks will be done individually and which collectively? Keep in mind that the final version should use one consistent style throughout, as if written by one person only.

  Note: Be sure to spell out *in writing* clear expectations for each team member.
- **Establish a timetable.** Gantt charts (see pages 161 to 163) help teams visualize the whole project as well as each part, along with start-up and completion dates for each phase.
- **Decide on a meeting schedule and format.** How often will the group meet? Where and for how long? Who will take notes or minutes? Set a strict time limit for each meeting and for each discussion topic. Distribute copies of the meeting agenda and timetable to each member beforehand, and stick to this plan. A meeting works best when each member prepares a specific contribution ahead of time.

- **Establish a procedure for responding to the work of other members.** Will reviewing and editing be done in writing, as a group, face-to-face, one-on-one, or online?
- **Develop a file-naming system for various drafts.** It's often too easy to save over a previous version and lose something important.
- **Establish procedures for dealing with interpersonal problems.** How will gripes and disputes be aired and resolved (by vote, by the manager, other)? How will irrelevant discussion be curtailed?
- **Select a group decision-making style.** To focus group effort, Intel Corporation requires every group to decide on a specific decision-making style before each meeting. Some possible styles:

  Authoritative—the group leader makes the decisions.
  Consultative—the leader makes decisions based on group input.
  Voting—decisions are made by majority vote.

- **Appoint an "observer" for each meeting.** At Charles Schwab & Co., a designated observer keeps a list of what worked well during the meeting and what didn't. The list is added to that meeting's minutes.
- **Decide how to evaluate each member's contribution.** Will the manager assess each member's performance and in turn be evaluated by each member? Will members evaluate each other? What are the criteria? Members might keep a journal of personal observations for overall evaluation of the project.
- **Prepare a project management plan.** Figure 1.2 on the next page shows a sample planning form. Distribute completed copies to members.
- **Submit regular progress reports.** Progress reports (see page 246) track activities, problems, and progress.

- **Instant messaging.** Instant messaging (IM), a form of online chat, is a fast and easy way to get an answer to a quick question.
- **Conference calls.** Conference calls are group telephone calls that connect the team for multi-person discussions in real time.
- **Track changes.** Microsoft Word and similar word processing tools have features that let you insert comments and changes in a way that everyone on the team can see. More sophisticated systems use something called "version control."
- **Blogs.** Blogs allow you to post material in reverse chronological order and are a very good way for the entire team to share ideas and link to each other's ideas.
- **Wiki.** Wikis can be used to conduct meetings and to have team members collaboratively edit documents.

Project Planning Form

Project title:
Audience:
Project manager:
Team members:
Purpose of the project:
Type of document required:

Specific Assignments	**Due Dates**
Research:	Research due:
Planning:	Plan and outline due:
Drafting:	First draft due:
Revising:	Reviews due:
Preparing final document:	Revision due:
Presenting oral briefing:	Progress report(s) due:
	Final document due:

Work Schedule

Team meetings:	Date	Place	Time	Note taker
#1				
#2				
#3				
etc.				

Mtgs. w/instructor
   #1
   #2
   etc.

Miscellaneous
   How will disputes and grievances be resolved?
   How will performances be evaluated?
   Other matters (internet searches, email routing, computer conferences, etc.)?

Figure 1.2 Sample Project Planning Form for Managing a Collaborative Project.

Societal Dimensions of Technical Communication

Good technical communication has a societal component, because it can make important topics in science and technology (such as genetically modified organisms, cloning, or computers that diagnose disease) understandable to the public. Such communication gives ordinary people access to new information—access that might otherwise remain closed if the information were hard to read, too technical, or impossible to interpret. They would be overwhelmed by the technical jargon, complex topics, and detailed presentations in technical journals. But if information is written in a way that matches the level of knowledge of the public, then ordinary readers can understand these important topics. In a world in which science and technology play major roles in everyone's lives, technical communication becomes increasingly important. When you create effective technical communication, you not only help others use the information but also help people learn about important ideas.

Ethical Dimensions of Technical Communication

Technical communication involves ethics because the words, fonts, graphics, and colours you choose to convey your information may influence your audience's perception, interpretation, and understanding. For example, advertising claims can indirectly hint that a new hair product can repair damaged hair. These claims are presented in technical-sounding jargon, but they often have no foundation in science. The writers of the ad chose words, language, and images to create impressions in the reader's mind that have no basis in fact. Moreover, writers often have to deal with workplace pressures: communicating what the boss wants or what will make more money for the company. These goals are often at odds with the goal of fair, accurate, and ethical presentation of information. In addition, technical communicators can also misuse visual communication, such as charts and graphs, to create impressions or confuse the facts for the reader. Later chapters address the ethical issues involved in technical communication. Generally, you will need to balance your own ethical stance against the interests of others, including your employer and your customers or end users.

 Checklist for Quality in Technical Communication

Accessibility
* Is the information *accurate*?
* Is the language *clear* and unambiguous?
* Is the information *complete?*
* Are the examples *concrete?*
* Is the material appropriately *organized?*
* Is visual information (layout, screen design, colour) used *effectively?*

Usability

- Can users find what they need *efficiently?*
- Is the language at an appropriate *technical level?*
- Does the document contain a *table of contents, index,* or other such device?

Relevance

- Is the material appropriate for this *audience?*
- Is the material appropriate for and relevant to the *purpose* at hand?

Exercises

1. Find an effective technical document and bring it to class. Use the above checklist to explain to other students why your selection can be called "technical communication." Explain how it is accessible, usable, and relevant.

2. Using the "Employability Skills 2000+" chart in Figure 1.1, assess what skills you currently possess and what skills you need to develop. Discuss ways you can start developing some of the crucial skills for job success.

3. **FOCUS ON WRITING.** Research the kinds of writing you expect to do in your career. (Begin your search with the National Occupation Classification in your library or on the web.) Interview a member of your chosen profession or a technical communicator in a related field or industry. What types of writing can you expect to do on the job? For what audiences will you be writing? How much of your writing will be transmitted or published in electronic forms (websites, intranets)? Summarize your findings in a memo to your instructor or in a brief oral report to your class.

4. **FOCUS ON WRITING.** Interview professionals in your field concerning the kinds and amounts of writing they do. In your interview ask what types of documents they prepare, the average length of these documents, how many hours they spend preparing them, to whom do they write, and what are the consequences for good or bad documents. Then prepare a memo on your findings.

5. **FOCUS ON RESEARCH.** Gather examples of different kinds of technical documents on the web. Use the webpages listed here as starting points, then expand your search by locating other webpages related to your career and interests. Bring printed copies of at least three sample pages to class and work in a small group to compare the examples you have collected. Identify key features of both good and bad technical communication, based on the criteria (accessibility, usability, and relevance) presented in this chapter.

- **www.ec.gc.ca**
  Environment Canada's website offers information to the public on environmental issues. A department of the Canadian government, Environment Canada provides scientific research, weather forecasts, and publications and reports.
- **www.imagescanada.ca**
  Images Canada stores over 65 000 images of Canadian events, people, places, and things dating from as early as the eighteenth century. The website also allows users to access photos from many collections, including Library and Archives Canada and the Canada Science and Technology Museum.
- **www.irb.gc.ca**
  The Immigration and Refugee Board of Canada's website houses reports, research, and information on the Canadian government's immigration policies and regulations.

The Collaboration Window

Most writing and communicating, especially in the workplace, is done collaboratively; that is, it is done by and among many people and takes numerous ideas and suggestions into account. In class, form teams of students who have the same or similar majors or interests.

To help other team members understand your perspective, create a miniature "dictionary" for your major or field. List 10 technical terms and concepts important in your major or career interest, and provide short definitions or explanations to help others understand these key concepts. Your list must fit on a single page. Collaborate on forming this list as follows:

- Each person in the group should create an individual list.
- When everyone is done, compile these lists into one master list.

Then negotiate among members of your group to reduce these compiled terms to just 10 terms and decide how to define these terms. Share your final list with the other groups in class.

The Global Window

Technical communication is an international activity. Technical products and services are used around the world, and communicators need to create information that is attentive to international needs. For example, if a company is shipping portable MP3 players to several countries, the documentation must be written in clear English that translates easily and contains internationally recognized symbols or visual information.

Find examples of multi-language technical documentation (instructions for household appliances, tools, or stereo equipment are often written in several languages). How many languages were used? Why did this company select these languages? Compare your findings with those of other students.

To learn more about global communication, use a web search engine to locate information about the International Organization for Standardization (ISO). This group specializes in creating technical and communication standards for worldwide use. Identify a particular aspect of this site related to your area of study or that you find interesting and share this information in class.

MyCanadianTechCommLab

Go to MyCanadianTechCommLab at www.mycanadiantechcommlab.ca for additional online exercises and problems.

CHAPTER 2

A World of People and Purposes

Chapter Objectives

By the end of this chapter you will be able to:

1. Analyze your audience.

2. Conduct an interview with an audience in mind.

3. Effectively use information from your analysis.

Roger Shuttleworth, London, Ontario

Having spent 20 years in medical microbiology, Roger Shuttleworth switched careers to technical writing. "I always enjoyed researching, writing, and training," he says, "so technical writing was a fit for me." He joined a start-up software company and has since spent eight years working in the industry.

"Everything was completely new to me. I had to create a whole document set from scratch, learning as I went. There were times when I wondered if I'd made the right decision!" As the company grew, Roger later found himself leading and training a team of three writers and becoming more and more involved in user interface design.

Usability, both of software and of documents, is one of Roger's new passions. "Our users don't want to read a book. They want enough information, *where* they want it, *when* they want it." Tailoring documents to the needs of users requires insight, a willingness to improve, and openness to new technologies. At his present company, agile programming methods result in ever-changing products and documents so content management is an issue. New XML-based technologies require the ability to learn quickly, and Roger finds himself training other writers. "You have to be willing to learn," he says. "I'm still researching better methods, and then training others to use them."

People, Purposes, and Communities

All forms of technical communication are ultimately intended for an *audience:* the readers, listeners, viewers, and users who need information to make decisions or perform tasks. A good technical communicator always designs information with an audience in mind, carefully reviewing the information, selecting what is important, and crafting it into a useful tool for a specific group. This group can also be thought of as a *community.* In other words, technical communicators must always take into account the needs of the community for whom they design information. Furthermore, technical communicators themselves are members of the community in which they work, and often the communities of technical communicators and the audiences for whom they design information overlap.

Identify Discourse Communities

The notion of community, and of *discourse community* in particular, has recently gained attention in organizational and professional settings, as well as in academic disciplines. A discourse community is "a group of people who share certain language-using practices . . . The key term *discourse* suggests a community bound together primarily by its uses of language, although bound perhaps by other ties as well, geographical, socioeconomic, ethnic, professional, and so on" (Bizzell, 1992, p. 222). Discourse communities have the power to influence and shape the way information is communicated within and outside of a group. Different types of discourse communities use language unique to themselves; for instance, a community of medical researchers uses technical or scientific language different from that of software programmers.

Ultimately, technical communicators need to analyze their audiences carefully in order to choose the right type of language. A technical communicator can belong to multiple discourse communities. For example, technical communicators belong to workplace project teams because that is what the employer pays them for. However, a good technical communicator is also an advocate of the needs of his or her audience or users, so technical communicators should also feel that they are part of their audience community as well. Common stylistic conventions (see Chapter 3) may help create a sense of community and interconnectedness among technical communicators and their collaborative teams in the workplace; however, the technical communicator will need an entirely different set of conventions for the external audience.

For example, the brochure in Figure 2.1 has been designed by a biomedical device company to inform physicians and other health care professionals who treat patients with heart conditions. Knowing the important features of this type of device for this community of doctors and nurses feels about meeting individual patient needs, the writing team begins the brochure with the following sentence: "The Adapta pacing system combines physiologic pacing with automacity." This sentence helps medical readers instantly connect the product with their workplace needs and goals. Having captured the readers' interest, the writers then outline the specific features of this product.

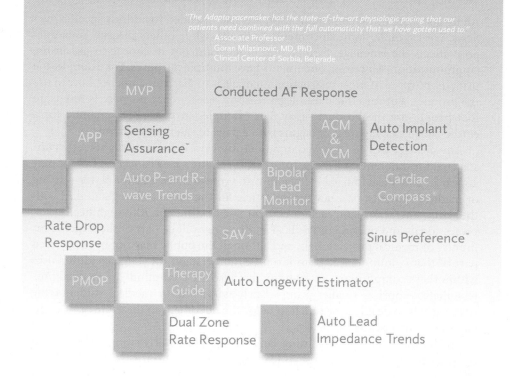

Adapta™ – Always Adapting

The Adapta pacing system combines physiologic pacing with automaticity.

Medtronic's exclusive MVP™ Mode monitors for natural intrinsic conduction. Atrial and Ventricular Capture Management™ (ACM and VCM) provide complete, long-term threshold management – **automatically**.

Completely Automatic – Simple to Use

Pacing thresholds, sensing, and lead impedances are continually evaluated, and associated parameters are automatically adapted for each patient – **enhancing safety and simplifying programming and follow-up.**

"The Adapta pacemaker has the state-of-the-art physiologic pacing that our patients need combined with the full automaticity that we have gotten used to."
Associate Professor
Goran Milasinovic, MD, PhD
Clinical Center of Serbia, Belgrade

MVP
Conducted AF Response
APP
Sensing Assurance™
ACM & VCM
Auto Implant Detection
Auto P- and R-wave Trends
Bipolar Lead Monitor
Cardiac Compass®
Rate Drop Response
SAV+
Sinus Preference™
PMOP
Therapy Guide
Auto Longevity Estimator
Dual Zone Rate Response
Auto Lead Impedance Trends

PACING REDEFINED

Figure 2.1 Technical Brochure   This brochure about a heart pacemaker system is designed to speak to a specific audience and to address its primary concerns. *Source:* Medtronic Adapta™ with MVP™ Pacing System. Reproduced with permission of Medtronic, Inc.

Provide Information that Your Audience Needs

The audience is an important consideration in all kinds of writing, but especially in technical writing, which is far more *user-centred* than other writing. When you write a poem or an essay, for example, you express your personal feelings and thoughts—you tell your audience what you want to say. In contrast, as a technical writer, your first concern is to provide information *the audience needs*.

According to technical communication expert Robert R. Johnson (1997), you cannot know every member of your audience, so you always have to do some guessing about audience needs. However, as much as possible, you should interact with and seek feedback from the community for which you write. This will help you eliminate false assumptions about who your audience actually is.

Define Your Primary and Secondary Purposes

All forms of technical communication are also intended to address specific *purposes*. For example, some documents persuade, while others inform. Your purpose affects the language, format, and other features you choose to use in the communication. Moreover, documents have multiple purposes. For example, the primary purpose of most instruction manuals is to teach an audience how to use the product. But for ethical and legal reasons, a secondary purpose is to ensure that people use the product safely. For example, an instruction manual for a cordless drill (see Figure 2.2) begins with a page of safety instructions.

Any message can be conveyed in numerous ways, depending on how it is constructed for different audiences. Information about a new cancer treatment may appear in a medical journal for health care professionals, a textbook for nursing or medical students, or a newspaper article for the public. Though all deal with the same general content, each document will be different. Although health care professionals and nursing or medical students may all be part of the larger community of medical professionals, and although the public may not be considered part of that community, it is important to understand the language differences within these communities. In addition, because the community of medical professionals comprises smaller groups, such as nursing or medical students, the writer needs to decide how much to tailor the document to these different audiences and purposes as well.

Furthermore, choices regarding language, jargon, and writing style need to consider the audience's purpose in reading the information, as well as their level of knowledge. For example, an audience of medical professionals has a thorough understanding of medical technical terms, but medical students understand a great deal less. How much should a writer tailor a document to medical students? The answer lies in the medical students' purpose: they are reading so that they can apply the information and learn to think and act like doctors. Thus, they expect to have to stretch their understanding and perhaps look up a few words.

IMPORTANT SAFETY INSTRUCTIONS

WARNING: When using Electric Tools, [always follow] basic safety precautions to reduce risk of fire, electric shock, and personal injury, including the following:

READ ALL INSTRUCTIONS

1. **KEEP WORK AREA CLEAN.** Cluttered areas and benches invite injuries.
2. **CONSIDER WORK AREA ENVIRONMENT.** Don't expose power tools to rain. Don't use power tools in damp or wet locations. Keep work area well lit.
3. **GUARD AGAINST ELECTRIC SHOCK.** Prevent body contact with grounded surfaces. For example: pipes, radiators, ranges, refrigerator enclosures.
4. **KEEP CHILDREN AWAY.** All visitors should be kept away from work area. Do not let visitors contact tool or extension cord.
5. **STORE IDLE TOOLS.** When not in use, tools should be stored in a dry, and high or locked-up place - out of reach of children.
6. **DON'T FORCE TOOL.** It will do the job better and safer at the rate for which it was intended.
7. **USE RIGHT TOOL.** Don't force small tool or attachment to do the job of a heavy-duty tool. Don't use tool for purpose not intended. For example, don't use a circular saw for cutting tree limbs or logs.
8. **DRESS PROPERLY.** Do not wear loose clothing or jewelry. They can be caught in moving parts. Rubber gloves and non-skid footwear are recommended when working outdoors. Wear protective hair covering to contain long hair.
9. **USE SAFETY GLASSES.** Also use face or dustmask if operation is dusty.
10. **DON'T ABUSE CORD.** Never carry tool by cord or yank it to disconnect from receptacle. Keep cord from heat, oil, and sharp edges.
11. **SECURE WORK.** Use clamps or a vise to hold work. It's safer than using your hand and it frees both hands to operate tool.
12. **DON'T OVERREACH.** Keep proper footing and balance at all times.
13. **MAINTAIN TOOLS WITH CARE.** Keep tools sharp and clean for better and safe performance. Follow instructions for lubricating and changing accessories. Inspect tool cords periodically and if damaged have repaired by authorized service facility. Inspect extension cords periodically and replace if damaged. Keep handles dry, clean, and free from oil and grease.
14. **DISCONNECT TOOLS.** When not in use, before servicing, and when changing accessories, such as blades, bits, cutters.
15. **REMOVE ADJUSTING KEYS AND WRENCHES.** Form habit of checking to see that keys and adjusting wrenches are removed from tool before turning it on.
16. **AVOID UNINTENTIONAL STARTING.** Don't carry plugged-in tool with finger on switch. Be sure switch is off when plugging in.
17. **OUTDOOR USE EXTENSION CORDS.** When tool is used outdoors, use only extension cords intended for use outdoors and so marked. (See page 4 for more information about extension cords.)
18. **STAY ALERT.** Watch what you are doing. Use common sense. Do not operate tool when you are tired.
19. **CHECK DAMAGED PARTS.** Before further use of the tool, a guard or other part that is damaged should be carefully checked to determine that it will operate properly and perform its intended function. Check for alignment of moving parts, binding of moving parts, breakage of parts, mounting, and any other conditions that may affect its operation. A guard or other part that is defective should be properly repaired or replaced by an authorized service center unless otherwise indicated elsewhere in this instruction manual. Have defective switches replaced by authorized service center. Do not use tool if switch does not turn it on and off.
20. **DO NOT OPERATE** portable electric tools near flammable liquids or in gaseous or explosive atmospheres. Motors in these tools normally spark, and the sparks might ignite fumes.

CAUTION: When drilling into walls, floors, or wherever "live" electrical wires may be encountered, DO NOT TOUCH THE CHUCK! Hold the drill only by the plastic handle to prevent electric shock if you drill into a "live" wire.

We understand that safety rules make some pretty dry reading, but they really are important. If you just skimmed them, please go back and thoroughly read them. Thank you.

SAVE THESE INSTRUCTIONS

Figure 2.2 Safety Instructions for Operating a Cordless Drill. This cordless drill manual begins with a page of safety instructions.

Source: Black & Decker Instruction Manual, © 1993. Black & Decker (U.S.) Inc. Reprinted by permission.

In contrast, general audiences reading about the same topic in a newspaper are usually looking for non-specific learning. They may be more interested in how the topic affects them personally, or how it might change their life. They don't expect to have to work hard to understand, and they may just give up. Thus, technical communication must consider the audience's purpose in reading, in addition to the writer's (or organization's) purpose in writing. Your task as a writer is to select the right language, content, organization, illustrations, and overall design to achieve both purposes. The more you understand about your audience's purpose in reading, the more your communication will meet user needs.

Figures 2.3 and 2.4 show two pieces of information, both about over-the-counter pain medications: Tylenol and Motrin. The website in Figure 2.3 is designed for a general audience of patients who have questions or want more information about Tylenol. The information from RxList (Figure 2.4) is intended for an audience of physicians and health care professionals, not patients. Both items answer questions and provide information about the pain medications, but they are designed and written for very different audiences. Notice the different uses of language and graphics for these two audiences.

Analyzing Your Audience

In preparing a technical communication product, you generally begin by analyzing your audience with a series of questions like these:

- Who will be reading, listening to, or using this material?
- What special characteristics does this audience have?
- Which discourse community or communities do they belong to?
- What is their background and attitude toward the subject?

Most people already know more than they think they do about analyzing an audience. Imagine that you are asked to give a presentation on global warming to a group of schoolchildren. Later you are asked to speak on the same subject to a group of manufacturing executives. In preparing to speak to the children, you would probably think of ways to make the topic easy to understand—for instance, using simple language and comparing your ideas to objects and events familiar to children. In preparing to speak to the manufacturing executives, you would change your approach, using more technical terms and referring to topics they care about, such as the effects of global warming on their industries.

In short, you would have performed a *basic audience analysis* by assessing the characteristics and interests of the two different audiences and then reshaping the information to fit what you know about each group. Yet it is best to be more systematic about analyzing an audience, because a communicator's assumptions are sometimes wrong. For example, you might assume that manufacturing executives know a great deal about global warming and you may decide to use

Figure 2.3 MedBroadcast website This website of medical information is designed for a general audience.

Source: Used with permission from MediResource Inc.

technical terms or refer to complex concepts. But what if your assumption is wrong? What if these executives actually know very little about the subject? Instead of relying on your assumption, learn as much as possible about the language and social dynamics of the community of manufacturing executives before the presentation. Then you can make informed judgments about the information that needs to be communicated to this group in the presentation.

DRUG DESCRIPTION

MOTRIN tablets contain the active ingredient ibuprofen, which is (±) - 2 - (p - isobutylphenyl) propionic acid. Ibuprofen is a white powder with a melting point of 74-77° C and is very slightly soluble in water (< 1 mg/mL) and readily soluble in organic solvents such as ethanol and acetone.

The structural formula is represented below:

MOTRIN (ibuprofen) tablets, a nonsteroidal anti-inflammatory drug (NSAID), is available in 400 mg, 600 mg, and 800 mg tablets for oral administration. Inactive ingredients: carnauba wax, colloidal silicon dioxide, croscarmellose sodium, hypromellose, lactose, magnesium stearate, microcrystalline cellulose, propylene glycol, titanium dioxide.

FOR PATIENTS

WHAT ARE THE POSSIBLE SIDE EFFECTS OF IBUPROFEN?

Get emergency medical help if you have any of these signs of an allergic reaction: hives; difficulty breathing; swelling of your face, lips, tongue, or throat.

Stop taking ibuprofen and seek medical attention or call your doctor at once if you have any of these serious side effects:

- chest pain, weakness, shortness of breath, slurred speech, problems with vision or balance;
- black, bloody, or tarry stools, coughing up blood or vomit that looks like coffee grounds;
- swelling or rapid weight gain;
- urinating...

Read All Potential Side Effects and See Pictures of Motrin »

WHAT ARE THE PRECAUTIONS WHEN TAKING IBUPROFEN (MOTRIN)?

Before taking ibuprofen, tell your doctor or pharmacist if you are allergic to it; or to aspirin or other NSAIDs (such as naproxen, celecoxib); or if you have any other allergies. This product may contain inactive ingredients, which can cause allergic reactions or other problems. Talk to your pharmacist for more details.

Before taking this medication, tell your doctor or pharmacist your medical history, especially of: asthma (including a history of worsening breathing after taking aspirin or other NSAIDs), blood disorders (such as anemia, bleeding/clotting problems), growths in the nose (nasal polyps), heart disease (such as congestive heart failure, previous heart attack), high blood pressure, kidney disease, liver disease, severe loss of body water (dehydration), stroke,...

Read All Potential Precautions of Motrin »

Last reviewed on RxList: 9/18/2007
This monograph has been modified to include the generic and brand name in many instances.

Figure 2.4 Motrin Information from RxList

This information is designed for a specialized audience of medical professionals.

Source: RxList from WebMD.

Most communication situations have an immediate audience. This is your *primary audience.* For example, instructions for installing new email software might be directed primarily at computer support staff. But most documents also have *secondary audiences*—people outside the circle of those who need the information urgently. A secondary audience for software instructions might be managers, who will check the instructions for company policy, or lawyers, who will make sure the instructions meet various legal standards.

Analyzing the Communication Purpose

As you analyze your audience, you also need to consider the purpose of your message by asking questions like these:

- Why is this communication important?
- Why is it needed?
- What will users do with this information?
- Do the users share common membership in a specific discourse community?

People use technical information for various purposes: to perform a task, learn more about a subject, or make a decision. If the communicator has one purpose in mind when preparing the information but the audience has several different purposes, then the document may be useless for some of the end users.

For example, you may have found websites where the purpose seems at odds with your purpose for visiting the site. Let's say you hear about a new website that sells books about birdwatching in South America. As an avid birdwatcher planning a trip to Brazil, you decide to check out this site. When you first connect, you are impressed with the bright colours and cute bird sounds. And as you click on each book selection, an array of birds fly across your screen. It's all very interesting, yet you still have not located any descriptive information about the books, and you cannot find the information about shipping costs. Also, you can't find an order form. It appears that your purpose—to locate and perhaps buy a book—conflicts with the purpose of the page, which appears to be a fancy digital advertisement.

Just as there are primary and secondary audiences, there is also more than one level of purpose. Often, the secondary purposes relate to the secondary audiences. For example, the primary purpose of a set of instructions for a new bicycle rack might be to help users assemble the rack, but a secondary purpose might be to meet the company's legal obligation to list all parts and inform users about potential hazards. Therefore, the instructions not only cater to the needs of the community of users but also fulfill the needs of the community of legal professionals working for the company.

Analyzing the Communication Context

Along with audience and purpose, it is also important to understand the context in which the document will be used. Context is related to purpose, but it suggests a slightly different set of questions:

- What are the organizational settings in which the document will be used? For example, will the document be used in training sessions? As part of overall policy documents? As a web-based customer support site?
- Are there legal issues to consider? For example, are you using printed material from another source, and if so, do you need to request permission? Are you discussing company projects that may be confidential?
- How much time do people at this company or with this job title have available to perform a task? For example, a service technician out in the field may have very little time to locate an answer in a long instruction manual, but a researcher working on a long-term experiment may have more time to mull over the theoretical aspects of a topic.
- Are the readers of this document associated with a larger community of professionals (nurses, scientists, teachers), and if so, what professional values might they bring to the situation? For example, medical professionals value the health and life of patients.
- Are audience members all from one culture, or is it a cross-cultural audience? Remember that Canada contains many diverse cultures: not everyone in Canada speaks English as their first language.

These and other issues affect every choice you make when writing and designing technical communication.

The chart on the following page summarizes important questions about audience, purpose, and context and provides a template worksheet for your own analysis. Modify this chart to suit your specific situations.

Conducting an Audience–Purpose Interview

Some documents have wide audiences. For example, manuals for household appliances are shipped to users worldwide. You may be able to interview only a few users of such a product, but if they represent the average reader or listener, you will have a good sense of how to proceed.

The first step, then, is to identify the people available for an interview. Try to interview people from various segments of your audience. Depending on your situation, you may interview people individually or in focus groups (small groups of people brought together for this purpose).

Before the interview, explain what you are doing and ask individuals for an appropriate time to meet or call. Email is a good way to make this initial contact, allowing recipients to respond at their convenience. If you can't set up a face-

AUDIENCE ANALYSIS WORKSHEET

Communication Aspect	Specific Features
Audience	
Demographic information	Age, gender ratio, education level, ethnicity?
Primary audience	Names, job titles?
Secondary audiences	Names, job titles?
Attitudes toward information	Level of interest and receptivity?
Technical understanding of or experience with topic	Extent of background knowledge?
Purpose	
Primary purpose:	
To learn	List what they want to learn
To obtain background information	List why they need this
To make a decision	List the decisions they will make
To perform a task	List tasks: to build, to design, to install, etc.
Secondary purpose or purposes	Legal, marketing, other
Context	
Role within the organization	Managers, engineers, etc.
Political or social situation	Power, decision making
Community membership	Specific vocabulary, discourse, social dynamics
Legal issues	Copyright, patents
Cultural considerations	Cross-cultural audiences
Professional values or affiliations	Engineers, teachers, nurses, etc.
Other contextual issues	Due dates, other constraints

to-face or phone interview, consider using email to conduct your audience analysis. But don't send out your analysis questions until your respondent has agreed to participate. (See Chapter 5 for more information on conducting interviews.)

During the interview, cover all the items on your audience analysis worksheet. Pay particularly close attention to the following items:

- **Levels of technical understanding.** How much technical knowledge does the reader have? Is the reader part of a discourse community that uses a specific technical vocabulary? Will technical terms be familiar or confusing? How much background will be needed to help explain concepts?

- **International issues.** Are audience members all from one culture or country, or are they from several countries and cultures? How can you adapt the document to make it accessible to everyone?
- **Workplace culture or hierarchy.** In what workplace setting will the document be used? Is there a certain style or tone appropriate to this company? Will all levels of employees be using this material, or should it be designed for just one or two groups? Does the company have its own style manual?
- **Gender.** How can the document be written and designed for audiences that are predominantly male or female? For example, advertisers try to tailor ads to what they believe are the perspectives, needs, and wants of male or female buyers. But many end up failing because they base their audience assessments on assumptions.
- **Mixed audiences.** In general, when preparing a set of procedures, you write one way for experienced users (people who have performed this or similar procedures before) and a different way for inexperienced users. But if your audience consists of both experienced and inexperienced users, you need to include different levels of information within the same document: some background and explanation of technical terms for the inexperienced users and some technical terms and concepts for those with experience. You can also use an approach called "context-sensitive communication," discussed in Chapter 3.

More Tools for Understanding Audience

Enhance your audience analysis by seeking out other information, such as the following:

- **Corporate style guides.** Stylistic conventions help regulate a discourse community, and companies often publish style guides with their own rules for corporate communication. These guides offer specific information on everything from grammar and punctuation to tone and style. A company style guide often describes the audiences for its products.
- **User preference documents.** Many manufacturing and software organizations create documents that assess user preferences. These documents are often created after detailed interviews with real customers.
- **Marketing surveys and focus groups.** Marketing departments spend a great deal of time with customers and have a wealth of information to share on customer attitudes, preferences, educational levels, and so on.

Using Information from Your Analysis

A thorough audience and purpose analysis will help you make the following decisions as you prepare your document or presentation.

- **Word choice.** Understanding your audience's level of technical expertise and the preferred linguistic and social conventions will govern the kind of language you use. A group of software engineers understands technical language about computing (for example, "remote analog loopback"), but a mixed audience of managers and supervisors may require less technical language and clear definitions of any technical terms you do use. Novices may need non-technical, reassuring language.
- **Examples.** Good examples can make a technical concept clear and easy to visualize. A document describing how a pacemaker works might compare the pacemaker's action to a more familiar concept, such as a ticking clock.
- **Document format.** An audience often expects a document to conform to a familiar format. Most companies have stylistic conventions that regulate the standard format for communicating new product information, such as a special type of company memo, a prepared form, or an email message with an attachment.
- **Length.** Some audiences, such as busy executives, have no time to read an entire report. For these audiences, the report needs an abstract that summarizes key information and conclusions. Length is also important in presentations. Some meetings limit individual presentations to 10 or 15 minutes.
- **Document genre.** Is your document meant to persuade or inform? Although all documents are implicitly persuasive (in that you want readers to appreciate the quality of your message), some are expected to be explicitly persuasive as well. A sales proposal, for example, explicitly attempts to persuade its audience to purchase the product or service; on the other hand, a research report is usually intended merely to describe the project and interpret the findings. It is important to remember that not only is the purpose of your document influenced by the genre you use, but the genre you use is also influenced by the conventions of the community for which you write.
- **Information to include.** Make sure the information you include in the document is interesting and useful to your audience. Consider carefully what to put in and what to leave out, based on what you know about audience and purpose. For example, details of what a new security system is designed to do are of marginal interest to the technician who has been brought in to install it.

Recognizing that Audiences Are Not Passive

Audiences are not merely passive recipients of information, and technical communicators are not merely passive designers of information. When people read a manual, listen to a presentation, or explore a website, they constantly form opinions about the material, learn new information, and consider new points of view. If they find the information difficult to use, unbelievable, or insulting, they will reject it. Therefore, as you analyze your audience and learn about its community, remember that the communication process works both ways. People will react to your ideas in ways that you may not anticipate. Keep an open mind, and be ready to modify your original ideas based on how your audience reacts.

Typical Audiences and Purposes for Technical Communication

The following list of audiences and their purposes suggests ways to think about different groups of people in different communication contexts and discourse communities. Obviously, these categories are not exclusive. People are members of multiple, overlapping discourse communities, and they shift in and out of various audience roles. For example, at work you may be a nurse or an engineer, but when you go home, you are a member of the public. Thus, you belong to several audience groups. Also, by tailoring too strictly to audience categories, writers run the risk of stereotyping. It's impossible to speak about *all* engineers or *all* musicians. Yet it is helpful to consider audience types, because a specific type of audience generally shares similar concerns and similar purposes. Consider these concerns as you plan and design your document or presentation.

- **Scientists** search for knowledge to "understand the world as it is" (Petroski, 1996, p. 2). Scientists look for at least 95 percent probability that chance played no role in a particular outcome. They want to know how well a study was designed and conducted and whether the findings can be replicated. Scientists know that answers are never "final" and that research is open-ended and ongoing. What seems probable today may well be rendered improbable by tomorrow's research.
- **Engineers** rearrange "the materials and forces of nature" to improve the way things work (Petroski, 1996, p. 1). Engineers solve problems: how to erect a suspension bridge that withstands high winds, how to design a lighter airplane or a smaller pacemaker, or how to boost rocket thrust on a space shuttle. The engineer's concern is usually with practical applications, with structures and materials that can be tested for safety and dependability.
- **Executives** focus on decision-making. In a global business climate of overnight developments (world markets, political strife, military conflicts, natural disasters), executives must often react immediately. In such cases, they rely on the best information available—even if this information is incomplete or unverified (Seglin, 1998, p. 54).
- **Managers** oversee the day-to-day operations of their organizations, focusing on problems such as how to motivate employees, how to increase productivity, how to save money, and how to avoid workplace accidents. They collaborate with colleagues and supervise multiple projects. To keep things running smoothly, managers rely on memos, reports, and other forms of information sharing.

- **Technicians** are the people who operate, construct, or fix things. They have expertise in how things work or why things don't work. While they may understand technical terms related to the equipment they use or the processes they are involved in, they may not be familiar with the theoretical concepts behind them. This audience is intensely practical. When reading technical documents, technicians are interesting in learning *how*: how to perform specific tasks, how to solve problems, how a new piece of equipment or device or procedure relates to their current jobs, or how to expand their knowledge base in order to perform their tasks more efficiently and/or effectively.
- **Sales representatives** often focus on selling technical products or services to a general audience. They need to understand how a piece of equipment or new technology works in order to discuss its application. They need to understand the pros and cons, and the similarities and differences between technologies or equipment but do not need to understand all the technical details.
- **Lawyers** focus on protecting the organization from liability or corporate sabotage by answering questions like these: Do these instructions contain adequate warnings and cautions? Is there anything about this product that could generate a lawsuit? Have any of our trade secrets been revealed? Lawyers carefully review documents before approving their distribution outside the company.
- **The public** focuses on the big picture—on what pertains to them directly: What does this mean to me? How can I use this product safely and effectively? Why should I even read this? They rely on information for some immediate practical purpose: to complete a task (what do I do next?), to learn more about something (what are the facts, and what do they mean?), to make a judgment (is this good enough?).

Because audiences' basic purposes vary, every audience expects a message tailored to its own specific interests, social conventions, ways of understanding problems, and information needs.

Checklist for Analyzing Audience, Purpose, and Content

Audience
- Have I identified my exact audience?
- Have I identified this audience's specific interests, information needs, and attitude toward this topic?
- Have I identified the level of technical understanding of the audience?
- Have I interviewed audience members beforehand?

Purpose
- Do I know exactly why this information is needed?
- Do I know exactly what will be done with this information?
- Have I considered all secondary uses of this information?

Context
- Have I considered the settings in which this information will be used?
- Have I considered the political, legal, and cross-cultural issues involving this document?
- Should I refer to a specific style guide for composing this document?
- Can I refer to any user preference or marketing surveys for composing this document?

 Exercises

1. Select a topic with which you are familiar: choose from your hobbies, your job, or your academic major. Assume that you will be writing a brochure on this topic and that your audience will be your classmates. Using the Audience Analysis Worksheet presented in this chapter, interview two or three classmates. From your notes, write an audience and purpose statement. It should begin: "The audience for my brochure is [describe it]. The purpose of my brochure is [describe it using verbs: to inform, to train, to convince, etc.]." Trade your statement with a classmate and exchange feedback.

2. Interview one or two professionals in a field that interests you. These professionals should have a job description that includes writing. Ask them the following questions:
    a) What types of documents do you write?
    b) How do you know who your audience is?
    c) How do you research your audience?
    d) What strategies do you employ to reach your audience?
    e) What typical obstacles do you face in trying to communicate?
    f) How do you write to more than one audience?

    Present your findings to the class.

3. **FOCUS ON WRITING.** Based on your experience in Exercise 1, modify the Audience Analysis Worksheet to include other questions, categories, or topics that you will need to learn about in order to understand your audience more fully. Write a memo to your instructor about your findings.

4. **FOCUS ON WRITING.** Find a short article related to your major (or part of a long article or a selection from your textbook for an advanced course). Choose a piece written at the highest level of technicality you can understand.

Using the Audience Analysis Worksheet, write down the assumptions about the audience made by the author. What kind of audience did the author have in mind? What audience characteristics did she or he assume? What are the purposes of this document? Now, working with a partner in class, discuss a different audience (laypeople, mixed audience, novices) for this topic. Write about the changes that you might make to turn this article into something accessible to a new audience.

5. Locate a technical or professional magazine in your field. Analyze the publication with the following questions in mind: Who is the primary audience for the magazine? Is there a secondary audience? What is the purpose of the magazine? What content items does the magazine have that make it attractive to its primary audience? Write a memo to the class answering these questions.

6. Write two paragraphs about a topic you know thoroughly. In the first paragraph, write to someone with your level of knowledge; in the second paragraph, write the same information to a non-expert. Make notes about the writing decisions you made to accommodate each audience.

7. FOCUS ON RESEARCH. Conduct an online search to identify four websites focused on weather information and forecasting. Try to find two that appear to be addressed to technical audiences and two addressed to general, non-technical, "consumer" audiences. Use the sites listed below as starting points.

How are these sites designed to present information to a specific audience? Are these sites designed primarily for one audience or one purpose?

How are secondary audiences and purposes addressed? Which site would be most useful to you if you were a meteorologist working on a weekend forecast? Which would be most useful to you if you were planning a family picnic? Why?

Make a list of the key features of each site that appeal to a specific audience, and present your findings in a brief report to your class. Be sure to consider visual presentation, site design, writing style, and other features (the presence or absence of advertisements, for example) when you analyze the sites.

- **www.msc-smc.ec.gc.ca**
  The official site of the Meteorological Service of Environment Canada, which provides information on current meteorological research, weather forecasts, and publications and links.
- **www.weathernetwork.ca**
  A national commercial weather information site directed at both technical and non-technical audiences.
- **www.bom.gov.au**
  The official site of the Australian government's Bureau of Meteorology.
- **www.cmos.ca**
  The Canadian Meteorological and Oceanographic Society website, with links to publications, universities, and organizations dedicated to the study of weather science.

The Collaboration Window

Form teams of three to six people. If possible, teammates should be from the same or similar majors (electrical engineering, biology, graphic design, etc.). Address the following situation: An increasing number of first-year students are dropping out of your major because of low grades, stress, or inability to keep up with the work. Your task is to prepare an online "survival guide" for incoming students. This website should focus on the challenges and pitfalls of the first year in this major. But before you can prepare the guide, you need to do a thorough analysis of your audience and purpose.

Assuming that some of you are in this major, perform an audience analysis using the Audience Analysis Worksheet on page 31 or a modified version of it. One team member should take notes, but all team members should participate, alternately, as interviewers and interviewees. Take turns interviewing students one at a time. Once you have a reasonable amount of information, draft an audience and purpose statement for your online survival guide (see Exercise 1).

The Global Window

Many websites and technical documents today are designed for truly global audiences. Consider the sites for multinational corporations, such as Canon and Sony. These sites are explicitly designed for multiple audiences around the globe, with screens in different languages specific to each region and country. Explore these and other international sites, and consider how they are designed to present information to global audiences. Create a list of specific features and elements of each site that differ from region to region. Consider language differences, visual presentation and images, navigation, units of measurement, idioms and slang, cultural biases, and marketing strategies for each. Discuss how you would redesign the site to make it even more accessible to an international audience.

- **www.canon.com**
  World gateway site for Canon Inc., a producer of cameras and business machines marketed and sold around the world.
- **www.sony.net**
  Sony Global, the world headquarters and internet portal site for Sony Group, a leading provider of consumer electronic devices, games, music, and movies.

MyCanadianTechCommLab
Go to MyCanadianTechCommLab at www.mycanadiantechcommlab.ca for additional online exercises and problems.

CHAPTER 3

Designing Usable Information

Chapter Objectives

By the end of this chapter you will be able to:

1. Write for a specific audience and for a specific usability.

2. Use the appropriate language for your target audience.

3. Recognize the elements of an effective paragraph.

4. Revise your work based on testing.

5. Create an outline with topics and subtopics to help you plan and organize your material/information.

6. Understand what readers are looking for (keywords, the ability to skim the work, concise writing).

Carole Sigouin, Gatineau, Quebec

With a diploma in Arts and Science from Algonquin College of Ottawa and a Bachelor of Arts from University of Ottawa, Carole Sigouin started her career in technical writing in 1990, working as a technical editor and translator at Public Works and Government Services Canada. In 1996, she accepted a Bilingual Technical Documentation Specialist role at Nortel, which had more than 100 000 employees worldwide in over 60 countries. In this position, she was trained in electronics, telecommunications, and information technology, as well as management of business administration.

After leaving Nortel, Ms. Sigouin founded her own consulting firm, Editch Documentation Inc., in Gatineau in 2001, which specializes in bilingual technical writing, translation, and editing for the high-tech industry in the private and public sectors. "Since I'm bilingual, freelance translation and editing helped me throughout my career—when the market didn't call for technical writing services, I could always fall back into other roles, having had various writing experiences. I do research and interviews to fully understand my clients' needs before I come up with a documentation plan."

Usability and Technical Information

When you plan, write, and design a piece of communication—a brochure, manual, online help screen, or report—you are creating a communication product. Like any other product, people will use it only if they can find what they need, understand the language, follow the instructions, and read the graphics. In other words, communication products must be *usable*. According to the International Organization for Standardization (ISO), the term *usability* refers to "a set of multiple concepts, such as execution time, performance, user satisfaction and ease of learning ('learnability') taken together" (Abran et al., 2003).

Some researchers have noted that "usability is often seen as an end-of-the-production-cycle affair" (Johnson, Salvo, & Zoetewey, 2007, p. 320). But to create a usable communication product, you must begin with a careful audience and purpose analysis (see Chapter 2). This analysis will provide you with much of the basic information you need to design your material. You can also take other more specific steps to ensure that your document is usable during the planning stages, during the writing and design process, and after the release of your document.

Usability During the Planning Stages

Before you begin writing or designing any information product, learn all you can about your audience and the intended use of your document. Then develop a clear plan.

Perform an Audience and Purpose Analysis

A systematic audience analysis is critical to any successful technical communication. To perform an audience analysis, customize the worksheet provided in Chapter 2 to fit your specific situation.

Perform a Task Analysis

Most audiences approach technical communication material with a series of tasks in mind. These tasks are most evident when the document is a set of instructions. For example, when users want to install a new oil filter, assemble a new gas grill, or install a new word-processing program. But other forms of communication, such as reports, memos, and brochures, also involve user tasks. When reading a report, a manager may need to extract information and write a response. When replying to a memo, a technician may need to explain why the company should purchase new equipment. In this way, most technical communication is task-oriented. People come to the information wanting to *do* something.

As one pair of experts notes, "It is all too easy to forget that the product exists because human beings are trying to accomplish tasks. Task analysis refocuses attention on users and on their tasks and goals" (Dumas & Redish, 1994, p. 44).

For your task analysis, you can create a worksheet similar to the one shown in Figure 3.1. Begin by defining the main tasks. For example, for an instruction manual to accompany a gas grill, you might define the primary user task as "Assemble the grill." But this task can be divided into several smaller tasks. Note that the tasks are listed using verb forms (assemble, locate, get, and so on):

1. *Locate* all parts.
2. *Get* the required tools.
3. *Lay out* parts in order.
4. *Assemble* parts into smaller units.
5. *Assemble* these smaller units into large units.

Even this list can be subdivided. For example, "Assemble parts into smaller units" probably consists of several smaller steps.

You can determine these tasks by interviewing users and watching them perform the actions. Once you understand the tasks, you can create an information

---

Main task: Assemble the grill

Subtasks
1. Locate all parts.
2. Get the required tools.
3. Lay out parts in order.
4. Assemble parts into smaller units.
5. Assemble these smaller units into large units.

Main task: Use the grill

Subtasks
1. Attach the gas canister.
2. Turn on the main gas valve.
3. Turn on the individual burners.
4. Press button to ignite.

Main task: Maintain the grill

Subtasks
1. Turn off the main gas valve when not in use.
2. Cover to protect from rain.
3. Clean the grate regularly.

Figure 3.1 **Sample Task Analysis Worksheet for a Gas Grill Instruction Manual**

plan (discussed next). Ultimately, your document will be more useful if you know what your audience wants to *do* with it.

Develop an Information Plan

Once you have a clear picture of the audience and purpose for your document, as well as the intended user tasks, you can draft an information plan: an outline of the assumptions, goals, specifications, and budget for your document. Information plans can be as short as a two- to three-page memo or as long as a five- to ten-page report, depending on your project. Begin with a clearly stated goal ("Users will be able to assemble a gas grill within 30 minutes") so that you can measure when a task has been successfully completed (Rubin, 1994). Figure 3.2 is a sample information plan created in a short-memo format.

Research Your Topic

Developing an information plan might require research. For instance, you might need to determine how often gas grill accidents occur because the burner unit was assembled incorrectly or because a faulty connection has been overlooked. This kind of research will certainly affect your decisions about what information to include and what to leave out. For more information on conducting research, see Chapter 5.

Usability During the Writing and Design Process

Once you have completed these first steps, you can write, design, and test your document. For a gas grill instruction manual, you would write the instructions, design the graphics, and select a medium (print, CD-ROM, web) for distributing the information. Most instructions are printed on paper and included with the product. You might choose paper but also make the information available on a website. Besides choosing a delivery method, you can take other steps at this stage to ensure usability.

Test Early Versions of Your Communication Product

Allow audience members to provide input as early as possible in the process. If time and budget allow, test your first draft of the brochure, webpage, or report on potential users. Ask them what they find useful and what they find confusing. Or watch people use the material and measure their performance. For example, if someone tried to assemble a gas grill but could not locate a part because of unclear instructions, this knowledge would be valuable to you as you revise the material.

GrillChef Corporation

To: Technical writing design team
From: Erin Green and Geoff Brannigan, team leaders
Date: January 21, 2003
Re: Information plan for gas grill manual

As you know, our team recently performed an analysis of user needs as we prepare to design and write the new User Manual for the new GrillChef Model 2000 double-burner grill. This memo summarizes our findings and presents a plan for proceeding.

Part One: Analysis

Audience—The audience for this manual is very broad. It consists of consumers who purchase the grill. This purchase may be their first gas grill, or they may be replacing an old grill. Some users are making a switch from charcoal to gas. Our analysis revealed that the primary users are male and female, ranging in age from 25–50. From a focus group, we determined that most users are afraid to assemble the grill. But all members expressed enthusiasm about using the grill. Also, according to marketing, this grill is only sold in the United States.

Purpose— The manual has several purposes:
1. Instruct the user in assembling and using the grill.
2. Provide adequate safety instructions. These are to protect the user and to make sure we have complied with our legal requirements.
3. Provide a phone number, Web address, and other contact information if users have questions or need replacement parts.

User tasks—Our task analysis revealed three main tasks this manual must address:
1. How to assemble the grill. Users need clear instructions, a list of parts, and diagrams that can assist them. Users wish to be able to assemble the grill within 30 minutes to one hour.
2. How to use the grill. Users need clear instructions for operating the grill safely. Because some users have never used gas for grilling, we need to stress safety.
3. How to maintain the grill. Users need to know how to keep the grill clean, dry, and operational.

Part Two: Design Plans

Based on our analysis, we suggest designing a manual that is simple, easy to use, and contains information users need. We will follow the layout and format of our other manuals.

Rough outline—Cover with drawing of grill, model number, company name.

Inside front cover: safety warnings (our legal department has indicated that these warnings need to go first).

First section: Exploded diagram, list of parts, drawings of parts, numbered list of instructions for assembly.

Second section: Numbered list of steps for using the grill, accompanied by diagrams.

Third section: Bulleted list of tasks users must perform to maintain the grill.

Final page: Company address, phone number, and Web address.

Production guidelines—Our budget for this project will not allow for color printing or any photographs. We suggest black ink on white paper, 8-1/2 x 11 folded in half vertically. We can use line drawings of the Model 1999 and modify these to the specifications of the Model 2000.

Schedule—The manual must be ready for shipping on April 1, 1999. We will follow our usual production and writing schedule, briefly summarized here:

February 21: First draft of manual is complete. Manual is usability tested on sample customers.

March 1: Manual is revised based on results of usability test.

March 3: Copyediting, proofreading, and final changes. Manual goes to the printer.

March 30: Manual is back from printer and sent to the warehouse.

April 1: Product is shipped.

Figure 3.2   **Sample Information Plan for the Gas Grill Manual**

Qualitative Testing.   To identify which parts of the document work or don't work, observe how users react or what they say or do. Qualitative testing employs either focus groups or protocol analysis (Plain English Network, 2008):

- **Focus groups.** Based on a list of targeted questions about the document's content, organization, style, and design, users discuss what information they think is missing and what is excessive, what they like or dislike, and what they find easy or hard to understand. They may also suggest ways of revising the document's graphics, format, or level of technical information.
- **Protocol analysis.** In a one-on-one interview, a user reads a specific section of a document and then explains what that section means. For long documents, the interviewer also observes how the person actually reads the document: for example, how often she or he flips pages or refers to the index or table of contents to find information. In another version of protocol analysis, users read the material and think aloud about what they find useful or confusing as they perform the task.

Quantitative Testing.   Assess a document's overall effectiveness by using a *control group*. For example, you can compare success rates between two groups using two different versions of your document, or you can compare the number of people who performed the task accurately to the number who performed it inaccurately (Plain English Network, 2008). You can also measure the time required to complete a task and the types and frequency of user errors (Hughes, 1999, p. 489). Although it yields hard numerical data, quantitative testing is obviously more complicated, time-consuming, and expensive than its qualitative counterpart.

When to Use Which Test.   If time, budget, and available users allow, consider doing both qualitative and quantitative testing. Quantitative testing is ordinarily done after qualitative testing, as a final check on usability. Each test has its benefits and limitations. Quantitative testing "will tell you *if* the new document is a success, but it won't tell you *why* it is or isn't a success" (Plain English Network, 2008). In short, to find out if the document succeeds as a whole, use quantitative testing; to find out exactly which parts of the document work or don't work, use qualitative testing.

Revise Your Plan and Your Product

Revise your information plan and your draft documents to conform to audience feedback. If your audience finds a technical term difficult to understand, define it clearly or use a simpler word or concept. If a graphic makes no sense, devise one that does. It is easier to make these changes earlier rather than later, after your information has already been printed, distributed, or posted to the web.

Create Documentation That Is Context-Sensitive

A useful way to think about providing documentation for your audiences is to consider that documentation is *context-sensitive*. Context-sensitive documentation considers the current situation and provides information specific to that situation, rather than providing general information. Computer programs often have embedded context-sensitive information that addresses the specific tasks that users want to complete. For example, if a user creating a memo template in Microsoft Word clicks on Help, the context-sensitive help system gives the user advice on how to create the template. Many online help systems today are context-sensitive, providing audiences with more closely focused help that pertains to their immediate needs.

Context-sensitive help is relatively new. In the past, software documentation was often designed as a series of paper-based materials, such as quick reference cards, "getting started" or "quick start" short manuals, or full-blown long manuals. Today, although these types of materials still exist, software documentation can usually be found on the same installation CD as the software itself and is usually context-sensitive. This kind of online software documentation often accompanies and sometimes replaces paper-based documentation.

Whether documentation is electronic or paper-based, you still need to know your audience when designing it. Software users range from novices to experts and therefore one single type of documentation simply won't suffice. Novices would be confused by the shorthand and technical terms that make sense to experts, whereas experts would be frustrated with the level of detail and explanation needed for a novice user. Depending on their level of expertise, different users need different types of information from documentation, and they should be able to use the documentation to find information that matches their needs. For example, user guides are primarily targeted at novices who want to learn about the product. Quick reference guides are targeted at users who know the product but need a quick reminder. Troubleshooting guides are targeted at both experienced and novice users who need a quick source of answers to solve specific problems. Whether the medium is electronic or paper-based, software documentation should address the specific needs of the users and the tasks for which they use the software.

Usability After the Information Is Released

Even after your instruction manual is on its way to the new gas grill owners or your report is being circulated among other engineers and managers, there are still ways to ensure usability in your information.

Provide Mechanisms for User Feedback

You can include ways for users to provide feedback on the documentation, such as customer comment cards, email addresses, telephone numbers, and websites. If your instructions contain a mistake on page 6, you can be sure customers will let you know, provided you give them a way to reach you.

Plan for the Next Version or Release

Continue collecting information, researching, and gathering user input as you plan the next version or release of your document. If you will need to revise the manual in a few months, begin collecting data as soon as possible. If the gas grill will be redesigned for next season, learn about the new design so you can plan the new manual. Establish an information file for quick access when you begin revising and updating.

Checklist for Designing Usable Information

Planning for Usable Communication
- Did I perform an audience and purpose analysis?
- Did I develop an information plan?
- Did I do enough research?

Writing and Designing Usable Communication
- Did I test an early version of the communication product?
- Did I make needed revisions to the plan or product based on testing?

Exercises

1. Think of an activity for which a novice would require instructions. Prepare a task analysis for this activity using a worksheet similar to the one in Figure 3.1. Exchange task analyses with another student in your class, and critique each other's analysis. With your class, discuss the challenges of doing a task analysis, and identify strategies for performing a task analysis effectively.

2. Examine technical reports to determine their arrangement strategies and content development. For each report, answer the following: Who is (are) the intended audience(s) for the report? What is the author's intended purpose?

What arrangement strategy is the author using? How does the author of each report develop the content information? How long and detailed are the paragraphs, and how are they organized? Examine and discuss how the report reflects the readers' informational needs.

3. **FOCUS ON WRITING**. Find a set of instructions or a similar type of technical document that is easy to use. Identify specific characteristics of the document that make it usable. Is the document well written? Does it have an overview? Can you quickly find the information you need? Next find a technical document that is hard to use. What characteristics make it unusable? In a memo to your instructor, define specific changes that you would make in revising the second document. Submit both examples along with your memo.

4. **FOCUS ON WRITING**. As a technical communicator, you will sometimes encounter technical terms that need to be defined or revised for a non-expert audience. But how do you define a technical term if you don't fully understand it yourself?

    Usable communication must be written in terminology and language consistent with the audience's background and level of understanding. Use online dictionaries and usability resources to help you revise the language of your documents for non-technical audiences.

    Find an article in a technical or science journal in your field or area of interest and create a list of unfamiliar terms. Use the following resources to look up definitions of these terms, and then write your own brief definition of each, directed at a non-specialist audience.

    *   **http://dictionary.langenberg.com**
        A portal site that connects to dozens of online dictionaries of various types and specialties.
    *   **www.webopedia.com**
        An online dictionary and search engine focused on computer and internet technology definitions.
    *   **www.techweb.com/encyclopedia**
        Definitions for over 20 000 information technology terms and acronyms.
    *   **http://upassoc.org**
        The website for the Usability Professionals' Association.

The Collaboration Window

Bring to class some children's connecting blocks, such as Tinkertoy, Mega Bloks, K'Nex, or Lego. Form several teams of four to six people, and assign two people to be the technical writers. The technical writers should assemble a few of the pieces into a simple design (don't use more than three or four pieces), then write up a quick instruction card explaining how to assemble the pieces into the design you've created. For example, the card for Lego blocks might read:

1. Select two large red blocks and two small green blocks.
2. Place one red block on its side.
3. Attach one green block to the red block.

Then present the "parts" and your instructions to the rest of your team. Watch as your team tries to assemble the blocks according to your instructions. Assess the instructions for usability. Were all tasks accounted for? Did any terms or language confuse the users? Go back and perform a task analysis, and discuss what you could do to improve the usability of your instruction card.

 ## The Global Window

Astronomy and planetary science have become truly global sciences, and space exploration is now conducted by multinational teams. Knowledge about astronomy belongs to everyone, regardless of nationality or language. Do the websites representing these disciplines succeed in making themselves accessible to and useful for a global audience?

Explore the websites in the following list, and assess their usability for international audiences. Would non-English speakers be able to access the information on these sites? What efforts are made to reach international readers? Are language and cultural differences accounted for in the design, content, and interface?

Draw up a list of key elements and features of each site that contribute to or detract from usability for international audiences. What changes would you recommend to make each site more accessible and usable for non-English-speaking readers? Summarize your assessment in a brief memo, including printed copies of specific pages from each website that you discuss.

- **www.unb.ca/fredericton/science/research/passc/**
  University of New Brunswick, Planetary and Space Science Centre
- **www.asc-csa.gc.ca/eng/default.asp**
  Canadian Space Agency
- **www.esa.int/esaCP/index.html**
  European Space Agency

MyCanadianTechCommLab

Go to MyCanadianTechCommLab at www.mycanadiantechcommlab.ca for additional online exercises and problems.

CHAPTER 4

Writing and Editing for Usability

Chapter Objectives

By the end of this chapter you will be able to:

1. Create an outline with topics and subtopics to help you plan and organize your material/information.

2. Create an effective sentence and paragraph.

3. Recognize the elements of an effective paragraph.

4. Identify the different types of paragraph organization.

5. Use transition devices effectively.

6. Avoid common grammar pitfalls.

7. Use the appropriate language for your target audience.

8. Understand what readers are looking for (keywords, the ability to skim the work, concise writing).

Andrew Brooke, Toronto, Ontario

Andrew Brooke graduated from Ryerson Polytechnical Institute in Toronto in 1988 with a degree in Graphic Communications Management. He worked as a print production coordinator, then changed careers to work in software. For five years, Andrew worked with computers and databases at an educational organization. Later, at Symantec, he worked in technical support, writing support documents and managing an online support tool. This led Andrew into technical communication.

In 1998, Andrew began work as a technical writer at i2 Technologies. In 2003, he moved to InSystems, where he is now the senior technical writer. Andrew firmly believes that technical communication is undergoing a major revolution: "The days of traditional 'user guide' publishing are ending. Instead, the profession will continue to split into its various specialties, with information developers creating the *content* of many, reusable pieces of information, information designers creating the *look* of information, and information architects creating the *containers* for the information."

Since 2002, Andrew has been active in the Toronto STC (Society for Technical Communication) chapter and is currently its newsletter editor and membership manager. Andrew enjoys exploring the philosophy of technical communication on his blog at http://techwriters-world.blogspot.com.

Writing Clearly and Correctly

As the Conference Board of Canada points out in "Employability Skills 2000+," the ability to communicate, especially in writing, is a valuable skill that all employees must possess. An employee needs to be able to take complex ideas and communicate them to the wider population. The main goal of a technical writer is to produce documents and presentations that are reliable, accessible, and usable for the intended audience. Thus in technical writing it is important to produce readable texts that your reader can easily comprehend.

Yet many writers forget that good technical writing must be "reader-centred." This means that the audience shapes the presentation of data or content, not the writer. As pointed out in the previous chapters, you must always identify the purpose or objective of your work, and then determine the best way to convey this message to your target audience. Therefore, efficient and effective technical writing is characterized by writing that focuses on the needs and reactions of the readers and then organizes the material to allow them to understand the issues. If you don't consider the informational needs of your reader, you may find that your message fails to get the desired reaction.

Once you have determined the purpose of the document or presentation, the next challenge is to determine how to organize the material you have gathered. To do this, you will need to address several questions regarding the audience's informational needs:

- What primary question am I trying to answer?
- What secondary questions will help clarify the original question?
- How does the data or content fit with these questions?
- What should be emphasized in the document?
- Where should the emphasis be placed?
- What is the take-away message for the audience?
- What is the appropriate level of detail for the audience?
- What information can I omit?
- What headings and subheadings will give the audience an overview of the document?

How you answer these questions will vary from document to document, based on your objectives and your audience. Remember that the document needs to make sense not just to you, but also to the readers. Your task therefore is to determine the best way to organize and present your ideas.

Creating an Outline

When you are answering these questions, a good strategy to determine the best organizational structure for your writing is to create an outline. An outline is "writer-centred"; it is a visual and conceptual design for your writing. In other words, it is the road map for your document—allowing you to see how your main message will unfold for the reader. An outline is a valuable tool because you can jot down ideas, then rethink and rearrange the structure of the document before writing the first draft. Remember, it is easier to make changes at this stage of the writing process than later. An outline must therefore be flexible, allowing you to arrange and rearrange ideas easily. The outline helps you present material in a logical form. It helps show relationships between ideas. It need not be formal or even written in complete sentences.

When drafting your outline, you will need to determine the best method for organizing the document as a whole. There are several ways to organize a document:

- **Chronological order.** This is a good organizational method if your document involves a linear process, such as step-by-step instructions.
- **Parts of an object.** This structure is often used to describe an object, such as an engine, that has many parts (pistons, spark plugs, values, etc.).
- **Simple to complex order (or vice versa).** Begins with the simplest and easiest ideas and gradually moves to more in-depth, complex ideas.
- **Specific to general order.** Starts with several ideas and then organizes the ideas into sub-categories.
- **General to specific order.** Begins with a small number of categories of ideas, and then becomes more in-depth.

There are two common types of outline patterns: the topic outline and the sentence outline (see Figure 4.1). The topic outline is the easiest and fastest form of outline to create. It uses words or phrases without punctuation to generate an overview of the document. In contrast, the sentence outline is more detailed and takes longer to produce. It provides compete topic sentences and uses full sentences and correct punctuation for all entries. Both methods make writing the draft easier because they allow you to pre-plan the scope and structure of the document. The outline style you use often depends on the type of document you are creating. Short informal documents may only require a quick topic outline, whereas longer, more complex documents may warrant a sentence outline.

Topic: The Benefits of Post-Secondary Education

Topic Outline

General Topic: Benefits of attending post-secondary school

I. Gaining life experience
   A. time management
   B. socialization skills
   C. responsibility

II. More job possibilities
   A. networking
   B. increased income
   C. more employment skills

Sentence Outline

General Topic: Benefits of attending post-secondary school

I. By attending a post-secondary school, one gains valuable life skills.
   A. One must learn to manage their time by balancing multiple tasks.
   B. Many courses and components of post-secondary school encourage students to work in groups.
   C. Attending higher education requires commitment and responsibility.

II. While attending post-secondary school, one gains crucial employment skills.
   A. Networking allows students to build contacts that may benefit them while they search for a job.
      1. Meeting potential employers gives students an opportunity to see what skills employers are looking for.
      2. Networking provides up-to-date information about trends in the field.
   B. Attending post-secondary school increases one's income potential upon graduation.
      1. Higher paying jobs are available to those with more education.
   C. Attending post-secondary school provides opportunities for students to participate in co-op programs or get jobs in their desired fields before

Figure 4.1   Examples of Topic and Sentence Outlines

Writing Clear Paragraphs

Once you have created your outline, it is time to begin to draft your paper. Good technical writing is characterized by *coherence*. Coherence means that your document holds together: it flows smoothly from one idea to the next. Readers want to be able to read a document from start to finish without getting lost. Moreover, many readers today skim documents quickly and selectively to look for information that is of interest to them. In the real world, because of time constraints, the technical reader does not linger over prose; he or she just wants to understand the main purpose of the document and the actions it recommends. Thus, your task is to create a document that is easy to skim. The main ideas and call to action must stand out for your reader.

One of the best ways to make the main ideas stand out is to write in good paragraph form. A paragraph is a sequence of related sentences that develops a single idea. As a rule, a good paragraph in technical writing is 60–100 words long, or three to five (or more) sentences. A good paragraph has *unity*, which means that it focuses on one idea. A paragraph must also have *internal coherence:* each paragraph must hold together, with one sentence leading logically to the next. Finally, an efficient and effective paragraph has *adequate content.* So as a technical writer you must ensure that you have selected an appropriate amount of information—not too much, not too little—to support the main idea of each paragraph.

Structure of a Paragraph

Readers expect paragraphs to have a predictable structure. Every paragraph must have a main idea that is expressed in a single sentence, which is called the *topic sentence* (see Figure 4.2). The best location for the topic sentence is at the beginning of the paragraph, since it helps the reader locate information easily. The remaining sentences in the paragraph simply support, elaborate, or explain the topic sentence. A paragraph may also end with a concluding sentence or sentences that provide a transition to the next paragraph.

A Closer Look at Paragraph Structure

The **topic sentence**

- starts the paragraph
- tells the reader what the paragraph is about
- allows the reader to skim past the paragraph if the subject matter is of no interest to them

The **supporting sentences**

- provide details such as facts, illustrations, and statistics to reinforce the main idea of the paragraph
- prove that the topic sentence is true
- provide detailed instructions for performing the task described in the topic sentence

The **concluding sentence**

- restates the topic sentence using different words or a different focus
- comments on the paragraph's topic (e.g., its usefulness, its connection to other parts of the document, etc.)
- often provides a transition to the paragraph that follows

(1) Mould is a public health problem. (2) Moulds are simple organisms that are found virtually everywhere, indoors and outdoors. The potential health effects of indoor mould are a growing concern. Mould can cause or worsen certain illnesses (e.g., some allergic and occupation-related diseases and infections in health care settings). (3) There is no conclusive evidence, however, that indoor mould is associated with other health problems, such as pulmonary hemorrhage, memory loss, and lack of energy.	**(1) Topic Sentence** tells the reader what the topic of the paragraph is. **(2) Supporting details** help illuminate the main idea. **(3) Concluding sentence** comments on the topic.

Figure 4.2 **Parts of a Paragraph**
Source: Adapted from the Centers for Disease Control and Prevention (2004), "Molds in the Environment," www.cdc.gov/MOLD/pdfs/pib.pdf..

Paragraph Types

When writing an effective paragraph, you must also consider how you will organize the information. It is important to place information where readers expect to find it. Skim-readers are more likely to read the first and last sentences of paragraphs. For this reason, place your key messages in either or both of these places.

In addition, the way you choose to organize information will affect the meaning your readers will derive from the text. The most common patterns of organization in technical writing are chronological order, exemplification, compare and contrast, cause and effect, classification, description, definition, process, and division. Each of these patterns has its own characteristic features.

Chronological Order paragraphs present the reader with material that is arranged in order of occurrence or sequence. If you are trying to convey a set of instructions or processes, or if you want illustrate the development of an object or idea, then use a chronological organization.

For example:

> **When making homemade ice cream, the ice cream maker must follow five basic steps.** The first step is to blend the milk solids, sugar, and water thoroughly. The next step is to pasteurize the mixture in order to destroy any harmful bacteria. The third step is to blend the mixture until it has a smooth consistency. The fourth step is to add colour and flavour to the mixture. Finally, the fifth step is to freeze the mixture to turn it into ice cream.

Exemplification paragraphs provide the reader with examples (such as illustrations, facts, and data) that clarify the topic sentence.
For example:

> **Bases are used in the home to neutralise acids**. For example, toothpaste is a weak base that is used to neutralise acids formed by plaque bacteria on your teeth. Bases can also be used to dissolve grease and dirt.
>
> (http://esolonline.tki.org.nz/ESOL-Online/Teacher-needs/Pedagogy/Principles-of-effective-teaching-and-learning-for-English-language-learners/Acids-and-bases/Learning-task-2)

Compare and Contrast paragraphs tell the reader about the similarities or differences between two objects, processes, or states. A comparison paragraph highlights the similarities, whereas a contrast paragraph highlights the differences.
For example:

> There are a number of skeletal differences between reptiles and mammals. For one, reptiles have a mouth filled with several teeth which are more or less uniform in size and shape; they vary slightly in size, but they all have the same basic cone-shaped form. By contrast, mammals tend to have teeth which vary greatly in size and shape; everything from flat, multi-cusped molar teeth to the sharp cone-shaped canines. In reptiles, the lower jaw is comprised of *several different bones*, which hinge on the *quadrate* bone of the skull and the *angular* bone of the jaw. In mammals, however, the lower jaw is comprised of only one bone - the *dentary*, which hinges at the *quadrate* of the skull.
>
> (http://genesispanthesis.tripod.com/fossils/rept_mam.html)

Cause and Effect paragraphs explain the reasons for or *causes* of something.
For example:

> **A warming climate in Canada will have impacts on water quantity and quality across the country**. For example climate models for the Great Lakes basin predict decreases in annual streamflow and lake levels. More frequent heavy downpours may cause localized flooding and overwhelm current sewage treatment facilities with increased volumes of stormwater and sewage runoff.
>
> (Frequently Asked Questions, http://www.climatechange.gc.ca/default.asp?lang = En&n = 3F11F818-1, Environment Canada, 2010.)

Classification paragraphs group information about people, organisms, objects, or ideas into categories according to shared characteristics.

For example:

> **Normally, the term "outsider" is used for somebody who does not fit into society's accepted norms.** Firstly, there are those who are put into the "out" group for political, religious, or ethnic reasons. Secondly, some of the people who are often viewed as outsiders in our society are the homeless. Thirdly, the obviously eccentric people belong among outsiders. And last, but not least, teenagers too may form a group of outsiders.
>
> (http://lepo.it.da.ut.ee/ ~ edat/paragraph.htm)

Description paragraphs organize material by describing a person, object, place, situation, or event.
   For example:

> **In its free gaseous form, hydrogen is much lighter than air, rising and quickly dissipating when released into the atmosphere.** Its high energy-to-weight ratio makes it an ideal spacecraft fuel. Invisible, odourless, and non-toxic, hydrogen is also widely used in the food, metal, glass and chemical industries.
>
> (Hydrogen Properties and Sources, http://www.hydrogeneconomy.gc.ca/scie/ pro-pro-eng.htm, Natural Resources Canada, 2009.)

Definition paragraphs are very similar to description paragraphs. Definition paragraphs elaborate on the meaning of a word or concept.
   For example:

> **Diabetes (also known as diabetes mellitus) is a condition in which the body either can't make or can't use insulin properly.** Insulin is a hormone normally produced by the pancreas. Insulin is very important because it regulates the sugar level in the blood, and it allows the body to use this sugar for energy. Without enough insulin, the body's cells can't get the energy they need, the sugar level in the blood gets too high, and many problems can result. Diabetes is not curable, but, fortunately, it is treatable.
>
> (www.yourdiseaserisk.wustl.edu)

Process paragraphs explain how to do something, how to create something, or how something happens.
   For example:

> **Water should be placed in a heat-resistant container or in an electric kettle without an automatic shut-off and brought to a rolling boil for 1 minute to kill all disease-causing organisms.** Water can also be boiled in a microwave oven using a microwave-safe container, but it is advisable to include a glass rod or wooden or plastic stir stick in the container to prevent the formation of super-heated water (water heated above its boiling point, without the formation of

steam). The water should then be cooled and poured into a clean container or refrigerated until you are ready to use it. At elevations over 2000 metres, water boils at a slightly lower temperature and should therefore be boiled for at least two minutes to kill all disease-causing organisms.

(Boil Water Advisories and Boil Water Orders. Health Canada, 2008. Reproduced with the permission of the Minister of Health, 2011.)

Division paragraphs take a single item and break it into parts. For example:

What is known to most Westerners simply as "the samurai sword" is in fact a whole family of different specializations in the field of blade making. These families can largely be broken down into the Katana, the Wakizashi, and the Tanto. The Katana is the longest of the three types of swords, with a cutting edge generally between 24 and 28 inches. The Wakizashi is generally 18 to 20 inches. Together, a pair of these swords is called a *Daisho*. Samurai also often carried a short dagger called a *Tanto* or *Kozuka*. Each of these blades is the product of a lengthy and complex series of steps involving forging, plate laminating, shaping, composite welding, and quenching.

(Trevor Plint: *How the Katana got its edge*, student paper)

Creating Paragraph Coherence through the Use of Transition Devices

An important element of a well-crafted paragraph is the use of transitional devices—often called transitional words or phrases. Transitional devices help to create coherence by establishing relationships within and between paragraphs (see Table 4.1).

Table 4.1 Examples of Transitional Devices

Illustration	Thus, for example, for instance, namely, to illustrate, in other words, in particular, specifically, such as.
Contrast	On the contrary, contrarily, notwithstanding, but, however, nevertheless, in spite of, in contrast, yet, on one hand, on the other hand, rather, or, nor, conversely, at the same time, while this may be true.
Addition	And; in addition to; furthermore; moreover; besides; than; too; also; both–and; another; equally important; first, second, etc.; again; further; last; finally; not only–but also; as well as; in the second place; next; likewise; similarly; in fact; as a result; consequently; in the same way; for example; for instance; however; thus; therefore; otherwise.

(continued)

Time	After; afterward; before; then; once; next; last; at last; at length; first, second, etc.; at first; formerly; rarely; usually; another; finally; soon; meanwhile; at the same time; for a minute, hour, day, etc.; during the morning, day, week, etc.; most important; later; ordinarily; to begin with; afterwards; generally; in order to; subsequently; previously; in the meantime; immediately; eventually; concurrently; simultaneously.
Space	At the left, at the right, in the centre, on the side, along the edge, on top, below, beneath, under, around, above, over, straight ahead, at the top, at the bottom, surrounding, opposite, at the rear, at the front, in front of, beside, behind, next to, nearby, in the distance, beyond, in the forefront, in the foreground, within sight, out of sight, across, under, nearer, adjacent, in the background.
Concession	Although, at any rate, at least, still, thought, even though, granted that, while it may be true, in spite of, of course.
Similarity or Comparison	Similarly, likewise, in like manner, analogous to.
Emphasis	Above all, indeed, truly, of course, certainly, surely, in fact, really, in truth, again, besides, also, furthermore, in addition.
Details	Specifically, especially, in particular, to explain, to list, in detail, namely, including.
Examples	For example, for instance, to illustrate, thus, in other words, as an illustration, in particular.
Consequence	So that, with the result that, thus, consequently, hence, accordingly, for this reason, therefore, so, because, since, due to, as a result, in other words, then.
Summary	Therefore, finally, consequently, thus, in short, in conclusion, in brief, as a result, accordingly.
Suggestion	For this purpose, to this end, with this in mind, with this purpose in mind, therefore.

Within a paragraph, transition devices help create flow from one sentence to the next. Between paragraphs, transition devices help create flow from one paragraph to the next and help emphasize the relationships between paragraph topics. In the paragraph below, Stephen J. Gould skillfully uses transitional devices to lead the reader from one idea to the next.

I don't wish to deny that the flattened, minuscule head of the large-bodied "stegosaurus" houses little brain from our subjective, top-heavy perspective, **but** I do wish to assert that we should not expect more of the beast. **First of all**, large animals have relatively smaller brains than related, small animals. The correlation of brain size with body size among kindred animals (all reptiles, all mammals, for example) is remarkably regular. **As** we move from small to large animals, from mice to elephants or small lizards to Komodo dragons, brain size increases, but not so fast as body size. **In other words**, bodies grow faster than brains, and large animals have low ratios of brain weight to body weight. **In fact**, brains grow only about two-thirds as fast as bodies. **Since** we have no reason to believe that large animals are consistently stupider than their smaller relatives, we must conclude that large animals require relatively less brain to do as well as smaller animals. **If** we do not recognize this relationship, we are likely to underestimate the mental power of very large animals, dinosaurs in particular.

(Stephen Jay Gould, "Were Dinosaurs Dumb?" Natural History 87)

Building Clear Sentences

Clear sentences build a clear message. Effective writers build ideas from sentence to sentence. Sentences need to be *short* so your reader can process new information. Sentences should be on average 15 words in length and no more than 25 words. However, a variety of sentence lengths and patterns makes your document more appealing. The beginning and end of a sentence draw the most attention. You can put the important points in short sentences and use your longer sentences for discussing the supporting points.

Sentences need to be *unpretentious*. You should avoid redundancies such as *at this point in time, each individual, past history,* and *true and accurate*. Similarly, wordy constructions such as *there are, it is interesting to note that, it may be recalled that,* and *it is important to add that* delay the delivery of information to the reader.

When appropriate, your sentences should focus on the *positive*. Positive sentences are more appealing to read, while negative sentences can discourage your reader from reading and trusting your opinion. Negative phrasing, however, can be used to allay fears, dispel myths, and emphasize dangers. When you are editing, eliminate any double negative constructions in a sentence, since they are confusing. The following is an example of revising a double negative construction.

Instead of: The business will not be unsuccessful.

Use: The business will be successful.

When you need to convey information, link your ideas with words such as *which, that,* and *who*. These linking words help clarify your sentences.

Another way to avoid ambiguity is to use pronouns correctly. In your document, you need to ensure that there is no doubt about which noun the pronoun represents.

In addition, you need to place adverbs and adverbial phrases such as *only, merely, just, even, both, also, mainly, at least,* and *in particular* properly to avoid confusing your reader.

Parallel Structure in Sentences

Good parallel structure influences the effectiveness of your document. All parts of a sentence need to be in the same grammatical form. The example shows how parallel structure improves the ideas in a sentence:

> **Instead of:** Good writing requires you to *plan outlines, write several drafts,* and *revise.*

> **Use:** Good writing requires you to *plan outlines, write several drafts,* and *revise your work.*

Sentence Patterns

When you use a variety of different sentence patterns, your writing flows more smoothly for the reader. There are four sentence patterns that you can use:

- **Simple** sentences contain only one independent clause. An independent clause is a subject-verb combination that can stand alone as a complete sentence:

> The rat ate the cheese.

- **Compound** sentences contain two or more independent clauses. These clauses are joined either by a semicolon or a comma, followed by a coordinating conjunction (and, but, or, nor, for, so, yet).

> The rat ate the cheese, but he did not drink the wine.
>
> The rat ate the cheese; he did not drink the wine.
>
> **Independent clause:** the rat ate the cheese
>
> **Independent clause:** he did not drink the wine

- **Complex** sentences contain one independent clause and at least one subordinate clause. A subordinate clause is a subject-verb combination that cannot stand alone as a complete sentence.

The rat ate the cheese because he was hungry.

Independent clause: the rat ate the cheese

Subordinate clause: because he was hungry

- **Compound-complex** sentences contain two or more independent clauses and one or more subordinate clauses.

Rather than go hungry, the rat ate the cheese; however, he did not drink the wine.

Subordinate clause: rather than go hungry

Independent clause: the rat ate the cheese

Independent clause: he did not drink the wine

Sentence variety helps retain your reader's interest. Imagine a piece of writing that only uses simple sentences—it would be tedious to read. When you use a variety of different types of sentences, your writing has greater appeal for the reader.

Editing for Grammar and Style

You can significantly increase the usability of any communication by focusing on three aspects of writing. First, use good grammar and style. Readers can't extract what they need from poorly written information. Moreover, bad writing makes you (and your company) look incompetent. Second, start each communication with an overview to give your audience a framework. Third, "chunk" information into units that make sense for the specific audience and purpose. (Chunking is described later in this chapter.)

The following is a snapshot of important grammar and style issues for technical writing. For more information, see Appendix A and this book's companion website, www.mycanadiantechcommlab.ca.

Use Proper Punctuation. A poorly punctuated sentence can be hard to interpret. One example is inconsistent use of the "series comma," the comma inserted before a coordinating conjunction in a list of items. For example:

The Orb weaver, wood, and lynx varieties are examples of biological diversity in spiders.

Inserting a comma before *and* indicates that there are three items (Orb weaver spider, wood spider, lynx spider) in this series. But some writers, particularly in journalism, omit the final comma before the *and*:

The Orb weaver, wood and lynx varieties are examples of biological diversity in spiders.

This usage seems to imply that "wood and lynx spiders" are only one kind of spider, which is not the case.

Punctuation is easy once you learn some basic rules. Refer to the chart in Appendix A as you work on your own writing.

Use Complete Sentences. Complete sentences have a subject (noun) and a predicate (verb), and they express a complete thought. Sentence fragments are incomplete sentences. They either lack a subject or a predicate, or they are subordinate clauses that do not make sense on their own, and must therefore be attached to a main clause.

> **Complete sentence:** I dance.
>
> **Sentence fragment:** Although I dance.

To determine if a sentence is a sentence fragment, ask yourself the following questions:

- Who or what is performing the action?
  If you can answer this question, you have identified the subject.
- What is the subject doing?
  If you can answer this question, you have identified the predicate.
- Does the sentence present a complete thought?
  If not, the sentence is a sentence fragment, even if it contains both a subject and a predicate.

Avoid Run-on Sentences. Run-on sentences occur when independent clauses are not separated properly. There are two types of run-on sentence: the fused sentence and the comma splice.

- Fused sentences occur when there is no punctuation and no coordinating conjunction between two independent clauses.

  > The iPod has revolutionized the digital music market music will never be the same again.

- Comma splices occur when two independent clauses are joined with a comma but no coordinating conjunction (and, but, or, nor, for, so, yet).

  > The iPod has revolutionized the digital music market, music will never be the same again.

Run-on sentences can be revised in one of four ways:

- Insert a comma and a coordinating conjunction between the dependent clauses.

> The iPod has revolutionized the digital music market, and music will never be the same again.

- Insert a semicolon between the dependent clauses.

> The iPod has revolutionized the digital music market; music will never be the same again.

- Insert a period between the independent clauses to turn them into separate sentences.

> The iPod has revolutionized the digital music market. Music will never be the same again.

- Insert a conjunction to turn one of the independent clauses into a dependent clause.

> Since the iPod has revolutionized the digital music market, music will never be the same again.

Use Active Voice Whenever Possible. Sentences in active voice are easier to read and understand than sentences written in passive voice. In active voice sentences, the agent of the action in the sentence is the subject of the sentence:

Active Voice	*Agent*	*Action*	*Recipient*
	(subject)	(verb)	(object)
	Joe	lost	your report.

In a passive voice sentence, this pattern is reversed. The recipient of the action is the subject of the sentence. Sometimes the agent is appended to the end of the sentence with the word *by*:

Passive Voice	*Recipient*	*Action*	*Agent*
	(subject)	(verb)	(prepositional phrase)
	Your report	was lost	by Joe.

Note that passive voice adds a form of the verb *be* (was) next to the actual verb.

Some writers mistakenly rely on passive voice because they think it sounds more objective and important. But passive voice decreases usability by making sentences wordier and harder to understand.

In addition, writers often use passive voice deliberately to obscure the agent by leaving out the final *by* phrase:

Passive Voice	*Recipient*	*Action*	*Agent*
	(subject)	(verb)	
	Your report	was lost.	?

"Your report was lost" leaves out the responsible party. Who lost the report? Using passive voice to obscure the person or other agent who performed an action is unethical. However, passive voice is appropriate when the agent is not known or when the object is more important than the subject. For example, if a group of scientists performed an experiment and wanted to explain the results, they might write

> The data were analyzed, and the findings were discussed.

Even here, active voice ("We analyzed the data...") might sound better, but passive voice is considered the norm in this sort of scientific writing. Using passive voice can also be justified when the goal is to ease the blow that a direct sentence might deliver. For example:

> You have not paid your bill.

The passive form is indirect and thus less confrontational:

> Your bill has not been paid.

Consider this technique when you want to avoid a hostile tone. But in general, to create usable, readable technical information, use active voice.

Avoid Nominalizations. A nominalization is a noun form of a verb. Verbs are generally easier to read because they are usually short and signal action that can be visualized. Turning them into nouns changes an action into a thing, which makes it harder to visualize. You can usually spot a nominalization in two ways:

1. Look for words with a -tion ending:

> My recommendation is for a larger budget.

Strike the ending to find the root verb: recommend. Then rewrite the sentence in a more direct form:

> I recommend a larger budget.

Nominalizations may sound more "important" than a simpler verb form, but this kind of abstraction makes for difficult reading. A usable document is a readable document.

2. Look for "the [noun] of [noun]" formula:

> The managing of this project is up to me.

This sentence is wordy and cumbersome. Identify the root verb form (manage) and create a more accessible sentence, such as

> I manage this project.
>
> or
>
> Managing this project is my job.

Unpack Nouns. Too many nouns in a row can create confusion and reading difficulty. One noun can modify another (as in "software development"). But when two or more nouns modify a noun, the string of words becomes hard to read and ambiguous. For example:

> Be sure to leave enough time for today's training session participant evaluation.

Is the evaluation of the session or of the participants? With no articles, prepositions, or verbs, readers cannot sort out the relationships among the nouns. Revise this sentence for clarity and readability:

> Be sure to leave enough time for participants to evaluate today's training session.
>
> or
>
> Be sure to leave enough time to evaluate the participants in today's training session.

Use Simple, Short, Familiar Words. Effective communication requires you to be clear and concise. Avoid the impulse to use words simply to show your reader that you possess an impressive vocabulary. In today's busy business world, readers often scan text for meaning and the use of long, unfamiliar words slows down this task. Examples of words to avoid:

obviate	=	prevent
peruse	=	read, examine
utilize	=	use
furnish	=	send, give
modifications	=	changes

Avoid Wordy Phrases, but Don't Overedit. Wordy phrases can often be reduced to one word:

at a rapid rate	=	rapidly
due to the fact that	=	because
aware of the fact that	=	know
in close proximity to	=	near

But don't overedit, leaving out so many words that your audience cannot follow your line of thinking. A sentence such as this is confusing:

| Proposal to employ retirees almost died.

What or who "almost died," the proposal or the retirees? A few more carefully chosen words would help:

| The proposal to employ retirees was nearly defeated.

Short sentences are good, but not at the expense of clarity. Clear information is usable information.

Avoid Ambiguous Pronoun References. To make your writing as clear as possible for the reader, ensure that pronouns (I, you, he, she, they, their, it, etc.) refer clearly to one and only one noun (the antecedent). For example:

| Remove the battery from the cell phone casing and inspect *it.*

Should the reader inspect the battery or the cell phone? The pronoun *it* could refer to either. To make the sentence clearer for your reader, you simply need to clarify what the "it" is.

| Remove the battery from the cell phone casing and inspect the battery leads.

Here is another example:

| Amrita has changed her major twice this year, despite the requirement that she has to stay an extra semester. *This* might suggest she is unsure of her career goal.

What does *this* refer to? Amrita's major or staying an extra semester? It is not tied to a clear antecedent, so a reader may become confused. You can correct this type of error easily by using an explicit noun after the word *this.*

| Amrita has changed her major twice this year, despite the requirement that she has to stay an extra semester. *This change* might suggest she is unsure of her career goal.

Avoid Ambiguous Modifiers. A modifier is a word, phrase, or clause that describes words or phrases. You need to place the modifier close to the word or phrase it is modifying (usually next to the word it modifies) to avoid confusion.

A **dangling modifier** is a descriptive word, phrase, or clause that does not clearly point to the words it modifies. The reader then attaches the modifier to the closest noun or noun phrase in the sentence, often creating illogical constructions. Dangling modifiers often occur when a writer begins the sentence with a modifier that contains a participle (eating, published) or an infinitive (to be).

> **Confusing:** While eating my lunch, a bee stung me.
>
> **Clear:** While I was eating my lunch, a bee stung me.

The first sentence suggests that the bee not only stung me, but ate my lunch as well.

> **Confusing:** Published in the paper, the man believed the story.
>
> **Clear:** The man believed the story that was published in the paper.

The first sentence suggests that the man was published in the paper.

> **Confusing:** To be a successful student, good study habits need to be developed.
>
> **Clear:** If you want to be a successful student, you need to develop good study habits.

The first sentence suggests that good study habits themselves can be a successful student.

A **misplaced modifier** is a word, phrase, or clause whose position in the sentence causes the reader to misinterpret the intended meaning.

> **Confusing:** I have only eaten one egg in my entire life.
>
> **Clear:** I have eaten only one egg in my entire life.

The first sentence suggests that all I have ever eaten is one egg. The second sentence suggests that I have eaten no more than one egg in my lifetime.

> **Confusing:** The dog jumped the obstacle with its tail wagging.
>
> **Clear:** The dog, its tail wagging, jumped the obstacle.

The first sentence suggests that the obstacle has a wagging tail.

> **Confusing:** She put the hat on her head that she bought in Toronto.
>
> **Clear:** She put the hat, which she bought in Toronto, on her head.

The first sentence suggests that she bought her head in Toronto.

Use Parallel Structure. Parallel structure means that similar items should be expressed in similar grammatical form. For example, the structure of the following sentence is not parallel:

> She enjoys many outdoor activities, including running, kayaking, and the design of new hiking trails.

This sentence is essentially a list of items. The first two items, *running* and *kayaking*, are expressed as gerunds, with *-ing* endings. The third item, *the design of new hiking trails*, is not a gerund but a nominalization. To make this sentence parallel, you would revise as follows:

> She enjoys many outdoor activities, including running, kayaking, and designing new hiking trails.

Avoid Unnecessary Jargon. Every profession has its own shorthand and accepted phrases and terms. Among specialists, these terms are an economical way to communicate. For example, *stat* (from the Latin *statim*, "immediately") is medical jargon for "drop everything and deal with this emergency." For computer engineers, a *virus* is not the common cold but a program that makes its way onto a computer's hard drive and causes problems.

Jargon can be useful when you are communicating with specialists. But some jargon is useless in any context. For example, the sentence

> We will bilaterally optimize our efforts on this project.

may contain some popular buzzwords, but it would be much easier to understand if simplified to

> We will co-operate on this project.

Only use jargon that improves your communication, not jargon that bogs down the information and sounds pretentious. Keep in mind that general audiences are unlikely to know the meaning of jargon that experts use. Depending on the situation, you will need to explain such terms or avoid using them altogether.

Avoid Clichés. A cliché is an expression that has been used so many times it is considered corny and overused. If you've heard a certain phrase repeatedly, then it may be best to omit it from your writing. Some examples include:

acid test	paint the town red
as easy as pie	pale as a ghost
beat a hasty retreat	pass the buck
beyond the shadow of a doubt	pick and choose
blind as a bat	pretty as a picture
bottom line	proud possessor
break a leg	quick as a flash
calm, cool, and collected	rise and shine
cold, hard facts	rise to the occasion
deep, dark secret	sadder but wiser
every dog has his day	shoulder to the wheel
few and far between	sink or swim
flat as a pancake	sneaking suspicion
give 110 percent	state of the art
hit the nail on the head	straight and narrow
in this day and age	there's no place like home
ladder of success	tired but happy
last but not least	tried and true
live from hand to mouth	walking the line
the other side of the coin	worth its weight in gold

Avoid Biased Language. Language that is offensive or makes unwarranted assumptions will put off readers and make your document less effective. Avoid sexist pronoun usage, such as referring to doctors, lawyers, and other professionals as "him" or "he" while referring to nurses, secretaries, and homemakers as "her" or "she." Words such as *mailman* or *fireman* automatically exclude women; terms such as *mail carrier* or *firefighter* are far more inclusive.

Also, communication should respect all people regardless of cultural, racial, or national background, sexual and religious orientation, age, or physical condition. References to individuals and groups should be as neutral as possible. Avoid any expression that is condescending or judgmental or that might violate a reader's sense of appropriateness. When in doubt, consult a reputable reference book for the most widely accepted terms.

Write from the User's Point of View. As one team of technical communicators notes, "Writing from the user's point of view brings the user into the 'story,' so it is easy for the user to imagine doing what you are describing" (Hargis, Hernandez, Hughes, & Ramaker, 1997, p. 14). Techniques include performing an audience and purpose analysis (so you understand where your audience is coming from), writing in active voice, and creating headings in the form of reader questions. Another technique noted by Hargis and colleagues is to use *you* (second person) or command forms whenever possible. Sentences such as "Insert the bolt into the large wheel frame" speak directly to the reader and are presented in a clear, active voice; whereas, "The bolt is next inserted into the large wheel frame" is a passive construction that doesn't make clear who is supposed to do what.

Don't Rely Solely on Grammar and Spelling Checkers. Some people mistakenly assume that the computer can solve all grammar and spelling problems. This is simply not true. Spelling checkers are very important, because they will find words that are spelled incorrectly, but they cannot find words that are used incorrectly (for example, *it's* and *its*, or *there* and *their*). Grammar checkers are also useful tools to help you locate possible problems, but do not rely on what the software tells you. For example, not every sentence that the grammar checker flags as "long" should be shortened. Use these tools wisely and with common sense. Also, ask someone to proofread your material. Some companies have full-time technical editors who are happy to look over your writing.

Consider International Issues and Write for Translation. Technical communication
is a global process. Documents may originate in English but then be translated into other languages. In this case, writers must be careful to use English that is easy to translate. Idioms, humour, and analogies are often difficult for translators. One famous example is the case of the Kentucky Fried Chicken slogan, "finger lickin' good" that, when translated for the Chinese market, became, "eat your fingers off"! In addition to terms, certain grammatical

elements are also important for translation. The lack of an article (*a, the*) or of the word *that* in certain crucial places can cause a sentence to be translated inaccurately. Consider the following example (Kohl, 1999, p. 151):

> Programs that are currently running in the system are indicated by icons in the lower part of the screen.

> Programs currently running in the system are indicated by icons in the lower part of the screen.

The first sentence contains the phrase "that are," which might ordinarily be left out by native English writers, as in the second sentence. This second sentence is harder to translate because the phrase "that are" provides the translator with important clues about the relationship of the words *programs, currently,* and *running*.

The Use of Idiomatic Expressions. When thinking about writing for a cross-cultural audience, you should avoid the use of idiomatic expressions. An idiom is a group of words that when used together have a different meaning from when the words are used individually. The same words could have a literal meaning in one situation and a different idiomatic meaning in other situation. Idioms are often slang terms that are grounded in a cultural context. The following phrases can cause difficulty for cross-cultural audiences:

> **junk mail:** unsolicited mail (usually advertisements for something you're not interested in)

> **make a mountain out of a molehill:** make something seem much more important than it really is

> **a piece of cake:** very easy

> **sleep on it:** take at least a day to think about something before making a decision

> **on the road:** travelling

> **bent out of shape:** needlessly worried about something

> **blow one's top:** become extremely angry

Idioms cause trouble for cross-cultural readers because they do not translate well or they require the reader to understand the cultural term. Moreover, the use of such expressions could make your writing too informal, which may reduce the effectiveness of your message. Consider your audience and your purpose, as well as the type of document before deciding if you should use many idioms.

Document Layout and Usability

How your document looks affects how people read it. Is it tiring to the eye? Does the layout of the document allow for easy skimming and scanning? Is information easy to find? Chapter 7 discusses layout in more detail, but here are some of the basic principles.

Use White Space and Effective Page Design

White space, typography, and page design play big roles in a document's usability. Pages with tiny type crammed onto the page with no graphics and no white space are hard to read. Chapter 8 provides more information on graphics and visuals.

Create an Overview

Information is usable when people can answer several key questions before they start reading:

- What will I learn from this document?
- Why am I receiving this information?
- What can I anticipate finding in this document?

To help answer these questions, always provide an overview at the beginning of your document, before launching into the details. Think about it this way: If you were taking a long road trip, you would probably study a map first to get the "big picture" of your journey and to know exactly where you will be headed. Overviews provide a sort of road map.

You can provide an overview in many forms within a document. Some documents begin with a section called "About This Document," which previews the entire document. Within a document, you can also provide an overview of each chapter. Figure 4.3 shows a book overview from a manual for an IBM laptop computer. This particular overview explains what users will learn, how long this process should take, and what steps they should already have completed.

Overviews are important in oral communication as well. At the beginning of a presentation, outline for your audience the main points you will be covering. For example, you might begin a presentation about electric cars by saying, "Today, I would like to give you more information about electric cars. Specifically, I will cover three main points: the way electric cars operate, certain new designs in electric batteries, and the usefulness of electric cars in cold climates." Your presentation would then cover these points, in that order.

Handling the ThinkPad Computer

By using common sense and by following these handling tips, you will get the most use and enjoyment out of your computer for a long time to come.

This section provides tips for handling notebook computers in general. Some descriptions may not suit your situation. Check your shipping checklist to confirm the items you get with your computer.

Notebook computers are precision machines that require careful handling. Though your computer is designed and tested to be a durable notebook computer that functions reliably in normal work environments, you need to use some common sense in handling it.

ThinkPad don'ts

- Do not subject your computer to physical punishment, such as dropping or bumping.
- Do not place heavy objects on your computer.
- Do not spill or allow liquids into your computer.
- Do not use your computer in or near water (to avoid the danger of electrical shock).
- Do not pack your computer in a tightly packed suitcase or bag. Your LCD might be damaged.

A scratchlike marking on your LCD might be a stain transferred from the keyboard (including from the TrackPoint stick) when the cover was pressed from the outside. Wipe such a stain gently with a dry soft cloth. If the stain remains, moisten the cloth with LCD cleaner and wipe the stain again. Be sure to dry the LCD before closing it.

- Do not disassemble your computer. Only an authorized IBM ThinkPad repair technician should disassemble and repair your computer.
- Do not scratch, twist, hit, or push the surface of your computer display.
- Do not place any objects between the display and the keyboard or under the keyboard.
- Do not pick up or hold your computer by the display. When picking up your open computer, hold it by the bottom (keyboard) half.

Figure 4.3 **Book Overview from the IBM Thinkpad 240 Manual.** This page is designed to help users understand the purpose and structure of the manual.
Source: Reprinted by permission from *IBM ThinkPad 240 User's Reference*, 1/e. © 1999 by Lenovo.

Chunk Information

Chunking means dividing information into small units or modules, based on the topics or types of information that will be covered in a given section. When you chunk information into topics, you should "include information in a topic that the user thinks of as a unit" (Horton, 1990, p. 101).

For example, if you were designing a quick reference card for using an ATM, you might organize the information in three general chunks:

- How to make a withdrawal
- How to make a deposit
- How to check your balance

You would design the card around these three chunks of information. If any one of the chunks became too long and unwieldy, you might subdivide it. "How to make a deposit," for example, might become two chunks: "How to deposit cheques" and "How to deposit cash."

If you've ever created an outline to help you write a paper or speech, you've had experience in breaking down information into smaller units. When you chunk information for an audience, you create these units based on the audience's needs and the document's purpose.

Create Headings

Another way to enhance usability is to create headings in the form of questions your audience might ask. This approach isn't appropriate for all documents, and overuse of questions can become repetitious and annoying. For certain documents, such as patient information brochures, questions can help guide readers to the appropriate section of the document. Questions also create an inviting, user-friendly tone. If the question sounds like something readers would actually ask, they will feel as if the document has been written just for them.

For example, a patient information brochure about a laparoscopy (a medical procedure that uses a small camera to look inside the body) begins as follows:

LAPAROSCOPY

Activities
Your return to normal activities will depend on how quickly you recover from surgery, which may take a few days or as long as 2 to 4 weeks.

Source: BC Health Guide, http://www.healthlinkbc.ca/kb/content/surgicaldetail/tw9171.html.

This information would be more useful and friendly if it addressed an actual patient question:

> **WHAT ACTIVITIES CAN I PERFORM AFTER MY LAPAROSCOPY?**
> You should rest until you feel up to resuming your normal activities—usually in a day or two. Do not lift objects weighing more than 10 to 15 kilograms for one week.

Use the Margins for Commentary

You can use the margins to call out or highlight particularly important information, or you can leave them blank for readers to take notes or write comments (see Figure 4.3). Using white space and marginal cueing areas are discussed in more detail in Chapter 8.

Proofreading Your Final Draft

Writers proofread as a final step to ensure that everything is just right. No matter how engaging and informative the document, basic errors distract the reader and make the writer look bad. Here are some types of easily correctable errors you can spot through careful proofreading (refer to the page numbers in parentheses for advice on repairing these errors):

* Sentence errors, such as fragments, comma splices, or run-ons (page 346–348)
* Punctuation errors, such as missing apostrophes or unnecessary commas (page 342–344)
* Usage errors, such as *it's* for *its*, *lay* for *lie*, or *their* for *there* (page 349–350)
* Mechanical errors, such as misspelled words, inaccurate dates, or incorrect abbreviations (page 354–357)
* Format errors, such as missing page numbers, inconsistent spacing, or incorrect source documentation (page 128–136)

TIPS FOR PROOFREADING

* **Save proofreading for the final draft.** Proofreading earlier drafts might cause writer's block and distract your focus from the content, organization, and style of your document.
* **Take a break before proofreading.** After you complete a final draft, do something else for at least a couple of hours so that you can approach the document with fresh eyes.

- **Check for typographical errors (typos),** such as repeated or missing words and letters, omitted word endings (such as -s, -ed, or -ing), or left-out quotation marks or parentheses.
- **Work from hard copy.** Research indicates that people read more perceptively (and with less fatigue) from a printed page than from a computer screen. Also, the page is easier to mark up. Some people like to proofread in a comfy chair or even lying down.
- **Proofread slowly.** Read each word—don't skim. Force yourself to slow down by placing a ruler under each line or by moving backward throughout the document, sentence by sentence.
- **Be especially alert for troublesome areas in your writing.** Do you have difficulty with spelling? Do you confuse commas with semicolons? Do you make many typographical errors? If punctuation is a problem, make one final pass to check each punctuation mark.
- **Proofread more than once.** The more you do it, the more errors you're likely to spot.
- **Don't rely only on computerized aids.** In the end, nothing substitutes for your own careful reading.

Checklist for Proofreading

- Does each paragraph have a topic sentence?
- Does each paragraph contain one main idea?
- Does each sentence state a complete thought?
- Is the document free of sentence fragments, comma splices, and run-on sentences?
- Has the document been checked for proper punctuation?
- Have you used active voice wherever possible?
- Do your subjects and verbs agree?
- Have you eliminated wordy, pompous, and inflated words that could alienate your reader?
- If using jargon or industry buzzwords, have you defined them sufficiently for your audience?
- Have you eliminated biased language?
- Have you avoided using clichés?
- Have you reviewed all sentences to make sure that modifiers are correctly used?
- Have you checked that all pronoun references are clear to the reader?
- If writing for a cross-cultural audience, have you ensured that your audience can understand the words you have used?
- Have you organized the content in a way that allows the reader to access information easily?

Exercises

1. **FOCUS ON WRITING.** Select one of the general topics below and create a topic and a sentence outline.

   - Fuel cells
   - Cable modems
   - Volcanoes
   - Ritalin
   - Proportional representation
   - Affirmative action

   Once you have written an outline for one of the topics above, write two paragraphs on the topic using two different paragraph types.

2. If you're unclear about any aspect of grammar, visit the University of Western Ontario's writing centre website to obtain free self-help grammar and punctuation handouts:

   - **www.sdc.uwo.ca/writing/index.html?handouts**

The Collaboration Window

Many writers find it difficult to rely on their own judgment of whether their writing is clear to their readers. If we have laboured over our writing, we may become too familiar with the material to be aware of how a reader might respond to it. A peer review provides writers with an opportunity to learn how clear their message is to an objective reader.

In pairs, exchange one of the assignments you have been working on in this class and conduct a peer review. Peer reviewers should focus on key questions when reviewing a peer's manuscript:

- Does the document answer the writer's purpose?
- Is the document written at a level that is just right for the target audience?
- Does the document answer the audience's purpose?
- Is the document organized so that it is easy to follow?
- Is the document's content clear and concise?
- Is the document free from grammatical or spelling problems?

To answer these questions adequately, ensure that you discuss the document with the writer in advance so that you understand his or her purpose, the intended audience, and the audience's information needs.

Read through the text twice, the first time to become familiar with the topic and the second to answer the questions above. As you read, pretend that you are the intended audience. Has the writer provided you with enough content? Is the content presented in a logical, organized, and clear manner?

When looking at the sentences of the document, avoid editing with a red pen. Instead, bring the errors to the writer's attention. Remember that this is the writer's work, not yours. Comment on the clarity and conciseness of the sentences and on grammar and spelling.

It is important to be honest and provide specific constructive feedback to the writer. Don't simply tell the writer what you liked or didn't like; you should explain why something worked or didn't work.

When someone is peer editing your documents, remember that they are not evaluating your writing skills. All writers use peer editors and "test" audiences to ensure that their documents work. For this reason, don't let your ego get involved. Thank your peer editor for his or her time, ask questions about the comments and concerns, and use this new information to make your document stronger.

The Global Window

Many Canadian universities and colleges have writing centres with excellent resources for you to gather information and practice your writing skills. The following websites provide useful information for making your documents clear and effective:

- **www.ryerson.ca/writingcentre/handouts_slides/index.html**
  Ryerson University's Writing Centre website provides handouts covering a variety of topics that will help you improve your writing, such as effective group writing, writing an effective resume, and the importance of critical reading.
- **http://writing.utoronto.ca/about-this-site/pdf-links**
  "Writing at the University of Toronto" is aimed at helping students improve their writing. It offers links to websites, a list of hardcopy resources, and tips for academic writing. In particular, "Computers and Writing" demonstrates how to write efficiently and get from the composing to the revising stage using a Word document.
- **http://umanitoba.ca/student/u1/lac/handouts/handouts.html**
  The University of Manitoba's Learning Assistance Centre offers online handouts on topics such as academic writing, effective reading, note taking, and time management.

MyCanadianTechCommLab

Go to MyCanadianTechCommLab at www.mycanadiantechcommlab.ca for additional online exercises and problems.

CHAPTER 5

Conducting Research for Technical Communication

Chapter Objectives

By the end of this chapter you will be able to:

1. Interview participants and ask properly formulated questions.

2. Understand where to find a variety of different sources.

3. Conduct research using a variety of different online and text sources.

4. Successfully complete a checklist for research.

Brendon Culliton, London, Ontario

In his teen years, Brendon Culliton decided to combine his passion for working with computers with his desire to tell stories and his artistic skills. He started making films and working on his high school's news broadcast program in order to gain hands-on experience. After enrolling in the University of Western Ontario and Fanshawe College's joint Media Theory and Production program, he learned to make different types of videos based on special criteria, his audience, and his message.

After working at the Epilepsy Support Centre in London, Ontario, Brendon's film company, Joint Media Group Inc., produced *If I Should Fall*, an award-winning documentary about the Canadian war experience. Combining interviews, historical footage, and research, Brendon uses his skills to tell stories: "You have to make something the audience will enjoy and, most importantly, something that will make them think, ask questions, and encourage them to want to know more."

Thinking Critically About Research

Most major decisions in technical communication are based on careful research. Often, the findings are recorded in a written report, in a long memo, on a website, or in some combination of documents. Research includes the development, testing, and evaluation of information to discover or contribute to a body of general knowledge and to compare information to published findings and theories (Bjork & Ottoson, 2007). The type of research you will perform as a technical communicator depends largely on your workplace. For any topic you research, for the classroom or workplace, you can consult numerous information sources. As Gary Radford and Stuart Goldstein point out: "Research methods are not only tools for collecting information, they also form the basis of strategic decisions in the creation of persuasive messages" (2002, p. 255). An excellent way to begin is by conducting primary research—conducting interviews and surveys and observing people in action. This allows you to start with information "from the source." The internet is also a great starting place, because it's quick and convenient; but you need to verify that any information you find on the internet is from a credible source. Other electronic sources include CD-ROM databases and online retrieval services. Finally, traditional sources such as encyclopedias, print indexes, and journals can be valuable because their contents are usually subject to close scrutiny before they are published. Many of these traditional sources are also available electronically.

Primary Research

Informative interviews, surveys and questionnaires, inquiry letters, official records, and observations and experiments are considered *primary sources* because they afford an original, first-hand study of a topic.

Informative Interviews

An excellent primary source of information is the interview, conducted in person, by telephone, or by email. Much of what an expert knows may never be published, so an interview is often the only way to get that information. Also, a respondent might refer you to other experts or sources of information.

Of course, an expert's opinion can be just as mistaken or biased as anyone else's. Like patients who seek second opinions about serious medical conditions, researchers need to seek a balanced range of expert opinions about a complex problem or controversial issue—not only from one company engineer and environmentalist, for example, but also from independent and presumably more objective third parties, such as a professor or journalist who has studied the issue.

INTERVIEW TIPS

- Research your topic and interviewee beforehand. Make sure that you have enough knowledge about what you will be talking about and who you will be talking to so that you can ask questions that you may have not originally planned to ask.
- Prepare a list of questions you want to ask or topics that you want to cover. Have follow-up questions or ideas prepared in order to steer the conversation. For example, "How do you feel about genetically modified food?" could be followed by "Where do your feelings on this come from?" if you want more detail and background information.
- Make each question clear and specific.
- Avoid questions that can be answered yes or no.
- Avoid loaded questions, such as "In what ways do you think the hazards of genetically modified foods have been overstated?" Ask impartial questions instead, such as "In your opinion, have the hazards associated with genetically modified foods been accurately stated, overstated, or understated?"
- Save the most difficult, complex, or sensitive questions for last.
- Be polite and professional.
- Let your respondent do most of the talking.
- Ask for clarification if needed, but do not put words in the respondent's mouth. Questions such as "Could you go over that again?" or "What did you mean by [word]?" are fine.

Always go into an interview with a clear purpose and do your homework before the interview so you won't waste time asking questions you could have answered yourself.

Surveys and Questionnaires

Surveys help you form impressions of the concerns, preferences, attitudes, beliefs, or perceptions of a large, identifiable group (a *target population*) by studying representatives of that group (a *sample*).

The questionnaire is a tool for conducting surveys. Whereas interviews give your research greater clarity and depth, questionnaires give you a large quantity of information from many sources. Respondents can answer privately and anonymously—and often more candidly than in an interview. The following guidelines will help you design effective surveys.

SURVEY AND QUESTIONNAIRE TIPS

- **Define the survey's purpose and target population.** Why is this survey being performed? What, exactly, is it measuring? How much background research do you need? How will the survey findings be used? Who is the exact population being studied (the chronically unemployed, part-time students, computer users)?
- Identify the sample group. How will intended respondents be selected? How many respondents will there be? Generally, the larger the sample surveyed, the more valid and reliable the results (assuming a well-chosen and representative sample). Will the sample be randomly chosen? In the statistical sense, *random* does not mean "haphazard": *random* simply means that each member of the target population stands an equal chance of being in the sample group.
- **Define the survey method.** What type of data (opinions, ideas, facts, figures) will you collect? Is timing important? How will the survey be administered—in person, by mail or email, by phone? How will the data be collected, recorded, analyzed, and reported? (Lavin, 1992, p. 277). Phone, email, and in-person surveys yield fast results and high response rates, but respondents consider phone surveys annoying, and without anonymity, people tend to be less candid. Mail surveys are less expensive than phone surveys. Electronic surveys, conducted via a web form or an email message, are the least expensive, but these methods can have pitfalls. Computer connections can fail, and you have less control over how many times the same person completes the survey.
- **Decide on the types of questions.** Two types of questions can be used in surveys: open-ended and closed-ended questions. Open-ended questions allow respondents to create their own answer. Open-ended answers require more time to measure the data gathered, but these types of questions provide a rich source of information. An open-ended question would be worded like this:

How much do you know about genetically modified food products?

In contrast, closed-ended questions give respondents a limited number of choices for answers, and the data gathered are easier to measure. A closed-ended question would be set up like this:

Are you concerned about genetically modified food products?

Yes _____   No _____   Don't know _____

- **Develop an engaging introduction and provide appropriate information.** Persuade respondents that the questionnaire relates to their concerns, that their answers matter, and that their anonymity is ensured:

  Your answers will help our company determine the public's views about genetically modified food products. All answers will be kept confidential. Thank you.

- **Make it brief, simple, and inviting.** Respondents don't mind giving up some time to help, but long questionnaires usually don't get many replies. Limit the number and types of questions to the most important topics.

Public Records and Organizational Publications

The *Access to Information Act* and provincial public-record laws grant public access to an array of government, corporate, and organizational documents. Obtaining these documents (from provincial or federal agencies) takes time (although more and more such documents are available on the web), but in them you can find answers to questions like these (Blum, 1997):

- Which universities are being investigated by Agriculture and Agri-food Canada for mistreating laboratory animals?
- Are auditors for the Canada Revenue Agency required to meet quotas?
- How often has a particular nuclear power plant been cited for safety violations?

Organization records (reports, memos, webpages, and so on) are also good primary sources. Most organizations publish pamphlets, brochures, annual reports, or websites for consumers, employees, investors, or voters. Of course, you need to be alert for bias in company literature. For example, in evaluating the safety of a genetically modified food product, you would want the complete picture. Along with the company's literature, you would want to consult studies and reports from government agencies and publications from health and environmental groups.

Personal Observation and Experiments

Observation should be your final step in primary research because you now know what to look for. Know how, where, and when to observe, and jot down observations immediately. You might even take photos or make drawings.

Experiments are controlled forms of observations designed to verify an assumption (e.g., the role of fish oil in preventing heart disease) or to test something untried (e.g., the relationship between background music and productivity). Each field has its own guidelines for experimental design, including the need for all experiments to be reviewed by human subject review boards to ensure protection of test subjects. Depending on the situation, you may be able to learn about your subject matter by interviewing a scientist who is conducting an experiment or by reading published results.

In addition, *workplace research* can involve the analysis of samples, such as water, soil, or air for contamination and pollution; foods for nutritional content; or plants for medicinal value. Investigators may analyze material samples to find the cause of airline accidents; engineers may analyze samples of steel, concrete, or other building materials to test for tensile strength or load-bearing capacity; and medical specialists may analyze tissue samples for disease. As a researcher, you may be able to access this information through interviews or published reports.

Internet and Digital Research

Almost every form of information—newspapers and magazines, government documents and research reports, corporate-sponsored websites, library databases—can be accessed on the internet. In fact, "Googling" a research topic is fast becoming the method of choice for almost all forms of research. For example, Statistics Canada reported that in 2009, 50 percent of internet users used the web for training, schoolwork, or educational purposes (Statistics Canada, 2009).

The internet can provide sources ranging from 12-year-olds who have their own blogs to electronic journals and national newspapers. Remember that although the internet is quick and easy to use, you need to be sure that the source of your information is credible and reliable. (See TIPS for Searching on the Internet on page 90). Following is a brief listing and description of various sources of information on the internet.

Online News Sites and Magazines

Most major news organizations offer online versions of their broadcast outlets and print publications. Examples include online newspapers (www.theglobeandmail.com) or television network websites (www.cbc.ca). Major magazines (www.macleans.ca) also offer web versions. Some news is available *only* electronically—for example, online magazines such as Canada.com and smaller news sites such as www.engineeringtoday.org.

Note: Make sure you understand how the publication obtains and reviews information. Is it a major news site, such as the CBC, or is it a smaller site run by a special interest group? Each type can be useful, but you must evaluate the reliability and objectivity of each source.

Government Research Sites and Other Government Documents

Almost every government organization—local, provincial, or federal—has a website and online access to research and reports. Examples include Health Canada (www.hc-sc.gc.ca), Statistics Canada (www.statcan.gc.ca), and provincial and local sites that provide information on car licences, tax laws, and local property and land issues. From some of these sites, you can link to specific government-sponsored research projects.

Note: Check the date on the report or data; for instance, if you are using Statistics Canada information, make sure the date fits the research question you are trying to answer. Also, find out how often the site is updated so that you can determine how current the posted information is.

Community Discussion Groups and Bulletin Boards

For almost any topic, there is a discussion group or bulletin board on the web that you can turn to. The good news is that these sites provide you with an abundance of information. But the challenge is to determine how to use this information. For example, if you are studying health issues related to smoking, you might visit a Yahoo! group to learn more about the challenges facing smokers who are trying to quit; this information may be very insightful, but it would not represent the full range of input from all smokers.

Note: Look at more than one such site in order to get a broader perspective on the discussion.

Blogs and Wikis

Blogs (weblogs) are websites where users post ideas and discussions. Blog postings are displayed in reverse chronological order (see Chapter 6). Blogs can also be used to connect to other similar discussions and to make comments and give feedback. As with discussion groups, you will find more blogs than you can use, so evaluate the information carefully and consider more than one source. Never lose sight of the fact that virtually *everything* posted on a blog reflects personal opinion, not objective evaluation.

Wikis are community encyclopedias where anyone can add or edit the content of a listing. The original wiki is Wikipedia (www.wikipedia.org). Launched in 2001, Wikipedia is one of the most commonly used resources on the internet. Easy to access and navigate, Wikipedia hosts articles of a bibliographic nature in which visitors to the website can update entries. Wikipedia quickly gained popularity because it offers information much like an encyclopedia does, except that articles are edited as events happen and therefore provide information on the most current topics.

Academics are split over forbidding or promoting students' use of Wikipedia. As Professor Shaye J. D. Cohen points out, "Wikipedia represents all that is great and all that is dangerous about the Internet… It is incredibly powerful and readily available, and yet can mislead the unwary and spread disinformation. One hopes that a good… education will enable students to assess what they are reading" (qtd. in Child, 2007). When used with a critical eye, Wikipedia can be an excellent starting point to the research phase. Most students are familiar with it and consult it for basic information in place of an encyclopedia. Most entries provide the bibliographic information on where the material originates from, making it easy to consult that source directly. There are also links to online news articles and journals that can replace more expensive books and online journal subscriptions.

Any institution that promotes the use of Wikipedia as a source is likely to do so with caution. Like most encyclopedias, Wikipedia has a disclaimer that states that they assume no responsibility or liability for any articles that are published; however, unlike encyclopedias where the information is updated by those considered neutral professionals, Wikipedia can be updated by anyone, and it is up to the user to cite their source. An "open source," Wikipedia is monitored by editors, but with over 8 million entries, this is a daunting task and editing is commonly done by the users. Articles considered to contain extremely controversial information or those frequently updated with purposely erroneous information will sometimes be marked as "protected," meaning that only Wikipedia editors can make changes. For the majority of entries, as Educause points out, "every article is only as good as those who have taken the time to write or edit it" (7 Things, 2007).

No matter what the topic, whether it be controversial or neutral, it must be examined in order to detect any bias, outdated information, or questionable content. Additionally, a "hot" topic is more likely to have visitors—and therefore editors (see the discussion of the C.A.R.S. method on pages 90–91). Ultimately, the decision of whether or not to use Wikipedia should be based on the quality of the information provided.

Email Lists

Many topics can be researched by subscribing to an email list devoted to that subject. For instance, if you are an engineer studying alternative energy (wind turbines, solar energy), you can probably find an email list for this topic. Email lists are usually very focused on the topic at hand, and subscribers are usually experts in this content area. There are several choices for receiving the information: single email messages or a digest format that provides all of the postings in a single email at regular intervals (daily or weekly).

Note: After you join the list, pay attention to the main people who do the postings. If the list is dominated by two or three people, you might want to find another list with a more diverse set of subscribers.

Online Videos and Streaming

Instead of recording programs off the television, now people searching for videos can simply browse internet sites such as Youtube.com and Bing.com, or visit sites such as CBC Digital Archives (http://archives.cbc.ca), National Film Board of Canada (www.nfb.ca), and History Television (www.history.ca) for video clips that range from breaking news to historical footage. Additionally, many sites such as CNN.com and CTV.ca allow users to watch the news live. Videos can be extremely beneficial when researching, but they can also be removed from sites without notice, so effort should be made to see how long videos are stored on the websites. You may also choose to download a copy of any videos you cite in your research in a research file to ensure that you do not lose access to the material. The use of any downloaded content must conform to copyright rules for distribution and fair use.

Internet-Searchable Library Databases

Almost all libraries now have some form of website where you can search for books and articles, reserve material, and even pay overdue fines. Research libraries, such as those located in colleges and universities, also have websites that let users search not only the library itself but also the large databases and other digital resources subscribed to by the library, such as *Applied Science and Technology Abstracts*, which indexes journals in most major scientific areas.

Note: Before initiating a database search, meet with a librarian. Your local reference librarian can give you a quick tour of the various databases and instructions for searching them most effectively. You can then use the internet search engine from school or home.

Other Websites

Many other kinds of websites can be useful for research, including corporate information sites, advertising and marketing sites, and sites with specific points of view (e.g., special interest groups). Remember that you must evaluate each website carefully. (See TIPS for Evaluating and Interpreting Information on page 96.)

Evaluating Sources from the Web

Regardless of your topic, a web search typically yields a large number of hits. You need to evaluate every source you intend to use. If you can't clearly identify the author and his or her credentials, you should assume that the source is not credible. Why? Because the web is a *bottom-up* medium, allowing anyone with the technical resources to create a website. Fonts, colour, and images can make any site appear credible. Information can come from a multitude of sources, without any form of gatekeeping.

On the other hand, journal articles, newspaper reports, and television or radio stories are considered *top-down* information. These materials are usually subject to editorial or peer review and fact checking before being printed or delivered on the air. Nevertheless, *all* websites require particular critical attention.

For example, imagine you are researching the topic of voting in Canada; in particular, you are looking into the pros and cons of Canada's current voting system and the benefits of a reformed voting system. You use a search engine and search on the term "voting reform in Canada." One of your hits is the website shown in Figure 5.1.

At first glance, this website appears to have a clear point of view. The left side of the page offers many links to information about reforming the voting system, and the centre of the page features news articles relevant to the subject.

But does this website offer objective information? If you look at the statement at the top of the page—"all regions and all walks of life are joining FVC to demand a fair voting system"—the proclamation suggests that all Canadians want this reform to occur. Clearly, this is a website designed to encourage readers to write to their representatives, media outlets, the government of Canada, and others, and lobby for changes to be made to the voting system. On the top left

Figure 5.1 **A Website That Advocates a Particular Viewpoint. One of the websites found during a search on the term "voting reform in Canada."**
Source: Reproduced with the permission of Fair Vote Canada. www.fairvote.ca.

side of the page is a button that states "Join Us" and leads to a page where you are encouraged to donate money or subscribe to the newsletter in order to support the possible reform. Overall, the website offers questions and answers that provide some useful information, but its purpose is not to be objective or neutral. Does this mean that the website is an invalid source of information? Not at all. It does mean, however, that this information source advocates a point of view and should therefore be considered biased. Balance your research by also consulting sources such as government websites, academic journals, documentary radio or television programs, technical manuals, and reputable media reporting that will reflect a range of other points of view.

Managing Your Information

Walker and Ruszkiewicz (2000) suggest the following options for keeping track of the vast amount of information you are likely to find on the internet:

- **Cut and paste.** You can copy URLs (www addresses) and text from websites, newsgroups, and listservs directly into your word-processing or database files. This saves time because you won't have to retype or rewrite information to integrate it into your own documents.
- **Download or print files.** If you find information on a website that appears to change frequently (e.g., Wikipedia) or is hard to access, you should either download and save the information or print it. Make sure you accurately record the URL where you found the information and the date on which you accessed the site. Most web browsers can be configured to print this information when they print the page—you can usually specify this option in your browser's page setup menu.
- **Use your bookmarks file/RSS feeds.** Most browsers provide some kind of bookmarking system that allows you to save and organize links to websites you've found useful. Typically, this feature allows you to create folders for the different kinds of sites that you visit repeatedly or wish to return to. You can also save your bookmarked files to USB memory sticks or SD cards, which is especially useful if you work in a public computer lab. Many websites, particularly those that are frequently updated, allow you to subscribe to the site using an RSS feed and will notify you about updates.
- **Use electronic note cards and bibliography programs.** Software programs such as ProCite or EndNote allow you to store complete bibliographic information as well as abstracts and quotations from various kinds of sources. This kind of software provides a useful system for managing all your research, not just internet research.

TIPS FOR SEARCHING ON THE INTERNET

- **Select specific keywords or search phrases that are varied and technical.** Some search terms generate more useful hits than others. In addition to "cell phone radiation," for example, try "electromagnetic fields," "cell phones and brain tumours," or "electrical fields." Specialized terms (such as "vertigo" instead of "dizziness") offer the best access to reliable websites.
- **Use Boolean operators.** Using words like "and," "or," and "not" can help you narrow down the results you get when using a search engine. Instead of typing "environmental science," you can search for "environmental science AND global warming," and receive fewer hits that will be specific to what you are searching for.
- **Look for discipline-specific websites.** Specialized newsletters and trade publications offer good site listings.
- **Expect limited results from any one search engine.** No single search engine can index more than a fraction of ever-increasing web content.
- **Save or print what you need before it changes or disappears.**
- **Download only what you need.** Unless they are crucial to your research, omit graphics, sound, and video files. Be aware that downloading files can increase your exposure to computer viruses.
- **Before downloading *anything* from the internet, ask yourself, "Am I violating anyone's privacy (as in forwarding an email or a blog entry)?" and "Am I decreasing the value of this material for its owner in any way?"** For information on copyright, see Chapter 10.
- **Consider using information retrieval services such as Inquisit or DIALOG.** For a monthly or per-page fee, users can download full texts of articles. Schools and companies often subscribe to these internet-accessible databases.

C.A.R.S. Method for Evaluating Online Sources

Whether you use a website for research or personal information, you should evaluate the source carefully. The C.A.R.S. checklist has you judge websites according to their credibility, accuracy, reasonableness, and support. Using the C.A.R.S. checklist allows you to narrow down your research to the best evidence available.

Credibility

- Is there a publisher or sponsoring organization? Is the organization an authority on the subject?
- Is the author listed? Is the author an authority on the subject? How do you know?
- Are there spelling errors, grammar errors, dead links, or other problems that indicate a lack of quality control?

Accuracy

- Does the information on the site agree with other sources?
- Does the site contradict itself?
- What is the date of publication or copyright?
- How recently has the site been updated?

Reasonableness

- Does the author, host, publisher, or sponsor have a bias?
- What is the motivation or purpose for creating the site? (To sell a product? To advance a viewpoint or belief? To educate?)

Support

- Are the sources listed? Can they be checked?
- Is there a way to contact the author or organization?

Other Electronic Research Tools

Several other electronic technologies are available for storing and retrieving information. These technologies are accessible at libraries and in many cases via the web.

Google Scholar

Hosted by Google, Google Scholar allows you to search for information considered scholarly, such as legal opinions, articles, and patents. The information you find will not come from a Wikipedia entry but from a whole host of scholarly publications, including peer-reviewed journal articles, conference proceedings, conference papers, and professional and industry publications. Articles most commonly cited by other authors will appear as the top results of your search.

Compact Discs (CD-ROMs)

A single CD-ROM can store the equivalent of an entire encyclopedia and serves as a portable database, usually searchable via keyword. One useful CD-ROM for business information is ProQuest. Its ABI/INFORM database indexes countless journals in management, marketing, and business published since 1989; its UMI database indexes major U.S. newspapers. A useful CD-ROM for information about psychology, nursing, education, and social policy is SilverPlatter.

Online Retrieval Services

University libraries and corporations subscribe to online services that can access thousands of databases stored on centralized computers. Compared with CDs, mainframe databases are usually more specialized and more current, often updated daily (as opposed to weekly, monthly, or quarterly). Online retrieval services offer access to three types of databases: bibliographic, full text, and factual:

- *Bibliographic databases* list publications in a particular field and sometimes include abstracts for each entry.
- *Full-text databases* display the entire article or document (usually excluding graphics) directly on the computer screen and will print the article on command.
- *Factual databases* provide facts of all kinds: global and up-to-the-minute stock quotations, weather data, patient lists, and credit ratings of major companies, to name a few.

Four popular database services are:

- **OCLC and RLIN.** The Online Computer Library Center (OCLC) and Research Libraries Information Network (RLIN) are electronic consortiums that allow you to compile a comprehensive list of works on your topic at any member library. OCLC and RLIN databases are essentially giant electronic card catalogues. Using a networked terminal, you can search the databases by subject, title, or author.
- **DIALOG.** Many libraries subscribe to DIALOG, a network of independent databases covering a wide range of subjects and searchable by keywords. This system provides bibliographies and abstracts of the most recent journal articles. DIALOG databases include Conference Papers Index, Electronic Yellow Pages (for retailers, services, manufacturers), and ENVIROLINE.
- **BRS.** The Bibliographic Retrieval Services (BRS), another popular network, provides bibliographies and abstracts from life sciences, physical sciences, business, or social sciences. BRS databases include Dissertation Abstracts and International and Pollution Abstracts.

Comprehensive database networks such as DIALOG and BRS are accessible via the internet for a fee. Specialized databases, such as MEDLINE and ENVIRO-LINE, offer free bibliographies and abstracts, and you can order copies of the full text for a fee. Ask your librarian for help searching online databases.

Library Catalogues

Library catalogues used to be card catalogues, but today electronic files can be accessed through the internet or at terminals in the library. You can search a library's holdings by subject, author, or title in that library's catalogue system. Visit the library's website or ask a librarian for help.

Hard Copy Research

Traditional printed research tools (books, journals, newspapers) are still of great value. Unlike much of what you may find on the web (especially if you aren't careful about checking the source), most print research tools are carefully reviewed and edited before they are published. True, it may take more time to go to the library and look through a printed book, but often it's a better way to get solid information. Many print books and journals have online versions, which are identical to the print version.

Bibliographies

Bibliographies are comprehensive lists of publications about a subject, generally issued yearly. However, they can quickly become dated. To see which bibliographies are published in your field, begin with the *Bibliographic Index,* which is a list (by subject) of bibliographies that contain at least 50 citations. To look for bibliographies on scientific and technical topics, consult *Scientific and Technical Publishing Services,* which is a list of everything published by the U.S. government in these broad fields. You might also look for bibliographies focused on a particular subject, such as *Health Hazards of Video Display Terminals: An Annotated Bibliography.*

Encyclopedias

Encyclopedias provide basic information. Examples include the *Encyclopedia of Building and Construction Terms,* the *Encyclopedia of Banking and Finance,* and the *Encyclopedia of Food Technology.* For example, the *Encyclopedia of Associations* lists over 30 000 professional organizations worldwide (Canadian Medical Association, Institute of Electrical and Electronics Engineers, and so on).

Dictionaries

Dictionaries may be general, or specific to a discipline; some give biographical or historical information. Examples include the *Dictionary of Engineering and Technology*, the *Dictionary of Telecommunications*, and the *Dictionary of Scientific Biography*.

Handbooks

These research aids contain key facts (formulas, tables, advice, examples) about a field in condensed form. Examples include the *Business Writer's Handbook*, the *Civil Engineering Handbook*, and the *McGraw-Hill Computer Handbook*.

Almanacs

Almanacs contain factual and statistical data. Examples include the *World Almanac and Book of Facts*, the *Almanac for Computers*, and the *Almanac of Business and Industrial Financial* Ratios.

Directories

Directories provide updated information about organizations, companies, people, products, services, or careers, often including addresses and phone numbers. Examples include *The Career Guide: Dun's Employment Opportunities Directory*, the *Directory of American Firms Operating in Foreign Countries*, and *The Internet Directory*.

Guides to Literature

If you simply don't know which books, journals, indexes, and reference works are available for your topic, consult a guide to literature. For a general list of books in various disciplines, see Walford's *Guide to Reference Material* or Sheehy's *Guide to Reference Books*. For scientific and technical literature, consult Malinowsky and Richardson's *Science and Engineering Literature: A Guide to Reference Sources*. Ask your librarian about literature guides for your discipline.

Indexes

Indexes are lists of books, newspaper articles, journal articles, or other works on a particular subject.

Book Indexes. A book index lists works by author, title, or subject. Sample indexes include *Scientific and Technical Books and Serials in Print* (an annual listing of literature in science and technology), *New Technical Books: A Selective*

List with Descriptive Annotations (issued 10 times yearly), and *Medical Books and Serials in Print* (an annual listing of works from medicine and psychology).

Periodical Indexes. A periodical index provides sources from magazines and journals. First, decide whether you seek general or specialized information. Two general indexes are the *Magazine Index,* a subject index on microfilm, and the *Readers' Guide to Periodical Literature,* which is updated every few weeks. Virtually all periodical indexes are now available in electronic form in library databases.

For specialized information, consult indexes that list journal articles by discipline, such as *Ulrich's International Periodicals Directory*, the *General Science Index*, the *Applied Science and Technology Index*, or the *Business Periodicals Index*. Specific disciplines have their own indexes: examples include the *Agricultural Index*, the *Index to Legal Periodicals*, and the *International Nursing Index*.

Citation Indexes. Citation indexes allow researchers to trace the development and refinement of a published idea. Using a citation index, you can track down the specific publications in which the original material has been cited, quoted, applied, critiqued, verified, or otherwise amplified (Garfield, 1973, p. 200). In short, you can use them to answer the question, "Who else has said what about this idea?"

The *Science Citation Index* cross-references articles on science and technology worldwide. Both the *Science Citation Index* and its counterpart, the *Social Science Citation Index,* are searchable by computer.

Technical Report Indexes. Government and private-sector reports prepared worldwide offer specialized and current information. Examples include *Canada Institute for Scientific and Technical Information, Canadian Research Institute,* and the *Government of Canada Publications.* Proprietary or security restrictions limit public access to certain corporate or government documents.

Patent Indexes. Countless patents are issued yearly to protect new inventions, products, or processes. Although patents originate in hard-text form, many institutes now publish their patents online to provide easy access to users. Examples include the *Canadian Patents Database,* the *Space Canada* website, and the *Derwent World Patents Index.*

Patents in various technologies are searchable through databases such as *Hi Tech Patents, Data Communications*, and *World Patents Index.*

Abstracts

Because abstracts index and summarize articles, they can save you time by eliminating the need to read every article before deciding whether it contains useful information. Collections of abstracts are usually titled by discipline: *Biological*

Abstracts, Computer Abstracts, and so on. For some current research, you might consult abstracts of doctoral dissertations in *Dissertation Abstracts International.* Abstracts are increasingly searchable by computer.

Access Tools for Government Publications

The Canadian government publishes maps, periodicals, books, pamphlets, manuals, monographs, annual reports, research reports, and other information, most of which are searchable by computer. Examples include *Environment Canada's Science Plan,* and the *Journal of Research of the National Bureau of Standards.* To access these complex resources, request assistance from a librarian familiar with government documents. The following are basic access tools for documents issued by or published at government expense, as well as for many privately sponsored documents:

- *Government of Canada Publications:* This searchable website (http://publications.gc.ca/site/eng/home.html) is the major pathway to government publications and reports.
- *Government of Canada Publications and Reports:* This website (http://canada.gc.ca/publications/publication-eng.html) is a listing of the government of Canada's publications, searchable by topic, department and agency, title, and so on.
- *Statistics Canada:* Updated weekly, Statistics Canada (www.statcan.gc.ca) offers an array of statistics collected on topics of interest to the Canadian government, such as population, health, and employment.

Many unpublished government documents are available under the *Access to Information Act.* The act grants public access to all federal agency records except for classified documents, trade secrets, certain law enforcement files, and records protected by personal privacy law. Contact the agency that would hold the records you seek. For example, for workplace accident reports, contact Human Resources and Skills Development Canada; for industrial pollution records, contact Environment Canada. If the information you seek is not public, then request access through the Act.

TIPS FOR EVALUATING AND INTERPRETING INFORMATION

Evaluate the Sources
- **Check the date of posting or publication.** The latest information is not always the best, but keeping up with recent developments is vital.
- **Assess the reputation of each source.** Check the copyright page, for background on the publisher; the bibliography, for the quality and

extent of research; and (if available) the author's brief biography, for credentials. For electronic sources, a reputable source will have the author's name and their credentials.

- **Identify the study's sponsor.** If the study acclaims the crashworthiness of the Hutmobile but is sponsored by the Hutmobile Auto Company, be skeptical.
- **Look for corroborating sources.** A single study rarely produces dependable findings. Learn what other sources say, why they might agree or disagree, and where most experts stand on the issue.

Evaluate the Evidence

- **Decide whether the evidence is sufficient.** Evidence should include more than the author's personal experience, anecdotes, or popular news reports. It should be credible enough for reasonable and informed observers to agree on its value and accuracy.

- **Look for a reasonable and balanced presentation of evidence.** Suspect any claims about "breakthroughs" or "miracle cures" or any information that is presented in emotional or dramatic language. Expect to see a discussion of drawbacks as well as benefits.

- **Try to verify the evidence.** Examine the facts that support the claims. Look for other studies that have replicated or repudiated these findings.

Interpret Your Findings

- **Don't expect to find certainty.** Complex questions are mostly open-ended, and a mere accumulation of facts doesn't prove anything. Even so, the weight of solid evidence usually points toward some reasonable conclusion.
- **Be aware of your personal biases.** Don't ignore evidence simply because it contradicts your assumptions.
- **Consider alternative interpretations.** What else might this evidence mean?

Check for Weaknesses

- **Decide whether the evidence supports the conclusions.** Suspect any general claim not limited by a qualifier such as *often, sometimes,* or *rarely*.
- **Treat cause-and-effect claims with healthy skepticism.** Consider other possible causes and effects, as well as confounding factors.
- **Look for statistical fallacies.** Determine where the numbers come from and how they were collected and analyzed—information that legitimate researchers routinely provide. Study graphs closely to make sure they present the information honestly.

- **Consider the limits of computer analysis.** A computer model is only as accurate as the assumptions and data programmed into it. So studies based entirely on computer analysis may not be any more reliable than those based on surveys and interviews.
- **Interpret the reality behind the numbers.** Consider the possibility of alternative and possibly more accurate interpretations of the data.
- **Consider the study's possible limitations.** Small, brief studies are less reliable than large, extended ones; epidemiological studies are less reliable than laboratory studies (which have their own flaws); animal or human exposure studies are often not generalizable to larger human populations; "masked" (or blind) studies are not always as objective as they seem; and measurements are prone to error.
- **Look for the whole story.** Bad news may be underreported; good news may be exaggerated; bad science may be camouflaged and sensationalized. Research on promising but unconventional topics (say, alternative energy sources) might be ignored.

Summarize your Information

- **Select the main points of the articles.** What sentences are the most crucial to understanding what you have just read? Limit yourself to only two to five sentences or points per paragraph to keep your summary concise.
- **Use your own words.** If you are summarizing an article or text that uses jargon that you are not familiar or comfortable with, use words that you are comfortable with while taking note of technical terms that are common to the discipline you are writing in.
- **Review your summary.** Does your summary provide you with a clear, concise overview of what you read? Are the main points from the original work included in your summary?

Checklist for Research

Methods
- Are my sources appropriately up to date?
- Is each source reputable, trustworthy, and relatively unbiased? Is the research supported by similar reputable sources?
- Does the evidence clearly support the conclusions?
- Is a fair balance of viewpoints represented?
- Can all the evidence be verified?

Reasoning

- Can I rule out other possible interpretations or conclusions?
- Have I accounted for all

- Am I confident that my causal reasoning is accurate?

  - Can I rule out confounding factors?
- Can all the numbers, statistics, and interpretations be trusted?
- Can I rule out any possible error or distortion?
- Am I getting the whole story and getting it straight?

Exercises

1. Locate a research article from the past four years (not one that is too recent). Using a citation index, track down the specific publications that cite this article. If your article is from a scientific or technical field, try the *Science Citation Index.* Based on the number and type of citations of the article, what is your opinion about the importance of the article's findings?

2. Locate an expert in your field or on a topic for an upcoming project (such as a long report). Arrange to interview that person. You may wish to make your initial contact via email. Follow the tips on page 81. In groups of three or four, discuss your interview experience and your findings with your classmates.

3. Choose a short interview from a popular Canadian news show such as *Mansbridge One on One, George Struombouloupoulos Tonight,* or *Marketplace* (10–20 minutes). In groups of three or four, discuss whether the interviewer followed the guidelines described at the beginning of this chapter. Does the interviewer use open-ended questions? Does the interviewer ask for clarification when needed?

4. Choose a specific topic to research. Then look through an abstracts database for articles related to your topic. Identify which articles would be useful to your research topic. What information does each abstract provide to help you determine its usefulness?

5. **FOCUS ON WRITING.** Use two major indexes to locate research articles for your field or topic. One source should be a traditional periodical index and the other should be an internet search engine. Find a recent article on a specific topic (for example, privacy laws in your province) and write a short summary.

6. **FOCUS** on **RESEARCH**. Researchers often have difficulty determining how to judge the validity of information found on a website. Working in small groups of three or four, research and develop a set of criteria that can be used to evaluate a website for research purposes.

Begin by visiting one or more of the websites listed here. Compile a working list of criteria based on these sites, then work as a group to expand your list. For example, do you consider good design to be a sign of credibility? What else do you look at when you are assessing the relevance, currency, and validity of information on a particular site? How do you know if a website is commercially or politically biased?

Test the criteria you have developed by using a search engine to locate websites on a current topic (for example, global warming, genetically modified foods, software piracy, or MP3 file downloading). Select one website that interests you and evaluate its credibility as a source for research information using your own criteria. Revise your list of criteria as needed, and then format it as a document that can be shared with the rest of your class.

- **http://libraries.dal.ca/using_the_library/tutorials/evaluating_web_resources.html**
  "Evaluating Web Resources," developed by the library at Dalhousie University
- **http://help.library.ubc.ca/researching/evaluating-internet-sources/**
  "Evaluating Internet Sources," from the library at the University of British Columbia
- **www.vuw.ac.nz/staff/alastair_smith/evaln/index.htm**
  "Criteria for evaluation of Internet Information Resources," from the Department of Library and Information Studies, Victoria University of Wellington, New Zealand

The Collaboration Window

In small groups, prepare a comparative evaluation of literature search media. Each group member will select one of the resources listed here and create an individual bibliography of at least 12 recent and relevant works on a specific topic of interest selected by the group:

- conventional print media
- electronic catalogues
- CD-ROM services
- a commercial database service such as DIALOG
- the internet and the World Wide Web
- an electronic consortium of libraries, if applicable

After carefully recording the findings and keeping track of the time spent in each search, compare the ease of searching and quality of results obtained from each type of search. Which medium yielded the most current sources? Which provided abstracts and full texts as well as bibliographic data? Which consumed the most time? Which provided the most dependable sources? Which provided the most diverse or varied sources? Which cost the most to use? Finally, which yielded the greatest depth of resources? Prepare a report and present your findings to the class.

 The Global Window

FOCUS ON WRITING.

The International Space Station (ISS) is undoubtedly the largest and most complex international scientific project in history. Begun in 1995, the project requires the collaboration, expertise, and technological resources of 16 nations. The ISS encountered delays and difficulties for a variety of reasons, including funding problems and the grounding of the NASA space shuttle program following the 2003 *Columbia* disaster. (For background information on the Columbia disaster, visit www.aerospaceguide.net/spaceshuttle/columbia_disaster.html.)

Do some preliminary research on the scope and history of the project by visiting www.shuttlepresskit.com/ISS_OVR, and then follow the links from that website to the websites for the European, Japanese, and Canadian space agencies. How does each website differ? Do you find any differences in the way the mission of the ISS is described? In the ways the roles of each nation are defined?

Imagine that you have been assigned to produce a campaign to rally and re-energize public support around the world for the ISS project. What information would you use to persuade citizens of the participating nations that in today's world, it is worth their nation's time and money to support continued development of an international space station? Would you use different strategies to persuade people in different countries? Why?

Develop a one-page proposal that outlines the key features of your campaign, detailing how you would customize the style and argument of your campaign to persuade public audiences in the diverse nations involved in the ISS initiative.

MyCanadianTechCommLab

Go to MyCanadianTechCommLab at www.mycanadiantechcommlab.com for additional online exercises and problems.

CHAPTER 6

Technical Communication in a Digital World

Chapter Objectives

By the end of this chapter you will be able to:

1. Design a webpage that is visually appealing and that contains text that is easy to read.

2. Present your information in an aesthetically pleasing way (adequate text size, proper spacing and layout, organized information, etc.).

3. Understand and be able to use various methods of electronic communication to reach the target audience/reader.

Glenn Ruhl, Calgary, Alberta

For Glenn Ruhl, writing and design have always played a large part in his career. "Some of my earliest projects were to design the logo for the college hockey team I was coaching and to write and prepare study materials for the department of student services."

After the completion of his doctoral degree in education, Ruhl served as a college registrar and was responsible for producing institutional calendars. "It wasn't conventional technical writing," Glenn adds, "but it provided valuable experience in applied writing and learning new technologies."

With over 30 years of writing and editing technical documentation ranging from curricula, calendars, and style guides to brochures, student handbooks, proposals, and websites, it was a natural progression for Glenn to assume his current position as program chair for electronic publishing and technical communication at Mount Royal College.

"My work," Ruhl adds, "has always included writing, research, and design, and not necessarily in that order. Seeing how these areas continue to emerge and develop beyond traditional boundaries is the most fascinating aspect of my work at Mount Royal."

Communicating in Digital Space

Computer technologies are often touted as the answer to communication problems. Much of what formerly took hours to accomplish by hand takes only seconds on a computer. For example, creating a pie chart or line graph once required careful hand drawing using ink and coloured overlays. Now, clicking on a button in any spreadsheet program to create a chart, graph, or other visual display takes only a moment.

However, these technologies by themselves do not guarantee quality communication. In fact, the information overload that often results from the use of so many technologies can make communication more, rather than less, confusing. By understanding the unique features of digital communication, you can use these technologies to create quality technical communication.

Note that all the elements discussed in Chapter 1 (accessibility, usability, and relevance) apply to electronic communication as well. In addition, there are many unique aspects of communication in the digital realm.

Designing Information

Traditionally, print newspapers have always been different from television news, radio ads distinct from brochures, software manuals different from CD-ROMs. Yet the trend today is toward "convergence": the distinctions between these forms of communication are becoming blurred. For example, online newspapers blur the distinctions between a newspaper and an interactive website. As more and more of this convergence occurs, technical communicators face information design issues unique to this type of media.

For instance, if you are a technical writer at a software company, you may be asked not only to research and write the information for a user's guide but also to design this information for a website or an online help screen. In some organizations, these tasks are done by different communication specialists. Companies may have employees who focus solely on writing while others focus on web design. Even so, each technical communicator must know the principles involved in designing for new media. As Mary Susan Ryan-Flynn notes, technical communicators "should be willing to pursue learning throughout their careers . . . (a)s technology changes" (2009).

Writing Issues

Writing for websites, like writing on paper, must conform to the principles of effective technical communication. In addition, writing for websites involves several audience considerations.

Addressing the Needs of Impatient Readers. Garth A. Buchhulz notes that it is important for writers to be aware that "print content is structurally and functionally different from online content. Print is . . . linear, narrative . . . and presents a continuous view. Online content is informally written, chunked out," and "interactive" (2009). Readers generally have less patience with on-screen material than with hard copy; experts claim that "one characteristic to all website audiences is that they spend most of their time scanning material, and if they don't find what they want quickly—within the first minute—they will probably leave your site and may never return" (Krizen, Merrier, Logan, & Williams, 2008). In addition, people associate computers with speed, so they find long blocks of online information annoying. In addition, the light patterns of computer screens tire the eyes, causing people to resist reading long passages of text online.

To counter reader impatience, you should write online text in a *chunked* format, breaking down long paragraphs into shorter passages that are easier to access and faster to read. Chunking is also used in paper documentation (see Chapter 3), but is especially important for web documents.

How you chunk the information depends on the way you expect your audience to interact with your website. According to one expert, "chunking content creates natural breaks and helps readers absorb information in manageable pieces" (Rominger, 2010). Imagine that you are writing text for a website intended to explain a medical procedure to patients. After performing an audience analysis, you decide to organize this information by questions users might ask: "How long will the surgery last?" or "When will I be able to return to work?" You would chunk your information into these categories, possibly making each an individual link on the website.

Companies increasingly realize that chunked information is cost-effective and strive to create single sources of information that can be reused in various formats. A technical communicator may write the information once, store it in a database, and use the same chunks (or "modules") to create a manual, a brochure, a website, and a CD-ROM.

Addressing the Needs of Nonlinear Readers. People do not read websites in a linear fashion, as they would read a book. A typical website displays information in a *hypertext format,* which allows users to jump around and move from link to link, thereby abandoning the original sequence of information. For this reason, each chunk of text on a webpage must make sense on its own, regardless of the order in which it is read.

Addressing the Needs of a Diverse Audience. A webpage's audience may end up being far broader than you intend it to be. Unless you are designing an intranet site (for use only within a specific company or organization), your website can be accessed by almost anyone worldwide. Some websites, such as those for patients seeking specific medical information, begin with a brief description of the intended audience. This helps readers determine whether this website is right for them.

To accommodate a global audience, take the following steps:

- Provide links to websites and webpages that explain highly technical terms or complicated ideas in simpler language.
- Provide a feedback mechanism (email address, web form) for people who have questions.
- Write in short sentences, not only for ease of reading but also to permit translation of webpages into different languages.

Design Issues

Webpages are designed using *hypertext markup language,* or HTML. This HTML code appears as inserted commands, or "tags," which, when read by a web browser (such as Microsoft Internet Explorer), cause formatting features to appear on the screen. For example, a line of text tagged as follows

| <c>Privacy and Electronic Commerce</c>

would appear as bold () and centred (<c>) when viewed through a browser:

| **Privacy and Electronic Commerce**

The slash tags at the end of the text (and </c>) tell the browser to turn off the boldface and centring features.

In the web's early days, HTML coding was done by experts. Today, it is easy to write a webpage with little or no knowledge of HTML. You can use web editing software (such as FrontPage, Expression Web, or Dreamweaver), and most word-processing programs can create a webpage, much as you would create a word-processing document. The software then translates your document into HTML code. HTML also allows your website to encompass other commonly used programs, such as XML, Java, and Flash, all which can be downloaded via the internet. Ensuring that your website uses the most common and popular programs means that it will not become quickly dated.

But even though websites are easy to produce, effective design is no simple matter. Many websites created by novices are poorly designed and hard to use. Web design is the subject of many books, classes, and workshops. The following are some basic design features to consider.

Organization. One common source of frustration for web users is the "can't find it" problem (Rosenfeld & Morville, 1998, p. 4). Most of us have visited websites that have no links, no overview of the site's content, and no apparent logical organization. A well designed website is clearly organized so that users can follow the information flow (see Figure 6.1). The page should be organized so that the main purpose of the website is represented by the largest item and draws the eye. If information is presented in columns, each column should have a clear purpose

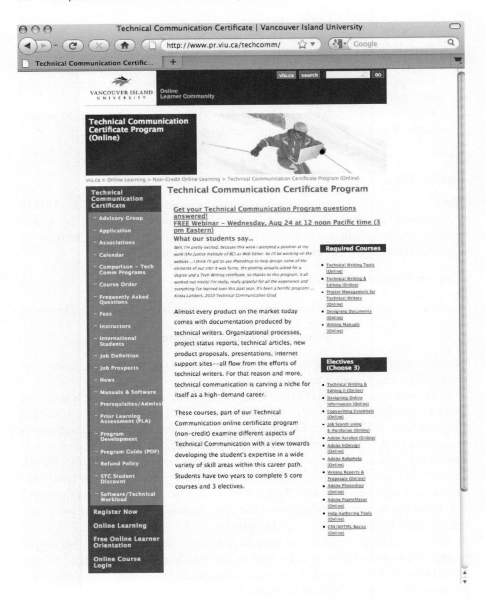

Figure 6.1 **A Well-Organized Webpage.** This webpage is pleasing in appearance and well organized. The photograph and text box at the top span the entire width of the page, providing cohesion and unity to the site and directing the eye to this information first. Three columns then provide information and links. Each column uses a different layout and font size. The page uses white space effectively and, while it offers many links and much information, it is not overcrowded or cluttered. The main links are in the left column and the other two columns provide a good balance.

Source: Vancouver Island University.

and differently sized fonts, and visuals should be used to differentiate between the columns of information. White space helps your reader move from section to section.

Typography. Typefaces on a computer screen show up less clearly and with less resolution than on a printed page. Also, predicting exactly how a typeface will appear on a given computer screen is almost impossible, since different browsers present fonts differently.

Mike Smith (2009) offers these recommendations for type designs on the web:

- Do not use too many fonts on one page
- Do not switch back and forth between serif and sans-serif fonts numerous times
- Do not use sans-serif fonts for large bodies of text
- Do not ignore the fact that the viewer may increase the font.

Note how most of these recommendations are embodied in Figure 6.2.

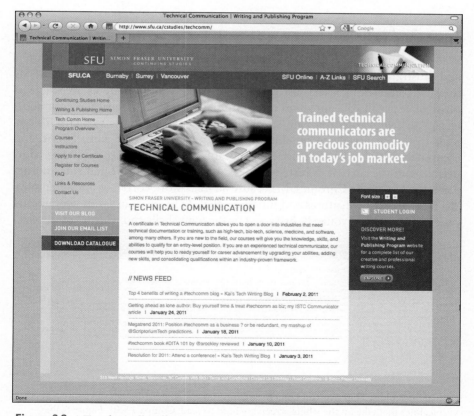

Figure 6.2 A Typologically Effective Webpage. This website uses typography effectively for the screen.

Source: Simon Fraser University Continuing Studies. www.sfu.ca/cstudies/techcomm/.

Line Length. HTML adapts a website's size to the size of a reader's screen, and long lines of text can be hard to follow, especially for readers with extra-wide screens. Never simply "dump" a page of print text onto a website. Chunk the text into smaller units. Control the width of the text by placing it inside a box or container of a specified size, or by using the padding or margins function in the container element. In general, line lengths should not exceed 60 characters per line (see Figures 6.3a and 6.3b). Also, set the text to have a "ragged right" margin, rather than a justified margin, because it will be easier to read.

Appearance. A well-designed, visually attractive website combines the information power of both printed text and visual information (such as a photograph, illustration, or live video). Colour can increase visual appeal, but don't add too many colours or your website will look cluttered and unprofessional. Select a few colours that complement each other well, and keep your choices simple. Use colours appropriate for your audience: for example, school colours might make an attractive background for a university website.

Technical Issues

Websites must be *accessible*. For example, a website that contains photographs and illustrations may be visually attractive but hard to access for users whose internet connections aren't fast enough. To make your website as accessible as possible, learn all you can about the computer use of the majority of your audience. Work with your company's technical support staff to use *standard file formats* to design a website suitable for the browsers, internet connections, and computers used by the audience. Websites for a global audience should be compatible with the current industry-standard browsers (Firefox, Microsoft Internet Explorer, or Google Chrome). Make sure all links work correctly, and remember "to avoid using any features and functions that do not support your overall purpose. . . . If you find yourself distracted by the many bells and whistles of the web,

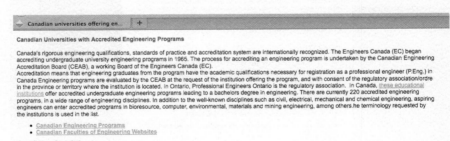

Figure 6.3a **Lines That Are Too Long for a Computer Screen.** Although the entire text is visible, lines that take up the whole screen are hard to read. Compare with Figure 6.3b.
Source: Reproduced from the website of Professional Engineers Ontario (www.peo.on.ca) by permission of the publisher.

Figure 6.3b **Shorter Line Lengths Are Easier on the Eye.**
Source: Used with the permission of the Engineering Institute of Canada www.eic-ici.ca.

remember that it's better to have a simple website that presents information clearly and effectively than a complex site that does not" (VanderMey et al., 2009). Finally, test the site to be sure it is *functional* and *usable*. Most organizations have staff who work specifically on the technical aspects of websites; they can help you make sure the technical design of your website is appropriate for your audience.

Online Documentation and Interface Design

Online documentation can be found either on a CD-ROM or in the software itself as a built-in feature. If you have ever used the "Help" command in your word-processing software, you have accessed online documentation. Many companies not only offer "Help" search engines in their programs but also allow users to connect to help websites. For example, users of Microsoft Word can quickly find the answers to their questions by clicking on the direct link to the Microsoft Office website. These functions are a part of interface design that is meant to make programs as functional as possible for the users.

Online Documentation

Online documentation (see Figure 6.4) is very popular with technology companies, because it saves the time and money that would be spent on printing paper documentation and manuals. In addition, some documentation is *context-sensitive:* if the user makes a mistake, the software with context-sensitive help functions will recognize the mistake and direct the user to the appropriate help screen. This process is faster for the user than identifying their own errors and then trying to find relevant information in the Help files.

You can use special software, such as RoboHelp or Doc-to-Help, to convert textual material into online help files.

Interface Design

The interface is the part of a software application you see on the screen. For example, when you open Microsoft Word, you see a menu bar, buttons, and a background screen. While the heart of the program—the computer code—runs

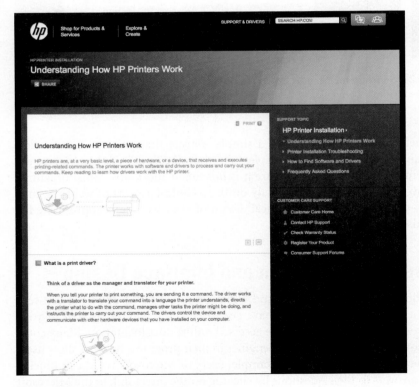

Figure 6.4   Online Documentation
Source: Used with permission of Hewlett-Packard (Canada) Co.

silently in the background, the interface—the clickable icons and menus—lets you interact with the software.

Software interfaces must be well designed. Menu commands must be consistent, visual images must appear in logical places, and features must perform in ways that make sense to the user. Items must be spelled correctly, and screens must appear in the proper order.

Interface design is such a complex subject that many schools offer degrees in this area. Technical communicators often work on the layout, functionality, and wording of software interfaces, and some go on to become interface designers.

Corresponding over the Wires: Email, Smartphones, Blogs, and Instant Messaging

The bulk of today's electronically mediated correspondence occurs via email, smartphones, blogs, instant messaging, and social media networks. While some of the traditions of paper communication apply to electronic communication, each technology has developed its own customs and practices.

Email

Email is electronic mail, which allows people to communicate computer to computer. Several features make it attractive for workplace communication.

- **Asynchronicity.** Communication is asynchronous if does not take place in real time. Unlike a face-to-face conversation, in which two or more people must be physically present, email allows you to communicate with someone at any time, day or night. You can send a message at 2:00 a.m., if that suits your schedule, and the recipient can read it on arrival at the office at 9:00 a.m.
- **Electronic "paper trail."** Unlike phone calls or face-to-face conversations, email messages are automatically stored and saved for future reference. It is also possible to cut and paste material from an email message into another document. Note that even if you delete your email files, the computer still holds a record of all the deleted files.
- **Easy forwarding.** Email messages can be forwarded to others with a single keystroke, thus simplifying the distribution of a message to multiple recipients.
- **Attachments.** Most email programs enable you to send attachments (see Figure 6.5) of entire documents with their original formatting. Most popular email programs make attachments between PCs and Apple computers interchangeable.

Technical communicators commonly share drafts of material via email or coauthor entire reports or other documents by collaborating through email.

The heavy use of email has resulted in new conventions for spelling, phrasing, and expectations of how quickly people will respond. Although many people

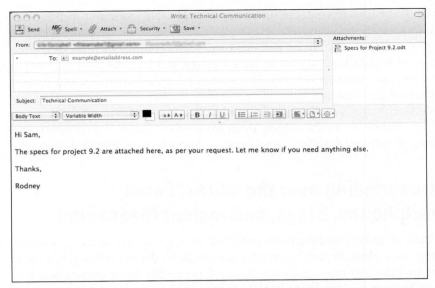

Figure 6.5 Most Email Programs, including Thunderbird, Allow the User to Send Attachments via Email.
Source: Thunderbird screenshot courtesy of Modzilla.

have tried to formalize the rules of "netiquette," these conventions continue to evolve. When communicating via email, consider the following issues:

- **Oral or written.** At first glance, email resembles a written document. The standard email format resembles that of a paper memo, with "To," "From," "Date," and "Re:" fields. Yet email tends to be informal and conversational. Even writers who are extremely careful with traditional written correspondence sometimes ignore spelling or grammar, instead writing an email message much as they might speak it. Proofread your email messages, spell-check them whenever possible, and avoid using all capital letters. (ALL CAPS in email is considered shouting.)

- **Speed and reach.** As with websites, people have a short attention span for reading email. Email is considered a *speed* medium, because people read the messages quickly. Don't send long messages or huge attachments unless you have warned the receiver in advance. Restrict an email to one topic, as you would for a written memo. Multiple topics in one email are likely to be ignored by the reader. Also, remember that accuracy is essential in technical communication. It is too easy to click on Send before you have considered how well and how appropriately an email has been worded. Be sure to check the content of your message carefully, and always pause before clicking on Send.

    Email is also a medium with a wide *reach*. Reach refers to the vast audiences and great distances an email can cover. Because of forwarding features, you never know who will read your message. A message intended only for your manager may accidentally be forwarded to the entire department. Or your manager may forward your message to others in the organization—and that message may be the only impression others have of you. In most organizations, email messages on company computers belong to the company, not to you. Never post an email message that you would not want to be seen by people other than your intended audience.

- **Flaming.** Some people use email to express anger and to attack others personally. Researchers speculate that this behaviour, called *flaming,* has various causes, including the speed at which people post messages and the fact that email writers can hide behind the screen, thus avoiding the repercussions of face-to-face rudeness. In addition, because email lacks facial expressions, gestures, and voice intonations to support the meaning of the words, readers can easily misinterpret messages and become insulted. If your email exchange becomes difficult, confusing, or angry, consider calling a meeting or making some phone calls to resolve the situation.

- **Hierarchy.** Email often lets you bypass "pecking orders" and send messages directly to someone you might never reach by phone. Because email tends to inspire informality, writers often forget that they are not writing to an old college roommate but to a manager, a respected scientist, or an important author. Even with email, politeness is always important; for example, if you don't know the recipient of your message, begin with a salutation—"Dear Dr. Raphani"—not with an informal "Hi!" or with no salutation at all.

TIPS FOR USING ELECTRONIC MAIL

Observe Rules of "Netiquette"

- **Check and answer your email daily.** Unanswered email is annoying. If you're busy, at least acknowledge receipt and respond later.
- **Check your distribution list before each mailing.** Verify that your message will reach all intended recipients and no unintended ones. Beware of the Reply All feature, which sends a reply to everyone who received the original message, including yourself.
- **Don't use email when a more personal medium is preferable.** Sometimes an issue is best resolved with a phone call or even voicemail.
- **Don't use email for most formal correspondence.** Don't use email to apply for a job, request a raise, resign from a job, or respond to clients or customers, unless someone has specifically requested this method.
- **Allow everyone in an email discussion to participate equally, regardless of gender.**

Consider the Ethical, Legal, and Interpersonal Implications

- **Assume that your email is permanent and could be read by anyone at any time.** Don't write anything you wouldn't say to someone's face.
- **Think twice before making wisecracks.** What seems amusing to you may be offensive to others, including recipients from different cultures. Any email judged to be harassing or discriminatory brings immediate dismissal and can result in legal action against the company as well as the guilty employee.
- **Don't use email for confidential information.** Avoid complaining, criticizing, or evaluating people, and handle anything that should be kept private (say, an employee reprimand) in some other way. Deleting old email files does not eliminate them from your hard drive. In a lawsuit, a court can confiscate your computer and order computer forensics to find those deleted emails.
- **Don't use the company email network for personal correspondence or for anything not work-related.** Employers increasingly monitor email networks.
- **Before you forward an incoming message, obtain permission from the sender.** Assume that anything you receive is the private property of the sender. (Email copyright issues are covered in Chapter 10.)

Make the Message Usable

- **Use a clear subject line.** Instead of "Test Data" or "Data Request," announce your purpose clearly: "Request for Beta Test Data for Project 16." Recipients scan subject lines when deciding which new mail to read immediately.
- **Refer clearly to the message to which you are responding:** "Here are the Project 16 Beta Test Data you requested."
- **Keep sentences and paragraphs short.**
- **Use block format. Don't indent paragraphs.**
- **Don't write in ALL CAPS—unless you want to YELL!**
- **Where appropriate in formal emails, use graphic highlighting.** Headings, bullets, numbered lists, boldface, and italics improve readability.
- **Where appropriate, use formal salutations and closings.** When addressing someone you don't know or someone in a position of authority, begin with a formal salutation ("Dear Doctor Benoit") and end with a formal closing ("Sincerely"). For a familiar recipient, you can be less formal ("Hello," "Regards").
- **Use emoticons (e.g., smiley faces) and abbreviations sparingly.** Smiley faces, made from a colon, dash, and right-hand parenthesis :-) or downloaded as small graphics, are used to signify humour or irony. Use these

and other emoticons infrequently and only in informal messages to people you know well. Also, common email abbreviations (for example,
FYI, BTW, and HAND—which stand for "for your information," "by the
way," and "have a nice day," respectively) may annoy some recipients.
Whenever in doubt, write it out.

- **Close with a standard signature.** Include the name of your company or
department, your telephone and fax number, and other relevant contact
information. Store your signature in the software's signature file so that
it automatically appears in every email.

- **Proofread.** A mechanically and grammatically correct message is always
more credible than a sloppy one.

Smartphones

Smartphones, such as the BlackBerry, the Android, and the iPhone, are a combination of mobile phone with other office software and multimedia functionality.
Smartphones have revolutionized the way work is done. These devices allow
users to conduct business wirelessly from virtually any location. Email can be
received or sent easily.

The BlackBerry, created by Canadian company Research In Motion (RIM),
has become "a tool of the trade now, rather than the status symbol they once
were when they were first introduced" (Batten, 2008). Organizations such as
Voda Training (blackberryclass.com) now offer online courses to teach Black-
Berry users how to use the device effectively and at their own pace. Websites such
as BlackBerryForums.com and CrackBerry.com allow users to connect with
other users and ask for tips and advice.

Tablet Personal Computers (Tablet PC)

The term "tablet PC" was made popular as a concept presented by Microsoft in
2001, but tablet PC now refers to any tablet-sized personal computer, even if it is
not running Windows but uses another operating system. Two popular tablets
PCs to enter the Canadian workplace are the iPad, from Apple, and the Playbook,
from Research in Motion. Tablet PCs are used increasingly in the workplace as a
convenient alternative to laptop computers because of their size, portability,
touchscreens and virtual keyboards, fast operating systems, expanded memory
capacity, and the number of computer applications specially designed for these
devices. All tablet PCs have a wireless adapter for internet and local network connection. Software applications for tablet PCs include office suites, web browsers,
games, and a variety of office applications.

A study by Deloitte Canada predicts that tablet PC and smartphone sales will outsell personal computers in 2011. The report also said that 425 million smartphones and tablets were expected to ship globally, compared to 400 million PCs, that same year. Moreover, a recent poll by the NPD Group (2011) reported that 6 percent of Canadians already own a tablet PC. Websites have had to adjust their content layout to meet the needs of the tablet PC user. Scroll ribbons and page turning that mimics the experience of print materials such as magazines and newspapers have allowed readers to use their touchscreens to navigate web content in more familiar and efficient ways.

Workplace Blogs

Blogs, once simply a popular online forum for sharing information and opinions, are becoming increasingly common as a workplace tool. Easily created with templates downloaded from a site such as Blogger.com, blogs enable colleagues to converse online on day-to-day matters ranging from solving a critical hardware problem at a nuclear power plant to brainstorming for new ideas in game software. Blogs can support the collaborative production of documents such as proposals, annual reports, and promotional literature, not to mention usability surveys among customers of various products and services.

One vital benefit of blogs is the gathering of real-time information from custom feeds (RSS) and e-newsletters on preselected topics—often in a preselected language—from outside sources. For example, NewsIsFree.com searches and updates the news from over 20 000 sources every 15 minutes. Knowledge centres offer the latest research reports on virtually any topic imaginable, ranging from data security to operating systems. Because blogs are inexpensive, efficient, and user-friendly, there are many mainstream applications, in academia as well as the workplace.

Several colleges and universities have begun promoting electronic interaction as a way to support classroom teaching and provide space for student discussions. One excellent example is the Centennial College Blog at centennialcollege-blog.com. (See pages 87–89 for precautions in relying on blogs as a sole source of information.)

Instant Messaging

A faster medium than email, instant messaging (IM), such as Facebook Chat, allows for text-based conversation in real time: the user types a message in a pop-up box, and the recipient can respond instantly. IM groupware enables multiple users to converse and collaborate from various locations. According to *Fortune* magazine, instant messaging has started replacing email for routine communication in North American businesses (Varchaver, 2003, p. 102). Many business BlackBerry users use RIM's BlackBerry Messenger system to send instant messages to both colleagues and clients.

Although instant messaging has been popular among teens and college students for years, its more recent advent as a business tool means that few rules govern its use in the business world. Also, most current IM software does not automatically save these messages electronically. But as IM becomes more common in the workplace, companies will likely monitor its use by employees and save all messages as a permanent record.

Social Media

Originally aimed at audiences looking for a way to socialize online, social media services such as Facebook and Twitter are now used by professional organizations as a way to reach out to customers and readers of all ages.

Facebook

Established in 2004 by Harvard University students as a way for their peers to connect with each other and share photos and interests, Facebook allows you to "friend" people and join common interest groups. Anyone can make an account and have either a personal profile page or a group page on any subject they choose. Status updates alert your "friends" to any activity on your page. Similarly, you can also "like" someone's post and post it to your own wall.

With half a billion users and half of them logging on each day, world-renowned companies such as Apple can reach millions of potential customers through official pages where they can control the content and post news updates, advertise new products, and get input from group members. In 2010, Facebook made approximately $2 billion through advertising; these ads appear when you search for friends or groups (Parfeni, 2011). The website's advertising feature allows you to upload images, run a campaign, and target certain demographics. Smaller companies and professional individuals can also take advantage of Facebook's popularity by realizing that "You need to be where your customers . . . and your prospective customers are" (Sinh, 2009).

Twitter

One of the most commonly used social networks, Twitter allows you to "tweet" your status and lets your followers catch up on the latest news. Founded in 2006, there are approximately 110 million "tweets" per day and 200 million registered account holders. Depending on what you are promoting, the tone of your messages can be serious, light-hearted, or it can advertise contests and answer customer questions. With nearly 30 000 businesses of all sizes listed on twibs.com, a Twitter environment that lets you search for business-oriented Twitter accounts, Henry J. Button cautions Twitter users to understand their own company culture, and to ask themselves, "What parts [of your company or organization] are you going to present? What parts do you want to keep hidden? What level of transparency are you comfortable with?" (2009, p. 33).

Companies can reach their target audience by using the Twitter for Business feature, which allows you to follow local trends, advertise to your followers and promote your "tweets," and include your company in the recommendation engine to any users that may find your company interesting. Since the introduction of the advertising function in 2010, Twitter has earned $45 million.

Digg

Digg provides its users with the most up-to-date news in a variety of categories, such as technology, science, and business. By becoming a member, you can "digg" any type of media—from a news story to a video—and promote its popularity on the website. By "digging" the news feature, the user is automatically redirected to the site where the feature was originally posted, and the feature, if popular enough, will be shown on the homepage. Active participation by members is necessary for the features to be popularized; as Curtis and Giamanco point out, "The real power of Digg lies in the conversation that can ensue around content . . . From a sales point of view, Digg is a place for you to learn what people are talking about" (2010, p. 122).

Since Digg's creation in 2004, the site has expanded from merely allowing you to favour a story, to allowing you to send questions to featured guests, to connecting to Facebook, and allowing users to connect their accounts from each social network and "digg" a feature that is then posted to the user's newsfeed. Digg can be useful to businesses because it allows users to network with other users who like the same newsfeeds as them.

Tumblr

Relying on micro-blogging, Tumblr hosts blogs specifically meant to be read on a smaller screen, such as the BlackBerry or iPhone, and made up of smaller file sizes, meaning that most of the bloggers will commonly post photos or links as opposed to text-heavy entries.

Foursquare

A location-based social networking site, Foursquare allows you to update your location to any smartphone and let friends and followers know where you are. Foursquare is appealing to businesses because it allows venues to advertise themselves, while allowing users to gain points for visiting their venue. This social networking tool is particularly appealing to smaller businesses; instead of competing in a "global marketplace," businesses can advertise deals and specials in "real-time" (Hall, 2010).

A Caution When Using Social Networking Sites

Although social networking sites allow you to connect with people, you must use caution when deciding to create accounts for users or for business. For example, Facebook allows users to adjust their privacy settings and determine how much they want their "friends" and other Facebook users to be able to see of their profile. Profile pages can be customized to show all information to friends and nothing to other users, or only certain features such as your name and basic information to all users. It is important to decide how much information to reveal as more and more prospective employers are using the personal information found on these sites when screening candidates. According to CareerBuilder, a popular job search website, nearly half of employers search for information on applicants online; they are able to compare information on your resume to information on the websites and judge your creativity from your postings, for example, on a blog.

Employers can also find information that will keep them from hiring someone. Some points that turn employers off applicants include: provocative or inappropriate photos, content about drinking or gambling, negative comments about previous or current employers, poor communication skills, discriminatory comments, lying about qualifications, and divulging private information related to their current employer (Haefner, 2010).

While many businesses are using sites such as Twitter and Digg to better their companies, they must also be prepared to deal with any technological consequences. Of those surveyed, 70 percent of businesses were hit with spam attacks when using social networking sites, and 72 percent of businesses believe that the actions of their employees on social networking sites can lead to security issues (Sophos, 2010). Viruses, malware, and spam attacks usually happen in the form of wall postings or from users requesting to be your "friend" or asking you to click on a link.

Even though setting up a Facebook account for your business may sound easier than building a website, companies must also remember that social media tools serve essentially the same purpose as a website: to advertise to potential clients. Likewise, the employee(s) who are in charge of maintaining these accounts should understand that anything they publish is an extension of the company itself. Grammatical errors, spelling mistakes, and other issues can take legitimacy away from the company. Testing and monitoring should be done frequently in order to ensure that the correct privacy settings are in place. Companies must be sure that the privacy rights of any visitors are protected, and that any necessary disclaimers are added to protect the company.

Choosing what type of social media to use is equally important. It is part of your marketing campaign and therefore you must know what type of audience you are trying to reach. Ask questions such as: What age bracket is my product aimed at? What language will most of my potential consumers speak? Should we target men or women? You should then gather demographic information about any social media tools you are thinking of using. For example, if your product is aimed at people over the age of 65, then Facebook may not be the right tool for you. According to www.checkfacebook.com, people between the ages of 18 and 34 use Facebook more than any other age bracket, while people over the age of 65 and under the age of 13 use it the least.

Telecommuting and Virtual Teams

Increasing numbers of employees work from home via a computer and a secure high-speed connection to the internet. This telecommuting requires great attention to detail. Information can be misconstrued, lost, or downloaded incorrectly when sent via computer. Sometimes the network server can go down, email speed can fall behind, or voicemail can be deleted; when these are your primary connections to the company, you need to have a back-up plan in place. Remember that for any projects conducted via telecommuting technology, you should always back up your data or make a hard copy daily.

Most organizations offer ways for employees to collaborate from remote locations. Your team may include members from various time zones in Canada as well as countries across the globe (China, India, Germany, Australia). Being part of a virtual team is almost a given in today's global business climate. Virtual teams work in two ways: in real time, using instant messaging (IM), videoconferencing, internet telephony (VoIP), and conference calls; and in ways that don't require real-time presence, such as email lists, blogs, or discussion boards, and special tools known as computer-supported cooperative work software. See Chapter 1 for more on virtual teams.

Another example of virtual teamwork is online education. Employees often take distance education courses via the web. Technical professionals take such courses to enhance their skills or pursue advanced degrees. Technical communicators are often part of the teams that design and deliver these courses.

Presentation Software

Presentation software (such as PowerPoint, discussed in Chapter 12) allows you to enter text, images, and animation and turn this information into presentation slides, which can be displayed via a computer or weblink, or printed out as overhead transparencies and handouts. Although this software can spice up an oral presentation with backgrounds, colour, and transitions, it is no substitute for a well-organized and well-prepared presentation. As Ray Shackleford and Kurt Griffis caution, "the success or failure of a presentation rests primarily on the thoroughness and care given to planning and designing a message" (2007).

Checklist for Digital Communication

Content
- Is the information chunked for easy access and quick reading?
- Is each chunk understandable regardless of order or context?
- Are all key terms defined?
- Are all necessary links provided?
- Are feedback and question mechanisms provided?
- Are all sentences short enough to facilitate reading and translation?

Design
- Is the document organized from the top down?
- Are links structured according to a hierarchy of importance?
- Is the typography appropriate and effective?
- Are the fonts designed to be read on a computer screen?
- Is the information chunked into small units?
- Are text lines left-justified and short?
- Does the document's appearance reflect cultural and organizational preferences?
- Is colour used appropriately?

Technical Features and Usability
- Have the technical capabilities of the audience's computers been considered?
- Are standard file formats used?
- Is the website compatible with industry-standard browsers?
- Are all links correct?
- Have gratuitous bells and whistles been avoided?
- Has the website been tested to ensure that it is functional and usable?

Email Conventions
- Have rules of netiquette been observed?
- Have all legal, ethical, and interpersonal implications been considered?
- Is the message designed for maximum usability?
- Has the message been proofread for correctness?

Exercises

1. **FOCUS ON WRITING.** With a classmate, locate one or two websites you might use as research sources for a project. Using the guidelines in this chapter, assess these websites for the quality of their writing, design, and technical features. How much does the visual attractiveness or choice of fonts affect your initial view of the website? Write up your findings in an email message to your instructor. Include the URLs for each of the sites you used.

2. Technical communicators are frequently asked to prepare multiple versions of a document, adapting similar content for presentation on a website, in a printed manual, or for a corporate digital archive, for example. Each version may have different purposes and audiences. For example, the word-processing software installed on your computer probably offers both online help and a CD-ROM manual. (Most companies post PDF versions of their documentation on their websites as well.) Compare the online or on-screen help information to the information in the CD-ROM manual. Notice in particular the use of chunking. Is the online information organized differently from the CD-ROM? Which is easier to use? Which allows you to find a topic more quickly and accurately? Write a short report comparing different types of help information.

3. Blogs are becoming an important means for professional groups to communicate ideas and concerns. Follow the discussion on a blog related to your major for at least a week. Prepare a report outlining the blog's target audience and what purpose the blog serves. Describe what type of subject matter is posted. How is the information presented? Discuss whether the information posted seems to be a useful source of information.

4. **FOCUS ON RESEARCH.** What are the elements of good web design? Colourful graphics? Catchy writing? Effective navigation? As the web has matured and expanded as a medium, principles for effective design have been developed, debated, and agreed on. Do some research to develop your own "top 10" list of effective web design principles.

5. Electronic communication is an important tool in the field of technical writing. While the internet has many benefits, there are also dangers. Read *A Matter of Trust: Integrating Privacy and Public Safety in the 21st Century* produced by the Office of the Privacy Commissioner of Canada. Discuss how the government aims to stop invasions of privacy against Canadians, and what steps are taken to do so.

   • **www.priv.gc.ca/information/pub/gd_sec_201011_e.cfm**

     A Matter of Trust: Integrating Privacy and Public Safety in the 21st Century, a report by the Office of the Privacy Commissioner of Canada.

6. What are the elements of effective web design? Begin by exploring the two websites listed here. Then use a search engine to find other resources on web style and web design. Based on what you find, put together your list of the 10 key elements of effective web design. Using your list as a guide, find three websites that best exemplify the principles of effective web design and style. Prepare a short presentation on your exemplary sites and explain why you selected them as examples of good design.

- **www.webstyleguide.com**

    Web Style Guide, by Patrick Lynch and Sarah Horton, is widely regarded as a "bible" of web design.

- **www.useit.com**

    Writing for the Web, by Jakob Nielsen, a leading web usability expert.

The Collaboration Window

Technical professionals often collaborate on projects, and many of them use technology to enhance their collaborations. In teams of three or four people, assume that you are all located in different parts of the world and must collaborate on a report on a topic that you choose. Determine an audience, purpose, and scope for your report. Then create a first draft, using the computer to share information. You may wish to set up an intranet website where group members can post their sections of the paper or use email attachments to pass the report back and forth.

As you work on this project, ask each team member to keep a log of any technical issues that arise. For example, if you use the web to post information, can all team members access the website? If you use email attachments, are all members able to open the same file types? Combine your log into one list, and based on this list, draft a set of guidelines for collaborating via the internet. Share these in a brief oral presentation to your class.

The Global Window

Find websites in different languages or based in different countries. Note any differences other than language. Also, note differences between American and Canadian websites. Here are some features you might look for:

- **Use of colour.** Different cultures often associate unique meanings with certain colours. For example, the colour red may be used in India to mean procreation or life, whereas red in North America is often associated with danger or warnings (Hoft, 1995, p. 267). In politics, for example, the colours associated with left-leaning and right-leaning parties are reversed in the United States and Canada. In the United States, blue is the colour of the Democrats and red is the colour of the Republicans, whereas in Canada, blue is the colour of the Conservatives and red is the colour of the Liberals.

- **Issues of privacy.** Canadian and American websites are permitted to send out cookies (files sent to your computer that give website providers information about you), but organizations covered by Canada's *Personal Information Privacy and Electronic Documents Act* (PIPEDA) must inform users that they are collecting personal information and give users the option of refusing cookies. Note if any of the sites mention their privacy policy in this regard.
- **Date formats.** The typical American format for dates is month, date, year (MDY), as in December 6, 2011, or 12/6/11, whereas the European format is date, month, year (DMY), as in 6 December 2011 or 6.12.11 (Hoft, 1995, p. 232). Search several Canadian websites to determine what the standard Canadian style is—European or American.

Keep track of what you find, and present your findings in class. If you can, create a class website that describes your findings and links to interesting sites on intercultural communication.

MyCanadianTechCommLab

Go to MyCanadianTechCommLab at www.mycanadiantechcommlab.com for additional online exercises and problems.

CHAPTER 7

Page Layout and Document Design

Chapter Objectives

By the end of this chapter you will be able to:

1. Understand how readers view a print or electronic document.

2. Create a visually effective document.

3. Recall the elements of good electronic document design.

Milan Davidovic, Toronto, Ontario

Before becoming a technical writer, Milan Davidovic worked in Japan in various corporate settings as an instructor of English for Specific Purposes. In the course of figuring out how to help his students do their jobs in English, he learned about the technical communication field. "When I trained people who were learning to use English as a foreign language to communicate on technical topics, I encouraged them to listen and read as much of that kind of material as they could—analyze, imitate, experiment, and figure out what works for you."

He subsequently decided that being a technical writer would be more interesting than being a trainer. Upon returning to Canada and settling in Toronto, Milan took classes in technical communication and got involved with the local chapter of STC (Society for Technical Communication). He got his first (and current) job—developing manuals and labelling for medical devices.

Milan finds that the skills involved in learning a foreign language and in learning to use your native language well are very similar: "Be a student of how others do it; pay attention to process as well as product, and always keep yourself in a cycle of improvement and reinvention."

Creating Visually Effective Documents

Like all decisions related to technical communication, layout and document design are based on informed choices. You make decisions about fonts, format, headings, page size, and other aspects based on the document's audience and purpose. For example, imagine that you are asked to produce a brochure for a physician's office. The brochure's audience is patients who have heart conditions and may need specific types of heart surgery. The brochure's purpose is to explain the procedure, answer frequently asked questions, and review the risks, while reassuring patients.

Before you would even begin to think about what to write or how to format the document, you would do an audience and purpose analysis (see Chapter 2). If you determined that the brochure also needed to include a list of tasks, such as a checklist of actions patients need to take, you might also conduct a task analysis (explained in Chapter 3). Your analysis would yield important information. For example, you might learn that patients who are frightened are often elderly, and may have difficulty reading small type. These facts would be important not only as you wrote the copy but also as you thought about designing the document. Frightened patients might prefer to read a document that is soothing to look at. You could choose a comforting typeface, pleasant graphics, and a warm colour for the paper. In addition, because your audience has difficulty reading small type, you would make sure the type is large enough to be read easily.

As you can see, document design, like all technical communication, puts audience and purpose first. In designing your document, consider the features discussed in this chapter.

How Page Design Transforms a Document

To appreciate the impact of page design, consider the fact sheets shown in Figures 7.1 and 7.2. The information presented in Figure 7.1 is very difficult to interpret and understand. Without design cues, we have no way of chunking this information into organized units of meaning. Figure 7.2 shows the same information after a design overhaul. A document that has been designed to match its purpose should improve the communication, whereas a poorly designed document may mislead or confuse readers and distort the author's meaning (Brumberger, 2004).

How Readers View a Page

When you design information, consider how most readers look at a page. Generally, they view it first as a whole unit, scanning the page quickly to get a sense of the overall layout, look, and structure. Readers try to make sense of the document and determine its "road map." They ask questions such as these:

- What is the main title?
- What are the primary headings?
- Where are the tables and charts?

By asking these questions, your audience is trying to determine the *visual hierarchy* of the page based on its layout and design. Technical writers use design to communicate with the readers and in effect link the visual elements and words and ideas together (Brumberger, 2004). The main items of importance should be in the primary headings, and the secondary items in the second level of headings.

Mold is a public health problem. Molds are simple organisms that are found virtually everywhere, indoors and outdoors. The potential health effects of indoor mold are a growing concern. Mold can cause or worsen certain illnesses (e.g., some allergic and occupation-related diseases and infections in health care settings). There is not conclusive evidence, however, about whether indoor mold is associated with a multitude of other health problems, such as pulmonary hemorrhage, memory loss, and lack of energy.

The Centers for Disease Control has accomplished much on the problem. The CDC has a mold Web site (http://www.cdc.gov/nceh/airpollution/mold) that provides information on molds and health and links to resources. In conjunction with the Council of State and Territorial Epidemiologists, the CDC has created an inventory of state indoor air quality programs which is available at http://www.cdc.gov/nceh.airpollution/indoor_air.htm. The CDC assists states in responding to mold-related issues, including offering technical assistance with assessment, cleanup efforts, and prevention of further mold growth and unnecessary exposure. The CDC is strengthening state, local and tribal capacity to respond to mold-related issues, including: determining the extent to which state programs establish coordinated responses to indoor mold exposures, working with federal and other organizations to coordinate plans related to indoor air and mold, developing a coordinated public response strategy, and identifying resources for developing and implementing responses. The CDC is also developing an agenda for research, service, and education related to mold. As a first step, the CDC contracted with the Institute of Medicine (IOM) to conduct a study on the relationship between damp or moldy indoor environments and the manifestation of adverse health effects and to provide recommendations for future research. The CDC's mold-related agenda is expected to address subjects such as the following: characterizing environmental conditions that allow mold growth indoors and the association between indoor mold and disease or illness; improving the capacity of state, local, and tribal health departments to prevent, investigate, and control mold exposures; and conducting and supporting research to define the association between damp or moldy indoor environments and harmful health effects.

The next steps the CDC will take include assisting states and others in responding to mold issues and developing an agenda for research, service, and education related to mold as described above. For more information, visit http://www.cdc.gov/nceh/airpollution/mold.

May 2004

Figure 7.1 Ineffective Page Design. Notice that the entire page is in the same font and does not provide the reader with any guidance on how the information is structured. A quick scan of this page imparts little new knowledge, if any.
Source: Centers for Disease Control and Prevention, www.cdc.gov/nceh/airpollution/mold/pib.pdf.

As you create your document, determine which subject areas constitute the first, second, or third level of headings. (Avoid using more than four levels of headings, since this can confuse your audience.) Make sure that headings at the same level use the same font and the same grammatical structure.

Look at Figure 7.2 for an example of a page that provides a clear visual hierarchy. Even if you view it from far enough away that you can't make out the actual words, you can still see that the page has a structure: main headings and explanatory text.

Electronic Pages

Readers view electronic pages much as they do the printed page. For instance, they skim the page looking for headings, tables, charts, main topics, and visuals, seeking the visual hierarchy. However, with electronic pages, there are some important differences.

Webpages can often become cluttered with too many links, flashing icons, and bright colours—more so than on a printed page because these features are easy to place on a website. These distracting features disorient, confuse, and annoy readers.

Computer screens are shaped very differently from the printed page, so items at the edge of the screen can get lost or become hard to track with the human eye.

Electronic text can be fuzzier than ink on paper when viewed on older monitors. Also, electronic text is actually made up of tiny pixels and can appear to be moving or "buzzing" on the screen. Both of these characteristics make it harder to read information on older monitors that use cathode ray tubes than on flatscreen monitors.

With these items in mind, make sure that electronic pages are designed for simplicity and ease of use. Keep text to a minimum, and avoid fancy icons and flashing fonts.

Formatting the Page Effectively

The term *page* is imprecise when you consider electronic documents. What constitutes a page? On the computer screen, a page can go on forever. Also, *page* might designate a page of a report, but it can also refer to one panel of a brochure or part of a quick reference card. The following discussion focuses primarily on traditional paper (printed) pages. See "Designing Electronic Documents" later in this chapter for a discussion of pages in electronic documents.

The design and layout of a page play an important role in how your audience will react to and interact with the information. If a page is poorly organized, readers won't be able to find what they need. If a page or document is unattractive, readers won't be enticed to explore it. Readers expect each page to be visually appealing, logically organized, and easy to navigate.

PROGRAM IN BRIEF

Mold

WHAT IS THE PUBLIC HEALTH PROBLEM?

Molds are simple organisms that are found virtually everywhere, indoors and outdoors. The potential health effects of indoor mold are a growing concern. Mold can cause or worsen certain illnesses (e.g., some allergic and occupation-related diseases and infections in health care settings). There is not conclusive evidence, however, about whether indoor mold is associated with a multitude of other health problems, such as pulmonary hemorrhage, memory loss, and lack of energy.

WHAT HAS CDC ACCOMPLISHED?

- CDC's Mold Web site (http://www.cdc.gov/mold) provides information on molds and health and links to resources. In conjunction with the Council of State and Territorial Epidemiologists, CDC has created an inventory of state indoor air quality programs, which is available at http://www.cdc.gov/nceh/airpollution/indoor_air.htm.
- CDC assists states in responding to mold-related issues, including offering technical assistance with assessment, cleanup efforts, and prevention of further mold growth and unnecessary exposure.
- CDC is strengthening state, local, and tribal capacity to respond to mold-related issues, including (1) determining the extent to which state programs establish coordinated responses to indoor mold exposures; (2) working with federal and other organizations to coordinate plans related to indoor air and mold; (3) developing a coordinated public response strategy; and (4) identifying resources for developing and implementing responses.
- CDC is developing an agenda for research, service, and education related to mold. As a first step, CDC contracted with the Institute of Medicine (IOM) to conduct a study on the relationship between damp or moldy indoor environments and the manifestation of adverse health effects and to provide recommendations for future research. CDC's mold-related agenda is expected to address subjects such as the following:
  - o Characterizing environmental conditions that allow mold growth indoors and the association between indoor mold and disease or illness;
  - o Improving the capacity of state, local, and tribal health departments to prevent, investigate, and control mold exposures;
  - o Conducting and supporting research to define the association between damp or moldy indoor environments and harmful health effects.

WHAT ARE THE NEXT STEPS?

CDC will continue to assist states and others in responding to mold issues and develop an agenda for research, service, and education related to *mold* as described above.

For more information, visit http://www.cdc.gov/mold.   *May 2004*

DEPARTMENT OF HEALTH AND HUMAN SERVICES
CENTERS FOR DISEASE CONTROL AND PREVENTION
SAFER·HEALTHIER·PEOPLE™

Figure 7.2 Effective Page Design. Notice that the first sentence of each paragraph has been recast as a question designed as a major heading. Note the use of bullets, white space, internal enumeration, and an identifying masthead at the top of the page, all of which make the material easier to read and remember. On the website, notice the effective use of hyperlinks and colour.
Source: Centers for Disease Control and Prevention, www.cdc.gov/nceh/airpollution/mold/pib.pdf.

Page and document design is an art that takes practice. More and more software is being developed to help people with layout and document design, but all the software in the world won't help unless you know something about how readers deal with text on a page.

Using a Grid Structure

Grids help readers make sense of material, because they create an underlying structure for the page. Figure 7.3 shows a sampling of grid patterns.

A two-column grid is commonly used in manuals. Brochures and newsletters typically employ a two- or three-column grid. Grids are used as frameworks or outlines to provide a coherent visual theme to a document. This consistent layout allows readers to anticipate what they will find on the next page. For instance, when reading a standard newspaper, you expect to find columns. When looking through a brochure, you expect the information to maintain a consistent look and feel throughout. Many layout programs have templates that allow you to create grids easily and quickly. For instance, when using Microsoft Word, you can select the "brochure" template after you have selected "new document." Word will automatically create a template document that has a proper grid structure.

Creating Areas of Emphasis Using White Space

Sometimes, it's what's *not* on the page that makes a difference. Areas of text surrounded by white space draw the reader's eye because the white space breaks up the regular visual pattern.

Well-designed white space imparts a shape to the whole document. It orients users and creates a visual form that keeps related elements together, isolates and emphasizes important elements, and provides breathing room between blocks of information (see Figure 7.4).

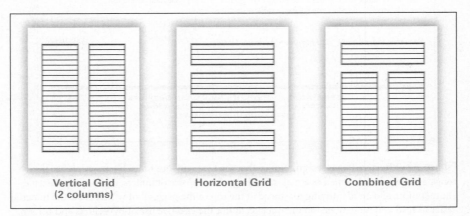

Vertical Grid
(2 columns)   Horizontal Grid   Combined Grid

Figure 7.3   Grid Patterns. Grids provide a blueprint for page design.

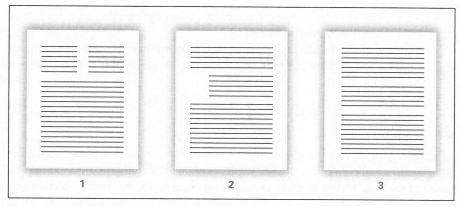

Figure 7.4 Use of White Space to Orient Readers.

Use white space to orient your readers. In the examples in Figure 7.4, notice how the white space pulls your eye toward the pages in different ways. In example 1, your eye moves toward the "gutter" (the white space between the columns). In example 2, the white space draws your attention to the middle paragraph. In example 3, white space falls between each paragraph but is equally placed. Each example causes the reader to look at a different place on the page first. White space can keep a page from seeming too cluttered; pages that look clean, inviting, and straightforward create an immediate impression of user-friendliness.

Provide Ample Margins. Small margins crowd the page and make the material look difficult. On a standard page, leave margins of at least 2.5 cm to 4 cm. If the manuscript is to be bound in some kind of cover, widen the inside margin to 5 cm.

Choose between unjustified text (uneven or "ragged" right margins) and justified text (even right margins). Each arrangement creates its own "feel." Justified text seems preferable for books, annual reports, and other formal materials. Unjustified text seems preferable for more personal forms of communication, such as letters, memos, and in-house reports.

Tailor each Paragraph to Its Purpose. Users often skim a long document to find what they want. Most paragraphs therefore begin with a topic sentence that clearly announces the paragraph's purpose. As you shape each paragraph, follow these suggestions:

- Use long paragraphs (no more than 15 lines) for clustering closely related material (such as history and background or any type of information best understood in one block).
- Use short paragraphs for making complex material more digestible, for giving step-by-step instructions, or for emphasizing vital information.

- For a series of short paragraphs, separate them by inserting an extra line of space instead of indenting them.
- Avoid "orphans" (leaving a paragraph's opening line at the bottom of a page) and "widows" (leaving a paragraph's closing line at the top of the page).

Using Lists

Whenever you find yourself writing a series of items within a paragraph, consider using a bulleted or numbered list instead, especially if you are describing a series of tasks or trying to make certain items easy to locate. Don't overuse bullets, however, and don't use fancy icons when a plain round dot will do. Most audiences prefer that bulleted lists have a streamlined look. Figure 7.5 compares in-text lists to bulleted and numbered lists.

There is no consensus on how to punctuate a list. Style guides, used by writers and editors to check punctuation and grammar issues, often disagree on this point. Many companies use their own style guides (see later in this chapter) and include directions for punctuating a list. In general, the move is away from any punctuation within the list itself unless each item is a full sentence or paragraph. But check with an editor in your organization or consult the company style guide.

Text	Bulleted list
The fire ant has now spread to three regions: the Galapagos Islands, the South Pacific, and Africa.	The fire ant has now spread to three regions: • The Galapagos Islands • The South Pacific • Africa

Text	Numbered list
There are three steps to installing your modem: Open the computer case, insert the modem in the slot, and close the case.	Installing your modem 1. Open the computer case. 2. Insert the modem in the slot. 3. Close the case.

Figure 7.5   Lists. Use a bulleted list for three or more items in a series. In cases where you are instructing an audience to perform a series of steps, a numbered list is more appropriate.

Using Headings

Readers of a long document often look back or jump ahead to sections that interest them most. Headings announce the document's organization, direct readers to specific information, and divide the document into chunks. An informative heading can help a reader decide whether a section is worth reading. Besides cutting down on reading and retrieval time, headings help readers remember information.

Size Headings by Level. Like a good road map, your headings should clearly announce the large and small segments in your document. When you write your material, think of it in chunks and sub-chunks. When you analyze the document's purpose and your user's intended tasks, you will generally create an outline of your document. An outline of a report for physicians on new medications for depression might begin as follows:

> Background: Current medications and their history
>
> Recent research into new medications
>
> Ongoing research and medications on the horizon

These are your primary, or level 1, headings. Your document might also contain subheadings for each section. You can use the marks *h1, h2,* and *h3* to indicate heading levels in your draft document.

> h1. Current medications and their history
>   h2. Medications before the 1980s
>   h2. Selective serotonin reuptake inhibitors (SSRIs)
>   h3. Prozac
>   h3. Effexor
> h1. Recent research into new medications
>   h2. Refining the SSRI approach
>   h2. Research on brain chemistry
> h1. Ongoing research and medications on the horizon
>   h2. Future trends in treatment of depression
>   h3. Medical
>   h3. Psychological
>   h2. Research implications

You would then design your document so that the heading levels are consistent. All h1 headings would use the same font and indent, as would all h2 and h3 headings. Your final document might look something like this (using "dummy text" to show the layout):

CURRENT MEDICATIONS AND THEIR HISTORY

Currently, several medications are popular andk dfkja fdkjdf jdasf dsfl ls ldf jdsfjdf-sjssdfkjakd aoiieu joieu ajoidu oi eruyao ghoikh ahogy henkajkd kanjkdntheoi heiou iao9j8ajfl d ald oaj glnkeyhioj

Medications Before the 1980s

Several medications were used prior to the 1980s when fkja sdfkjakd aoiieu joieu ajoidu oi eruyao ghoikh ahogy henkajkd kanjkdntheoi heiou iao9j8ajfl d ald oaj glnkeyhioj idu oi eruyao ghoikh ahogy.

Selective Serotonin Reuptake Inhibitors (SSRIs)

The increased research around the importance of serotonin fkja kd aoiieu joieu ajoidu oi eruyao ghoikh ahogy henkajkd kanjkdntheoi heiou iao9j8ajfl d ald oaj glnkeyhioj idu oi eruya

Prozac—The increased research around the importance of serotonin fkja kd aoiieu joieu ajoidu oi eruyao ghoikh ahogy henkajkd kanjkdntheoi heiou iao9j8ajfl d ald oaj glnkeyhioj idu oi eruyao gho

Effexor—The increased research around the importance of serotonin fkja kd aoiieu joieu ajoidu oi eruyao ghoikh ahofakljl gy henkajkd kanjkdntheoi heiou iao9j8ajfl d ald oaj glnkeyhioj idu oi eruyao gho

RECENT RESEARCH INTO NEW MEDICATIONS

New research indicates that andk jdf jdasfl dsfl ls ldf jdsfjdfsjssdfkjakd aoiieu joieu ajoidu oi eruyao ghoikh ahogy henkajkd kanjkdntheoi heiou iao9j8ajfl d ald oaj glnkeyhioj

Refining the SSRI Approach

The increased research around the importance of serotonin fkja kd aoiieu joieu ajoidu oi eruyao ghoikh ahogy henkajkd kanjkdntheoi heiou iao9j8ajfl d ald oaj glnkeyhioj idu oi eruya

Choose an Appropriate Heading Size. Headings, especially at the first and second level, should be larger than the body copy they accompany. A 2-point spread is the generally accepted rule: if the body text is 12 point, headings generally should be at least 14 point. Like all decisions, this choice should be based on audience and purpose. Some companies might determine that for their customers, a different arrangement is appropriate.

Address Reader Questions. Chapter 3 discusses the technique of creating headings in the form of reader questions. This approach may not be appropriate for all documents, and overuse of the technique can sound repetitious and become annoying to readers. But for some documents, questions can help guide the reader to the appropriate section of the document. For example, a patient information brochure about an outpatient surgical procedure called a laparoscopy might use question-style headings such as:

| What Activities Can I Perform After My Laparoscopy?

These headings create a more user-friendly document by letting the reader know that their questions are normal. Whenever you have a situation in which a user will approach a document with a series of questions in mind, consider using question-style headings.

Make Headings Visually Consistent and Grammatically Parallel. Heading levels should be consistent. For example, on a word-processed page, level 1 headings might be 12-point, bold, uppercase type set flush left with the margin; level 2 headings might be 12-point bold in upper and lower case, indented one tab setting; and level 3 headings might be 10-point bold, flush left, with the text run in (see Figure 7.6).

Along with visual consistency, headings of the same level should also be grammatically parallel (see Chapter 3). For example, if you phrase headings in the form of reader questions, make sure all are phrased in this way:

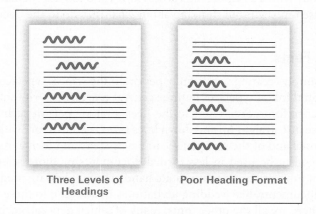

Three Levels of Headings   Poor Heading Format

Figure 7.6   Headings. When headings show the relationships among all the parts, readers can grasp at a glance how a document is organized.

TIPS FOR USING HEADINGS

- **Ordinarily, use no more than four levels of headings (section, major topic, minor topic, subtopic).** Excessive heads and subheads make a document seem cluttered or fragmented.
- **Below each higher-level heading, have at least two headings at the next-lower level.** This helps divide the information logically.
- **Insert one blank line above each heading.** For double-spaced text, triple-space before the heading and double-space after; for single-spaced text, double-space before the heading and single-space after.
- **Never begin the sentence right after the heading with *This, It,* or some other pronoun referring to the heading.** The opening sentence must stand on its own, independent of the heading.
- **Never leave a heading on the bottom line of a page.** Unless at least two lines of text can fit below the heading, move it to the top of the next page.

Using Typography Effectively

The style of type you choose makes a big difference to how audiences read and react to your document. Typefaces have personalities: some convey seriousness; others convey humour; still others convey a technical quality. Before desktop computing, the art of typesetting was in the hands of skilled graphic artists and typographers trained in selecting and using fonts for the most effective results. Today, anybody with a computer can access fonts, and too many amateur desktop publishers use fonts without thinking about what they do to the document.

Selecting Fonts

More than simply creating words on paper or on the screen, typefaces send messages. You can think of typefaces in three general categories: serif fonts, sans-serif fonts, and script fonts. *Serif* refers to the "feet" that are part of each letter; sans-serif fonts use just straight up and down lines (*sans* is French for "without"). Serif fonts are formal and of the sort you see in newspapers and formal reports. Sans-serif fonts tend to be used in less formal documents or more scientific documents. Script fonts are those that imitate handwriting. They are used in social or decorative documents, like wedding invitations. In addition to these three major categories, there are all the other fonts, many of which defy categorization, such as the decorative one shown in Figure 7.7. Decorative fonts, which can be serif, sans-serif, or script, are a powerful way to draw an audience's attention to the page. But such fonts must be used very sparingly, since they tend to be too difficult to read and too dramatic for a technical document.

> Times New Roman is a serif font.
>
> Arial is a sans-serif font.
>
> Optima is a display font.
>
> 𝔒𝔩𝔡 𝔈𝔫𝔤𝔩𝔦𝔰𝔥 𝔦𝔰 𝔞 𝔡𝔢𝔠𝔬𝔯𝔞𝔱𝔦𝔳𝔢 𝔣𝔬𝔫𝔱.

Figure 7.7 **Sample Typefaces.** Each typeface has its own personality. Select typefaces that enhance rather than conflict with the message of your text.

As you choose your typeface, consider the document's purpose. If the purpose is to help patients relax, use a combination that conveys ease. Script fonts are often a good choice, although they can be hard to read if used in lengthy passages. If the purpose is to help engineers find technical data quickly in a table or chart, use a sans-serif typeface—not only because numbers in sans-serif type are easy to see but also because engineers will be more comfortable with fonts that look precise.

Combining Fonts

With all these typefaces to choose from, many computer users use as many as they can and mix unrelated fonts in one document. When you do this, you end up with a document that looks like alphabet soup: a jumble of letter forms, sizes, and shapes. Too many fonts from too many type families create visual noise.

Follow these basic rules when mixing and matching typefaces within a document:

- **Use fonts from only one typeface.** The safest rule is to stick with just one typeface. For example, you might decide on Times (a popular serif font) for an audience of financial planners, lawyers, or others who expect a traditional font. In this case, use Times 14-point bold for the headings, 12-point regular (roman) for the body copy, and 12-point italic for the titles of books and periodicals or, sparingly, for emphasis.
- **If you mix different typefaces, be consistent.** If the document contains illustrations, charts, or numbers, use a 10-point basic sans-serif font (such as Helvetica or Arial) for these. Sans-serif fonts are good for captions and numbers. You can also use one typeface for headings and another for text. A common approach is to use a sans-serif font for headings and a serif font for body copy.

- **Use italics, boldface, and capital letters sparingly.** Various types of emphasis call for italic, boldface, or capital letters. For example, italic type is used to set the titles of books apart from the rest of the text:

| We read *The Grapes of Wrath* in English class.

Sometimes people use *italics* much as they would use a highlighter or marker, to set words apart and draw attention to these words. Using italics too frequently can make it difficult for your audience to decide what information is truly important.

The same is true for **boldface.** There are fewer rules about when to use bold, but too much bold makes it lose its power to draw the eye. Bold is good for headings, subheadings, or terms or concepts in a sentence that you want to emphasize. Within text, use bold very selectively.

Avoid all capital (ALL CAPS) letters for long phrases and headings, because long strings of uppercase words make the material difficult to read.

Choosing Fonts for Readability

It is important to use font sizes that are easy to read. In some cases, standard rules of design can help guide you. For example, use 12-point type for most papers, letters, and print correspondence. For electronic documents such as webpages, work with a web designer to ensure that the fonts you choose will be the same ones that show up on your readers' monitors. Also, you can follow guidelines to ensure that your website can be accessed by visually impaired readers. Keep in mind, too, the aging population and their need for larger type sizes. For more about accessibility and websites, visit www.w3.org/WAI/Policy/CA-Provinces.html.

- Do not use fonts smaller than 12-point type for most body text. (You can use 10 point, such as for figure captions and footnotes, but 12 is better.) However, point size may not look the same in all fonts; for example, in some fonts, 12 point may look small. So base your decision on how the font looks when printed or displayed.
- Make headings at least 2 points larger than body text.
- Double-space between blocks of text.
- Use italics, boldface, and capital letters sparingly.

For overhead transparencies or computer displays in oral presentations, consider larger sizes that can be read from a distance: 18- or 20-point type for body text, 20 points or larger for headings. To choose typefaces for computer displays, including webpages, see the section "Designing Electronic Documents" later in this chapter. In general, approach technical communication as something more than writing and then formatting; design must be an integral part of the process, rather than an afterthought meant to dress up the final product (Brumberger, 2004, p. 22).

Providing Effective Search Options

Nowadays when you think of internet search options, Google may be the first thing that comes to mind. But search options are also part of any good document. Traditional search features in books, such as a table of contents and an index, can be key aids in your documents for readers who are searching for specific information.

Table of Contents and Index

The layout and design process often involves creating a table of contents and an index (see Figure 7.8), especially for large reports, books, or similar publications. Even more than headings, tables of contents and indexes are the primary access points by which a reader will enter your text. Many readers start reading a document by checking the index for specific topics. Next, they scan the table of contents. If they still cannot locate the information, they either begin paging through the material at random, hoping to find something, or they decide that the information is not there and give up.

Most computer programs can automatically generate a table of contents or an index. You insert markers (tags) in the document, and the software will look for

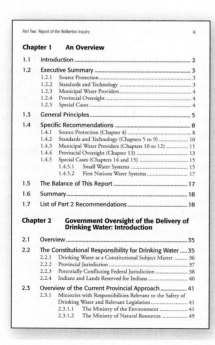

Figure 7.8 A Sample Table of Contents and Index.
Sources: © Queen's Printer for Ontario, 2002. Reproduced with permission.

the information in these tags and compile it into a table of contents or an index. For tables of contents, simply tag all the headings. Tagging for indexes is a little more complicated. The key to a successful index is not in the computer software but in knowing what categories, words, and topics your audience will look for. Most of us have had the frustrating experience of trying to look something up in an index and discovering that the term we use is not the term the index uses. To create a good index, you need to think the way your audience thinks and tag information that they are likely to want to find.

It is best to have your table of contents reviewed by an editor (for problems with parallelism or gaps in coverage) and to have your index prepared by a professional indexer. Many companies have technical writers on staff who specialize in these areas. You can also hire freelance editors and indexers to do these jobs.

For examples and further discussion of tables of contents, see Chapter 14.

Running Heads and Feet

Running heads and feet in a printed document help readers stay oriented to the particular part of the book or manual. Figure 7.9 provides examples of each. The head would be the same on each page of the chapter, and the foot lets readers know the title of the book. Microsoft Word and similar programs let you create running heads and feet easily.

Electronic Searching

With electronic documents, searching is not limited to tables of contents, indexes, and skimming, and there are no running heads and feet to scan. Most programs (for example, Word documents, websites, PDF files) have a "find" feature that lets you search for words or phrases. Moreover, you can search the entire web for content by using Google or a similar search engine.

As a technical communicator, you can make online searching easier for your readers by using keywords to help them get to your specific page quickly and easily. You will need to learn more about how each search engine works in order to create the most easily searched page or document. You might need to ask your company's web designer or technical expert how to do this. Alternatively, you might do an online search to research the material you are writing about. For more information on keyword searches, visit the Nova Scotia Community College library at http://library.nscc.ca/research_assistance/www_guide/index.asp. This website offers an intensive guide on successfully using the internet for research.

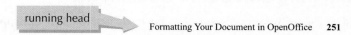 Formatting Your Document in OpenOffice **251**

About Headers and Footers

Headers and footers are areas in the top and the bottom page margins, where you can add text or graphics. Headers and footers are added to the current page style. Any page that uses the same style automatically receives the header or footer that you add. You can insert <u>Fields</u>, such as page numbers and chapter headings, in headers and footers in a text document.

- To add a header to a page, choose **Insert - Header**, and then select the page style for the current page from the submenu.
- To add a footer to a page, choose **Insert - Footer**, and then select the page style for the current page from the submenu.

 The page style for the current page is displayed in the **Status Bar**.

- You can also choose **Format - Page**, click the **Header** or **Footer** tab, and then select **Header on** or **Footer on**. Clear the **Same content left/right** check box if you want to define different headers and footers for even and odd pages.
- To use different headers or footers in your document, you must add them to different <u>Page Styles</u>, and then apply the styles to the pages where you want the headers or footer to appear.

Headers and Footers in HTML Documents

Some of the header and footer options are also available for HTML documents. Headers and footers are not supported by HTML and instead are exported with special tags, so that they can be viewed in a browser. Headers and footers are only exported in HTML documents if they are enabled in Web Layout mode. When you reopen the document in OpenOffice.org, the headers and footers are displayed correctly, including any fields that you inserted.

Related Topics

<u>Creating a Page Style Based on the Current Page</u>
<u>Defining Different Headers and Footers</u>
<u>Inserting a Chapter Name and Number in a Header or a Footer</u>
<u>Formatting Headers or Footers</u>
<u>Page Styles</u>

 *OpenOffice Help Manual*

Figure 7.9 **Running Head and Running Foot in a Sample Software Manual.**
Source: OpenOffice.

Designing Electronic Documents

Most of the techniques discussed so far in this chapter are appropriate for both paper and electronic documents. However, electronic documents require certain special considerations.

Webpages

To learn about webpage design in full, you will need to take classes or read books about this topic (see Lynch & Horton, 2001). Many large organizations have specific employees, with job titles such as webmaster or web designer, who are responsible for designing webpages. In general, web design requires you to consider some of the same items discussed so far in this chapter.

Typefaces and Layout. Web design experts point out that "although the basic rules of typography are much the same for both webpages and conventional print documents, type on-screen and type printed on paper are different in crucial ways" (Lynch & Horton, 2001, p. 115). For example, an older computer screen displays typefaces at a much lower resolution than a printed document, making them harder to read. Also, long lines of text on a computer screen can become blurred at the edges. This problem has improved with the invention of flatscreen monitors; however, technical writers need to consider this limitation because many users still have old monitors. Finally, even though you may select a special typeface for your website, you can't guarantee how it will appear on each individual computer screen. If the user's computer does not have that typeface in its fonts directory, then the computer will automatically substitute a different font. For this reason, it is wise to use standard fonts.

Therefore, keep your choices of type simple and readable:

- Don't mix and match too many typefaces.
- Use sans-serif type for body text.
- Don't use small type—anything smaller than 12 point is hard to read.

Headings. On webpages, web designers often include hypertext links as headings, which allow users to move to other related information either within the existing webpage or to another webpage in order to get a deeper level of information. This innovation allows users to interact with the webpage and thereby overcome the limitations of traditional written texts. As with printed text headings, links should be consistent. Use the same typeface and font for the same level of heading. Links also require testing to be sure they actually work.

In the end, you should work with a professional web designer to be sure your page will look and function the way you want it to. Figure 7.10 is an example of an effective webpage.

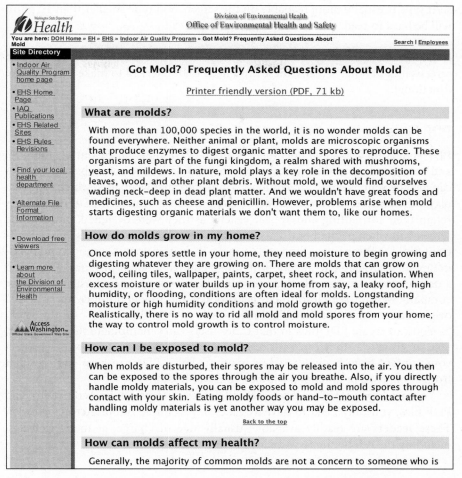

Figure 7.10 An Effective Webpage. The colour choices are consistent and easy on the eye. Text is written in short paragraphs, with headings in the form of questions. The left margin contains related links. The layout is balanced with plenty of white space.
Source: Washington State Department of Health, www.doh.wa.gov/ehp/ts/IAQ/Got_Mold.html.

Online Help

Like designing webpages, designing online help pages is a specialty. Many organizations, especially those that produce software, hire technical communicators who know how to produce online help screens. As with all page design, paper or electronic, producing online help screens requires consistency.

Typefaces. Like webpages, online help screens are usually shaped differently from printed pages, so lines cannot be set at the same length as in a book. Sans-serif type is usually more readable on the screen, and type smaller than 12 point will be hard to read.

Headings. The headings on an online help screen should be consistent. If help screens link to other screens, these links need to be checked to make sure they are functional.

PDF Files

PDF stands for "portable document format." PDF files can be put on the web, and users can link to these just the way they would link to any website. PDF files can also be sent as email attachments. Unlike normal webpages, which may display differently to users on different computers or browsers, PDF documents retain their formatting and appear exactly as they were designed, both on the screen and when printed out. This feature has made PDFs a very useful and efficient tool for companies who want to make their user documentation and product manuals available to anyone with a web connection. For instance, if you find a used item at a garage sale and the manual is missing, you can usually visit the company website, search for the exact product and model number, and find the original documentation (see Figure 7.11).

You can create PDF files so that other users can't manipulate the document, text, or visuals, as they can with regular web content. So if you want to protect your content from being altered or manipulated, a PDF can keep your content from being used or amended without your permission.

You need special software to create PDF files, such as Adobe Acrobat. To read PDF files, you only need to have a reader, for example Adobe Acrobat Reader. These readers are readily available, usually free of charge, at many websites, including the Adobe site (www.adobe.com).

CDs and Other Media

As a technical writer, you really can't predict the types of media that will be used to deliver your documents. You may design a print instruction manual or patient information brochure, yet the final document may be delivered and read on the web, on a hand-held device (like an iPod or PalmPilot), or on a CD. The PDF format is one method you can use to ensure that documents will look the same on the CD as in print. If you are designing for an iPod or PalmPilot, you will need to work within the specifications and software that is in current use for these devices. HTML is the current standard language for creating webpages, so web content needs to be converted to HTML. This may require a redesign of the layout. As much as possible, identify early in the process the ways in which your document will be used, and work with the design team in your organization to ensure that your readers will be able to access the information.

Figure 7.11 Product Manuals Online. Thermador has a website where users can quickly download product manuals using Adobe Acrobat Reader. When you click on the particular manual, it can be read on the screen or printed. The formatting of PDFs is exactly like the printed original.
Source: Courtesy of Thermador.

Creating and Using Style Sheets and Tools

Style sheets and tools are helpful devices that technical communicators use to ensure consistency throughout a single document or a set of documents. It's not hard to ensure consistency if you are the only writer, but if you are working as part of a team, it's important to be sure that all writers and designers are using the same grammatical conventions, typefaces, and formatting. Organizational style guides can help, and so can the tools available in Word, FrameMaker, other layout programs, and web design tools.

Organizational Style Guides and Style Sheets

Most large organizations have style guides that provide rules and guidelines for usage and design throughout the organization. Style guides tell you about high-level issues such as

- How and when you can use the corporate name and logo
- What colours must be part of the corporate logo
- How to describe certain products and processes
- How to use other trade and product names

As well as issues such as

- How to use punctuation according to the company's preferred style
- How to format a bulleted list
- When to use abbreviations and when to spell out words and phrases

If you work in a large organization, refer to the style guide. If you work in a smaller organization without a style guide, ask if you can help create one. If you change jobs, remember that the new company may have a very different approach to style and design issues. In the end, you must abide by the company's preferences.

If you are not familiar with style guides, read about them in this article by Jean Hollis Weber entitled *Developing a Departmental Style Guide*: www.jeanweber.com/newsite/?page_id=30.

Style Tools Using Word-Processing and Layout Software

Most word-processing and layout programs, including Word and FrameMaker, have tools that let you create styles for various parts of the document, such as headings at different levels, body copy (paragraphs), and lists. In the workplace, where it is important to ensure a consistent look and feel across the entire set of documents, using style tools is preferable to just using the bold or underline features. To learn more about style tools, use the Help section of the word-processing or layout program you are using.

Style Tools Using CSS and HTML for Webpages

CSS stands for Cascading Style Sheets. CSS is used to give web designers more control over how a webpage will look on any browser or computer. CSS is written into the web document in a manner similar to the use of HTML tags. In other words, CSS is written in at the code level of the document, which won't be seen by people viewing the website on their computer.

The CSS code tells the computer to look for a particular style sheet and then apply that style sheet consistently to the entire web document.

Learning both HTML and CSS is a specialized task. You may be able to rely on a web developer to help. The key, however, is to be aware of style sheets and know that it is crucial to use them to ensure consistency when creating a website. For more about CSS and web styles, see www.w3.org/Style/ (for definitions), http://webdesignledger.com/tips/developing-streamlined-and-efficient-css styles (article), and http://green-beast.com/build-css/ (how to).

Checklist for Layout and Document Design

Page Format
- Does the grid structure provide a consistent visual theme?
- Does the white space create areas of emphasis?
- Are the margins wide enough?
- Is each paragraph tailored to suit its purpose?
- Are series of parallel items formatted as lists (numbered or bulleted, as appropriate)?
- Do headings clearly announce the topics of large and small segments in the document?
- Are headings sized to reflect their specific level in the document?
- Are headings phrased to address reader questions?
- Are headings visually consistent and grammatically parallel?

Typography
- In general, are all fonts from one single typeface?
- If different typefaces *are* used, are they used consistently?
- Are *italics*, **boldface**, and ALL CAPS used sparingly?
- Are font sizes and styles chosen for readability?

Search Options
- Are the table of contents and the index complete and easy to navigate?
- Do running heads and feet announce each section of the document?

Electronic Documents
- Does the electronic document provide a "find" option along with keywords that helps users find specific pages easily?
- Have special design requirements for electronic documents been satisfied?
- For a complicated document, is appropriate layout software being used?
- Have you followed the appropriate style sheets and tools?
- Have you sought expert advice as needed?

Exercises

1. In this chapter, you learned that readers scan a document to make sense of it and to understand the document's organizational structure and visual hierarchy. To test this idea, try the following experiment. Take a page from a document that contains visual cues—headings, subheadings, tables, and so on. Make a transparency of this document. In class, put this transparency on the overhead projector, and turn the focus knob so that the document is out of focus. Make sure no one can read the actual text but everyone can see the structure of the page. Ask your classmates to point out the main headings, subheadings, and areas that contain graphics. In class, discuss how people knew this information without being able to read the text.

2. Find a truly bad website (go to www.webpagesthatsuck.com) and analyze the site according to the principles of usability and design. Prepare a report on your findings.

3. **FOCUS on WRITING**. With a partner, find two printed documents: one that demonstrates good use of typefaces and another that demonstrates confusing or inconsistent use. Imagine that you and your partner are a team of technical communication consultants. Write a memo to the manager of the organization that produced the effective document explaining its positive features. Write a memo to the manager of the organization that produced the confusing document making suggestions for improvement.

The Collaboration Window

Working in teams of three or four people, find a document that is intended to answer a question—for example, a patient brochure about an illness or medical procedure, a reference guide for new students on campus, or a personnel document from your company. Your team's goal is to redesign the document so that it uses headings in the form of reader questions, makes effective use of white space, and uses formatting, type fonts, headings, and other page design elements consistently and clearly.

Appoint one member of your group to serve as editor. The editor is responsible for making sure that the design elements are used consistently throughout the redesigned document.

Begin by developing a style sheet for your team to follow. You may want to refer to some of the websites listed here for more information on typefaces and page design.

Ask each team member to work on one section of the document. Bring all the redesigned sections back together, and ask your editor to review the materials. The editor should check your work against the style sheet. If some of the work is inconsistent with the style sheet, discuss ways you could improve the wording or layout of the style sheet to make it easier for writers to follow.

- **www.webdesignerdepot.com/2009/02/10-web-typography-rules-every-designer-should-know-2/**

  "10 Web Typography Rules Every Designer Should Know" features graphic demonstrations of each rule.

- **www.useit.com/alertbox/9605.html**

  Jakob Nielsen's "Top Ten Mistakes in Web Design," sets out many principles of design that apply to printed documents as well as webpages.

- **http://tc.eserver.org/dir/Document-Design**

  A directory of resources on document design written by and for technical communicators.

 ## The Global Window

Find a document that presents the same information in several languages (assembly instructions for various products are often written in two or three languages, for example). Evaluate the design decisions made in these documents. For example, are the different languages presented side by side or in different sections? Write a memo to classmates and your instructor evaluating the document and making recommendations for how it might be improved.

Also, talk to someone who is involved in translating documents. (Large cities often have translation companies, and your university or college will probably have an international student office.) Ask these professionals if type or page design has any effect on how a document might be translated. For example, if a series of headings were set in boldface in the English document, how would these be set in a German, Japanese, or Italian document?

MyCanadianTechCommLab

Go to MyCanadianTechCommLab at www.mycanadiantechcommlab.com for additional online exercises and problems.

CHAPTER 8

Graphics and Visual Information

Chapter Objectives

By the end of this chapter you will be able to:

1. Use the appropriate visuals for the appropriate audience.

2. Use charts and graphs to successfully turn statistics or numbers into images.

3. Use images to explain and enhance your point further.

4. Use colours that are universal in symbolism.

J. P. Pinard, Whitehorse, Yukon

After graduating from the University of Waterloo with an engineering degree in 1992, J. P. Pinard moved to Vancouver to work with a software firm before making his way to Whitehorse, where he ended up working for numerous engineering firms and teaching at Yukon College.

Interested in becoming involved with developing renewable energy in the territory, J. P. volunteered for a local not-for-profit organization, researching writing proposals for projects focusing on this subject. In 1997, one of his proposals for a wind-monitoring project in the Alsek Valley was accepted, allowing him to collaborate with the electrical provider Yukon Energy. This initial project eventually allowed J. P., now a wind energy expert, the opportunity to install more than 30 meteorology towers in Yukon, the Northwest Territories, and northern British Columbia.

Realizing early on in his career that he needed to educate himself about the physics of wind—an area that was slowly becoming more popular as a new way to produce energy for consumers—he applied to the University of Alberta in 1999 and eventually earned his master's and PhD. Continuously consulting for various organizations, J. P. also spends his time volunteering to help promote sustainable development in Yukon.

The Power of the Picture

According to Ray Shackleford and Kurt Griffis, "if a picture is 'worth a thousand words,' then understanding how visuals affect an audience's ability to grasp and retain the intended message (e.g., their learning) is important" (2007, p. 19). Visual communication is a very basic form of human communication, predating written language. Before there were alphabets or symbols for numbers, humans communicated visually. More than 15 000 years ago, humans created cave paintings of animals, hunting expeditions, and other activities. Today, we are surrounded by powerful images: charts that represent the stock market, television advertisements, and all sorts of photos and illustrations. Visual communication remains vital.

When people look at a visual pattern, such as a graph, they see it as one large pattern—a whole unit that conveys information quickly and efficiently. For instance, the line graph in Figure 8.1 contains no verbal information. The axes are not labelled, nor is the topic identified. But one quick glance, without the help of any words, tells you that the trend is rising. The graph conveys information in a way plain text never could. It would certainly be hard for audiences to visualize this trend by just reading a long list of numbers, such as:

> The stock began at 15⅞, then rose to 16. It rose again to 17, 18, 18½, and 19, then levelled off at 19 for several days....

Visuals are especially important in technical communication because they enhance accessibility, usability, and relevance.

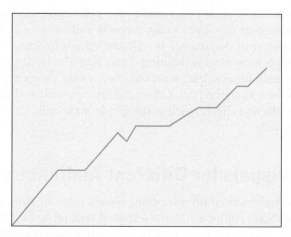

Figure 8.1 Line Graph with No Labels.

- **Accessibility.** Because humans understand visuals intuitively, visual information makes your content accessible to a wide audience. Also, if your manual or report is written in English, charts or graphs can often be easily understood by non-English speakers. For example, a report on the European economy written in English might be difficult for non-English speakers to read, but a graph of European financial trends would be more broadly accessible.
- **Usability.** Information is usable when audiences can find what they need and use it to perform the tasks at hand. Visuals can simplify this process, because they focus and organize information, making it easier to remember and interpret. A simple table, for instance, can summarize a long and difficult passage of text. A pie chart can show the relationship between parts and a whole.
- **Relevance.** Information is relevant if people can relate the content of the information to the task they need to perform. Sometimes a series of numbers or a long passage of text strikes some readers as irrelevant. But a well-designed visual, such as a pie chart or diagram, can help readers see the connection between this information and their task or project. For example, if you want to show that your project generates 35 percent of company revenues, a pie chart may have more impact on the audience than simply reading the percentage as text.

In the job market, the ability to read and understand information presented in a variety of ways (words, graphs, charts, and diagrams) is an important skill. Learning how to take information and present it to an audience based on their needs, abilities, and background—and on your purpose and the type of document you are presenting—can improve your audience's understanding of your message.

When to Use Visuals

In general, use visuals whenever they make your point more clearly than text or when they enhance your text. Use visuals to clarify and enhance your discussion, not just to decorate your document. As well, use visuals to direct the audience's focus or help people remember something. There may also be organizational reasons for using visuals; for example, some companies may always expect a chart or graph as part of their annual report. Certain industries, such as the financial sector, often use graphs and charts (such as the graph of the daily Dow Jones Industrial Average) as well.

Different Visuals for Different Audiences

Like all effective technical communication, visuals must fit your audience and purpose. For example, Figure 8.2 shows a special type of visual called a surface temperature plot. This visual takes specific pieces of temperature and other data and plots this information on a regional map, using symbols unique to the study of meteorology. Such a visual display using curves, lines, and other symbols

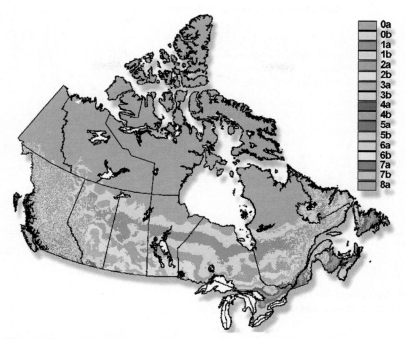

Figure 8.2 Surface Temperature Map and Visual, Designed for a Scientific Audience.
Source: Reproduced with the permission of Natural Resources Canada, 2011, courtesy of the Atlas of Canada.

makes complete sense to a trained meteorologist but would baffle a general audience.

Compare this chart with the line graph in Figure 8.3, taken from the NASA website, a website designed for a more general audience. This graph, which shows the global temperature change from 1880 to 2000, is much more accessible and familiar to general audiences than the visual shown in Figure 8.2. In short, a visual's content must be familiar to the audience, and the type of visual must be understandable.

Text into Tables

A table is a powerful way to illustrate dense textual information, such as specifications, comparisons, or conditions. Figure 8.4 shows instructions on how to operate a DVD remote control. In its purely textual form, this information is hard to follow, because it makes reference to icons that are not shown and requires readers to jump back and forth between the sentences to compare the different functions. But in a table format, parallel information can be listed in the same column and row, as shown in Figure 8.5.

The table shown in Figure 8.6 (on page 156) explains the various types of kayak paddles and provides an overview of the specifications for each. This tabular information is much more accessible than any text-based equivalent. Readers can

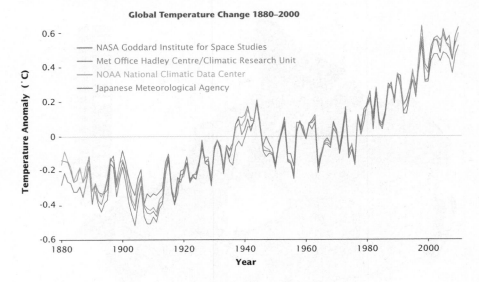

Figure 8.3 **Line Graph for a General Audience.**
Source: NASA Earth Observatory/Robert Simmon.

Operating a DVD remote control

There are five different buttons on the remote control that can be used when watching a movie:

1. By pressing the PLAY button, the movie will start. When the REW, FFWD, PAUSE, or STOP function is being used, pressing the PLAY button will resume the movie from that point. The PLAY icon does not appear on screen when function is being used.

2. By pressing the STOP button, the movie will stop. When this function is being used, the STOP icon will appear in the lower left-hand corner of the screen. To stop this function, press the PLAY button.

3. By pressing the PAUSE button, the movie will pause. When this function is being used, the PAUSE icon will display in the lower left-hand corner of the screen. It will flash while the movie is paused. To stop this function, press the PLAY button.

4. By pressing the REW button, the movie will rewind. When this function is being used, the REW icon will display in the lower left-hand corner of the screen. There are three different REW speeds: x2, x5, and x10. Press the REW button more than once to modify how fast the movie rewinds. To stop this function, press the PLAY button.

5. By pressing the FFWD button, the movie will fast-forward. When the function is being used, the FFWD icon will display in the lower left-hand corner of the screen. There are three different FFWD speeds: x2, x5, and x10. Press the FFWD button more than once to modify how fast the movie fast-forwards. To stop this function, press the PLAY button.

Figure 8.4 **Information from a DVD Player Manual in Text Format.**

Button	Icon	Function	Icon appears on screen when function is used?
PLAY	▶	Plays movie	N
PAUSE	❚❚	Pauses movie	Y
STOP	■	Stops movie	Y
REW	◀◀	Rewinds move at x2, x5, or x10 the normal viewing speed	Y
FFWD	▶▶	Fast-forwards movie at x2, x5, or x10 the normal viewing speed	Y

Figure 8.5   Information from Figure 8.4 Reformatted as a Table.

select the general type of paddle they are interested in (for example, Premium Touring). Readers can then determine which specific paddle (San Juan versus Little Dipper) is the length, weight, and type of material they need for their particular type of kayaking.

Numbers into Images

Visuals are especially effective in translating numeric data into shapes, shades, and patterns. Graphs and charts help you achieve this purpose.

Graphs

Graphs display at a glance the approximate values of a data set, the point being made about those values, and the relationship being emphasized.

Simple Line Graph. A simple line graph, as shown in Figure 8.7, uses one line to plot time intervals on the horizontal scale and values on the vertical scale.

Multiline Graph. The multiline graph in Figure 8.8 uses three lines to illustrate separate statistics showing the most common travel methods of U.S. visitors to Canada. Readers can see that the overwhelming majority travel to Canada by car.

Band Graph. Figure 8.9 is a type of line graph called a band or area graph. By shading in the areas beneath the main plot lines, you can highlight specific features. Despite their visual appeal, multiple-band graphs are easy to misinterpret. In a multiple-band graph, the top line depicts the total, with each band below it representing a part of that total. Always clarify these relationships for users.

Bar Graph. Bar graphs compare discrete changes and differences over time, such as year-by-year or month-by-month. Each bar represents a specific quantity. You can use bar graphs to focus on changes in one value or to compare values over time.

Specifications

Premium Touring

San Juan	full size blade
Paddle Length	220-260 by 10 cm
Blade Length	56 cm
Blade Width	17 cm
Weight for Size	230 cm
Standard	921 gr 32.5 oz
All Carbon	794 gr 28 oz
Ultra-Light	652 gr 23 oz

Camano	mid size blade
Paddle Length	220-260 by 10 cm
Blade Length	52 cm
Blade Width	16 cm
Weight for Size	230 cm
Standard	865 gr 30.5 oz
All Carbon	765 gr 27 oz
Ultra-Light	624 gr 22 oz

Little Dipper	small size blade
Paddle Length	220-260 by 10 cm
Blade Length	48 cm
Blade Width	15 cm
Weight for Size	230 cm
Standard	850 gr 30 oz
All Carbon	751 gr 26.5 oz
Ultra-Light	609 gr 21.5 oz

Kauai	mid size blade
Paddle Length	210-230 by 5 cm
Blade Length	48 cm
Blade Width	18.5 cm
Weight for Size	220 cm
Standard	865 gr 30.5 oz
All Carbon	751 gr 26.5 oz
Ultra-Light	609 gr 21.5 oz

Molokia	full size blade
Paddle Length	210-230 by 5 cm
Blade Length	49 cm
Blade Width	20.5 cm
Weight for Size	220 cm
Standard	907 gr 32 oz
All Carbon	794 gr 28 oz
Ultra-Light	638 gr 22.5 oz

Premium Whitewater

Rogue	full size blade
Paddle Length	194-203 by 3 cm
Blade Length	49 cm
Blade Width	19.5 cm
Weight for Size	200 cm
Standard	1049 gr 37 oz
Carbon Blades	1006 gr 35.5 oz
All Carbon	950 gr 33.5 oz

Quest	mid size blade
Paddle Length	194-203 by 3 cm
Blade Length	46 cm
Blade Width	18.5 cm
Weight for Size	200 cm
Standard	964 gr 34 oz
Carbon Blades	936 gr 33 oz
All Carbon	879 gr 31 oz

Freestyle	full size blade
Paddle Length	194-203 by 3 cm
Blade Length	48 cm
Blade Width	19.5 cm
Weight for Size	200 cm
Standard	992 gr 35 oz
Carbon Blades	964 gr 34 oz
All Carbon	907 gr 32 oz

Side Kick	full size blade
Paddle Length	194-203 by 3 cm
Blade Length	48 cm
Blade Width	19.5 cm
Weight for Size	200 cm
Standard	992 gr 35 oz
Carbon Blades	964 gr 34 oz
All Carbon	907 gr 32 oz

Nantahala	full size blade
Paddle Length	54-56 by 2 in
Blade Length	55 cm
Blade Width	21.5 cm
Weight for Size	58 in
Standard	737 gr 26 oz

Mid-Line

Mid-Tour	full size blade
Paddle Length	220-240 by 10 cm
Blade Length	52 cm
Blade Width	16 cm
Weight for Size	230 cm
Standard	1106 gr 39 oz

Mid-Tour S	mid size blade
Paddle Length	220-240 by 10 cm
Blade Length	48 cm
Blade Width	15 cm
Weight for Size	230 cm
Standard	1077 gr 38 oz

Mid-Sport	mid size blade
Paddle Length	210-220 by 5 cm
Blade Length	47 cm
Blade Width	18.5 cm
Weight for Size	220 cm
Standard	1077 gr 38 oz

Mid-WW	mid size blade
Paddle Length	194-203 by 3 cm
Blade Length	45 cm
Blade Width	18.5 cm
Weight for Size	200 cm
Standard	1021 gr 36 oz

Mid-WW 3 Pc.	mid size blade
Paddle Length	194-203 by 3 cm
Blade Length	45 cm
Blade Width	18.5 cm
Weight for Size	200 cm
Standard	1134 gr 40 oz

Point Paddles

Point Kids	small size blade
Paddle Length	180-230 by 10 cm
Blade Length	49 cm
Blade Width	12.5 cm

Point Canoe	full size blade
Paddle Length	54-62 by 2 in
Blade Length	54.5 cm
Blade Width	21.5 cm

Our Warranty: WERNER PADDLES are warranted to be free from defects in material and workmanship for a period of one year from the original date of purchase. Within that warranty period all paddles found to have defects will be repaired or replaced at no charge.

Figure 8.6 Kayak Paddle Information.
Source: Kayak paddle specifications. Courtesy of Werner Paddles, Inc.

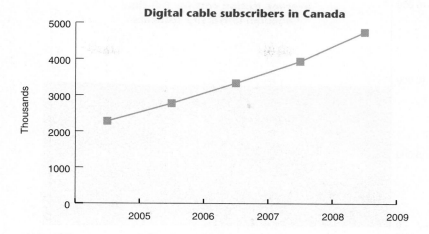

Figure 8.7 Simple Line Graph.

Source: Adapted from Statistics Canada's Summary Tables, Cable and other program distribution industry, financial and operating statistics, http://www40.statcan.ca/l01/cst01/COMM01A-eng. htm, July 18, 2011.

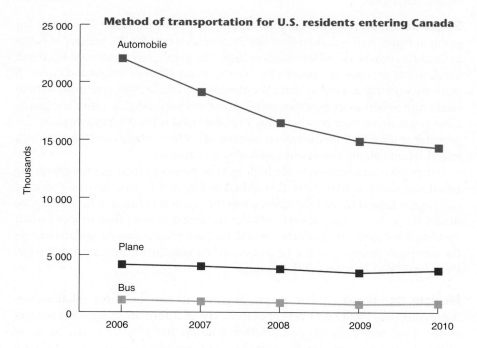

Figure 8.8   Multiline Graph.

Source: Adapted from Statistics Canada's Summary Tables, Non-resident travellers entering Canada, http://www40.statcan.ca/l01/cst01/ARTS34-eng.htm, July 18, 2011.

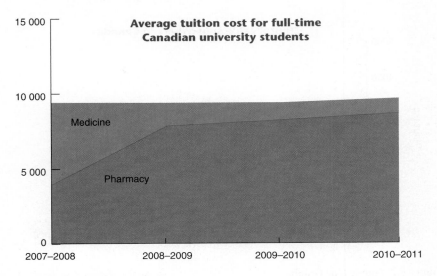

Figure 8.9 **Multiple-Band Graph.**
Source: Adapted from Statistics Canada's Summary Tables, Undergraduate tuition fees for full time Canadian students, by discipline, by province, http://www40.statcan.ca/l01/cst01/EDUC50A-eng.htm, July 18, 2011.

Simple Bar Graph. A simple bar graph displays one trend or theme. The simple bar graph in Figure 8.10 is derived from Statistics Canada data for the number of births in Canadian provinces and territories in 2008. This graph was created with Microsoft Excel, which provides instructions for creating many kinds of graphs and charts. If you were working on a report about the number of births in 2008, you might want to create such a chart to see how each province and territory differ. As with a line graph, a bar graph shows clear trends: in this case, the trend is the difference between the province or territory with the highest number of births (Ontario) and the ones with lowest (Nunavut, the Northwest Territories, and Yukon).

Bar graphs call attention to the high and low points by focusing the eye on the tallest and shortest bars. Note that although Figure 8.10 may be readable on a webpage, it is hard to read the labels when the graph is reduced to fit on the page of this book. You should always consider the sizing of your final product when creating a bar graph or any other visual, because what is easy to understand on the computer screen may not be as clear when you turn it into a printed page, transparency, or handout, and vice versa.

Multiple Bar Graph. A bar graph can display two or three relationships simultaneously. Figure 8.11 contrasts three sets of information, allowing readers to see three trends. When you create a multiple-bar graph, be sure to use a different colour or pattern for each bar, and include a key so your audience knows which colour or pattern corresponds to which bar. The more relationships you include on a graph, the more complex the graph becomes, so avoid including more than three colours or patterns on any one graph.

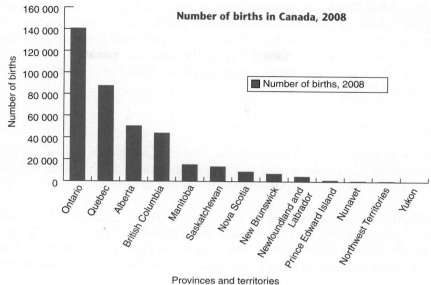

Figure 8.10 **Simple Bar Graph.**
Source: Adapted from Statistics Canada's Summary Tables, Births and total fertility rate, by province and territory, http://www40.statcan.ca/l01/cst01/HLTH85A-eng.htm, July 18, 2011.

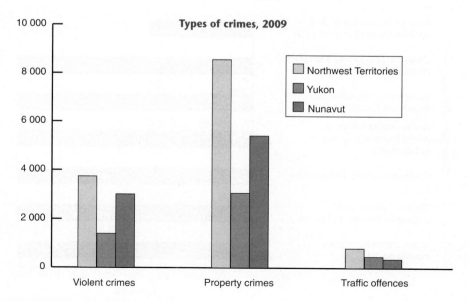

Figure 8.11 **Multiple Bar Graph.**
Source: Adapted from Statistics Canada, http://www40.statcan.ca/l01/cst01/legal50d-eng.htm, July 18, 2011.

Deviation Bar Graph. Most graphs begin at a zero axis point and display only positive values. In contrast, a deviation bar graph displays both positive and negative values, as in Figure 8.12. Note how the horizontal axis extends to the negative side of the zero baseline, following the same incremental division as the positive side of the graph. Deviation bar graphs are useful for illustrating trends in financial profits and losses.

Charts

The terms *graph* and *chart* are often used interchangeably. But a chart displays relationships that are not plotted on a coordinate system (*x* and *y* axes). Popular charts include pie charts, Gantt charts, tree charts, and pictograms.

Pie Chart. Pie charts are among the most common charts and are easy for almost anyone to understand. Pie charts display the relationship of parts or percentages to the whole. In a pie chart, readers can compare the parts to each other as well as to the whole (to show how much was spent on what, how much income comes

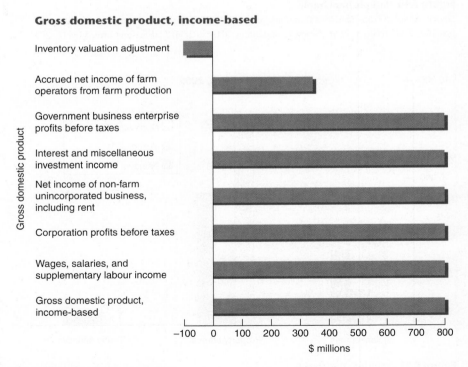

Gross domestic product, income-based

Figure 8.12 Deviation Bar Graph.
Source: Adapted from Statistics Canada, http://www40.statcan.gc.ca/l01/cst01/econ03-eng.htm, September 5, 2008.

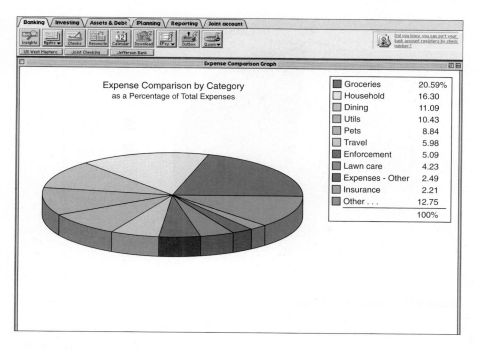

Figure 8.13 Pie Chart.
Source: Quicken™. Screen shots © Intuit, Inc. All rights reserved.

from which sources, and so on). Figure 8.13 shows a pie chart created with a personal finance program. This chart makes it very clear that for this household, groceries are the largest annual expense. Figure 8.14 is an exploded pie chart created in a spreadsheet program. Exploded pie charts help call out, or highlight, the various pieces of the pie. Once you have created a chart like this, you can easily save it as an image and include it in a word-processing file (for a report) or as part of a webpage.

With pie charts, make sure the parts add up to 100 percent. Use different colours or shades to distinguish between parts of the whole, or differentiate each slice by exploding it out. Include a key to help readers differentiate between the parts, or label each slice directly. Note that if most of the slices are very small or quite similar in size, the pie chart will not be useful; consider using a different format, perhaps a bar graph.

Gantt Chart. Gantt charts (named for engineer H. L. Gantt, 1861–1919) depict how the parts of an idea or concept relate to each other. A series of bars or lines (timelines) indicates beginning and completion dates for each phase or task in a

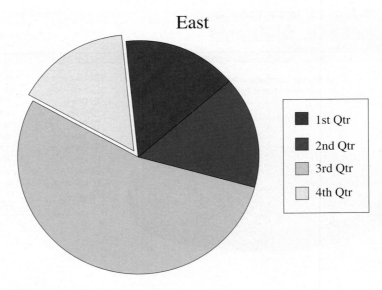

Figure 8.14 **Exploded Pie Chart.**

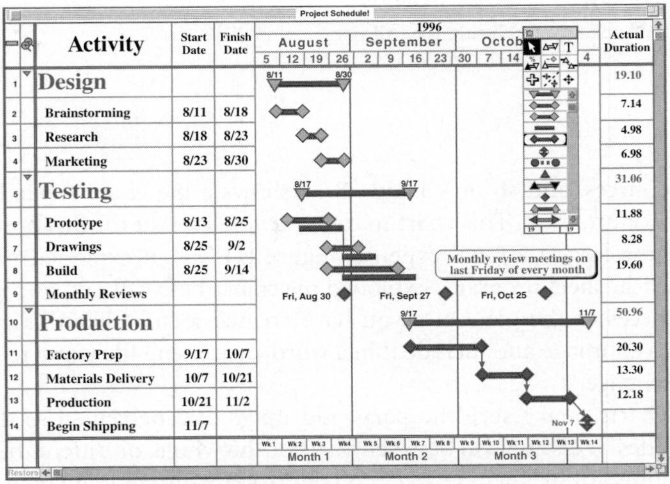

Figure 8.15 **Gantt Chart Showing the Schedule for a Manufacturing Project.**
Source: Chart created in Fast Track Schedule.™

project. Figure 8.15 is a Gantt chart illustrating the schedule for a manufacturing project. Many professionals use project management software to produce Gantt and similar charts (see Software and Web-Based Images later in this chapter).

Tree Chart. Many types of charts can be generally categorized as "tree" charts:

- Flowcharts, which use a tree structure to trace a procedure from beginning to end;
- Software charts, which use a tree structure to outline the logical steps in a computer program; and
- Organization charts, which show the hierarchy and relationships between different departments and other units in an organization.

Figure 8.16 shows an organizational tree chart.

Pictogram. Pictograms are a cross between a bar graph and a chart. Like line graphs, pictograms display numeric data, often by plotting it across *x* and *y* axes. But like a chart, pictograms use icons, symbols, and other graphic devices rather than simple lines or bars. Figure 8.17 is a pictogram that uses stick figure icons to illustrate population at different times. Pictograms are visually appealing and can be especially useful for non-technical audiences. Graphics software makes it easy to create pictograms.

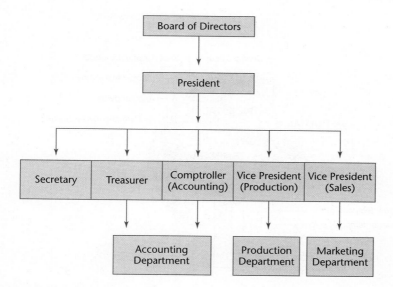

Figure 8.16 **Organizational Chart.**

School attendance of Canadians ages 15 and up, 1991–2001
(Each figure = 1 million)
(All symbols represent nearest million.)

Year

2001

Not attending school: 🧍🧍🧍🧍🧍🧍🧍🧍🧍🧍🧍🧍🧍🧍🧍🧍🧍🧍🧍🧍 (20,004,485)

Attending school full time: 🧍🧍🧍 (2,777,230)

Attending school part time: 🧍 (1,119,650)

1996

Not attending school: 🧍🧍🧍🧍🧍🧍🧍🧍🧍🧍🧍🧍🧍🧍🧍🧍🧍🧍🧍 (18,659,820)

Attending school full time: 🧍🧍🧍 (2,801,280)

Attending school part time: 🧍 (1,167,820)

1991

Not attending school: 🧍🧍🧍🧍🧍🧍🧍🧍🧍🧍🧍🧍🧍🧍🧍🧍🧍🧍 (17,523,570)

Attending school full time: 🧍🧍🧍 (2,537,715)

Attending school part time: 🧍 (1,243,450)

Figure 8.17 Pictogram.
Source: Adapted from Statistics Canada, http://www40.statcan.ca/101/cst01/educ40a.htm, September 5, 2008.

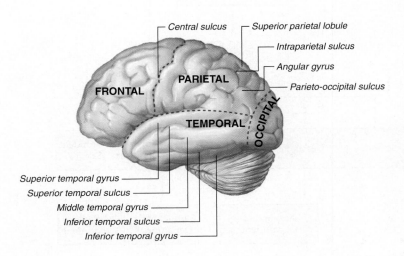

Figure 8.18 Illustration of the Brain.
Source: Davidoff, Jules., *Cognition through Color*, figure: "illustration of the brain", © 1991 Massachusetts Institute of Technology, by permission of The MIT Press.

Illustrations

An illustration is sometimes the best and only way to convey information. Illustrations can be drawings, diagrams, symbols, icons, photographs, maps, or any other visual that relies on pictures rather than on data or words. For example, the drawing of the brain in Figure 8.18 accomplishes what plain text cannot: it offers an overview of the brain's shape, the relative sizes of its segments, and its structure. Illustrations are especially valuable when you need to convey spatial relationships or help your audience see what something actually looks like. Drawings can be more effective than photographs, because in a drawing, you can simplify the view, remove any unnecessary features, and focus on what is important.

Diagrams

Diagrams are a useful way to illustrate a device or part of a device. Figure 8.19 is a diagram of a cloud-simulation chamber that shows readers the device as a whole and the parts that make up the device.

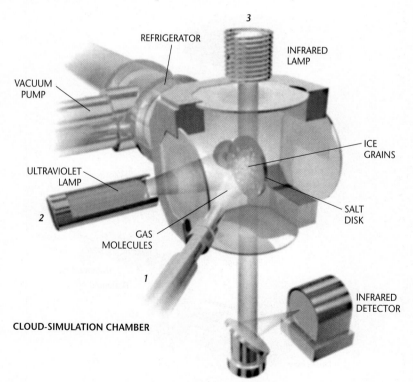

Figure 8.19 Cloud-Simulation Chamber. Diagrams are useful for illustrating devices.
Source: Illustration by Slim Films.

Exploded Diagrams

An exploded diagram is a diagram that has been pulled apart to show the parts. It is useful for explaining how a component fits into a product or how a user should assemble a product. The exploded diagram in Figure 8.20 illustrates the parts of a disk brake, a device for slowing or stopping the rotation of a wheel while it is in motion.

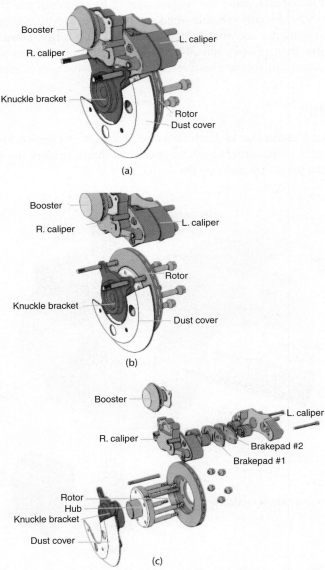

Figure 8.20   Exploded Diagram of a Disk Brake.
Source: Courtesy of Dr. Wilmot Li.

Cutaway Diagrams

Cutaway diagrams are extremely useful for showing your audience what is inside a device or helping explain how a device works. The cutaway diagram in Figure 8.21 illustrates the interior structure of Mars.

Symbols and Icons

Symbols and icons are useful ways to make information available to a wide range of audiences. Because such visuals do not rely on text, they are often more easily understood by international audiences, children, and people who may have difficulty reading. Symbols and icons are used in airports, shopping malls, restaurants, and other public places. They are also used in documentation, manuals, or training material, especially when the audience is international. Some symbols have been developed and approved by the International Organization for Standardization (ISO). The ISO makes sure the symbols have universal appeal and are standard, whether used in a printed document or on an elevator wall.

The words *symbol* and *icon* are often used interchangeably. Technically, icons tend to resemble the thing they represent: for example, an icon of a file folder on your computer looks like a real file folder. Symbols can be more abstract; symbols still get the meaning across but may not resemble precisely what they represent.

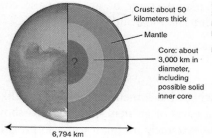

NEAREST NEIGHBOR — Based on research at the Advanced Photon Source and measurements by spacecraft, scientists have inferred the likely interior structure of Mars. The red planet's core is probably composed of an iron-sulfur alloy and about 3,000 kilometers (1,860 miles) across.

Return to article.

Figure 8.21 Cutaway Diagram.
Source: U.S. Department of Energy, http://www.anl.gov/Media_Center/News/2003/mars.html.

Figure 8.22 **Internationally Recognized Symbols.**

Figure 8.22 shows some international symbols used in airports and other public places. You should have no difficulty guessing what each means.

Note that the first three symbols represent nouns: things or objects. The last symbol (the arrow), however, represents a verb. It indicates that the person looking at it should do something—in this case, go forward and to the right. Nouns are easier to represent than verbs, because drawing a thing is easier than drawing an action.

If you are creating a document or website for an international audience, consider using ISO symbols. Check the ISO website at www.iso.ch or related sites, which you can locate using a web search engine.

Wordless Instruction

Many organizations with international audiences rely on wordless instruction: symbols, drawings, and diagrams that convey information completely without words. Flight information cards in the seat pockets of commercial airplanes are an example of wordless instruction, because they use diagrams, photographs, and drawings to explain how passengers can exit an aircraft in the event of an emergency. Figure 8.23 shows how the manufacturer of an automatic coffeemaker uses wordless instruction for its international audience.

Photographs

Photographs are especially useful for showing what something looks like. Unlike a diagram, which often highlights certain parts of an item, photographs show everything. So while a photograph can be extremely useful, it can also provide too much detail or fail to emphasize the parts you want your audience to focus on (see Figure 8.24). To obtain the most effective photograph, use a professional photographer who knows all about angles, lighting, lenses, and special film or digital editing options.

Maps

Besides being visually engaging, maps are especially useful for showing comparisons and helping users visualize position, location, and relationships among various data. The map in Figure 8.25 synthesizes information about plant hardiness zones in Canadian provinces and regions.

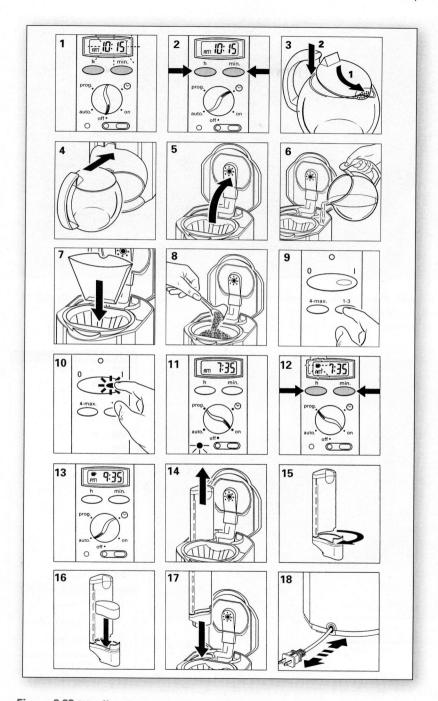

Figure 8.23 **Wordless Instructions in a Coffeemaker User's Manual.**
Source: Courtesy of Krups, Inc. (This instruction leaflet is from 1998; since then, instructions from Groupe SEB have greatly improved.)

Figure 8.24 Photograph. Photographs provide a good view of the entire product, such as this electronic car.
Source: Topham © The Image Works. Reprinted by permission.

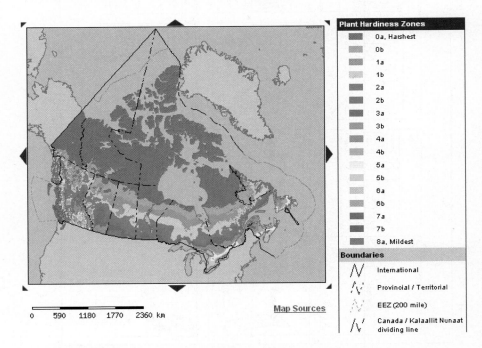

Figure 8.25 Map Showing Canada's Plant Hardiness Zones.
Source: Reproduced with the permission of Natural Resources Canada 2011, courtesy of the Atlas of Canada.

Visualization and Medical Imaging

Certain techniques from science and medicine can provide powerful and useful visuals for technical communication. Visualization is a process whereby scientists load complex mathematical data into a high-speed computer, and the computer generates an image. The image becomes a tool that can be used to understand the data. For example, NASA's Phoenix sends images of the surface of Mars back to Earth as numbers. Complex software then takes this numeric information and creates images. Similarly, the structure of DNA, which is also represented mathematically, can be converted into a visual image that scientists use to envision how DNA works.

Medical images such as CAT scans, ultrasounds, and photographs of the inside of the body via a laparoscopic camera give us a picture of organs, muscles, and tissue not visible from outside the body. These images, which are often available on the web, might be appropriate in a medical textbook or in a manual used by physicians to learn about a new imaging product.

Software and Web-Based Images

You can create most of the visuals discussed in this chapter with the wide assortment of computer graphics software, spreadsheets, presentation software, and related products that are available. Also, you can find clip art, icons and symbols, medical images, and a vast assortment of other visuals on the web. See Chapter 10 for information on copyright and web-based graphics.

Consider taking a class in computer graphics. With the continued growth of the internet, cable television, personal computing, and other visually based technologies, you can enhance your career by learning about visuals and computer technology.

Knowing about the following categories of computer software will definitely enhance your abilities as a technical communicator, whether this is your full-time job or just part of your job:

- *Graphics software,* such as Adobe Illustrator or CorelDraw, allows you to draw and illustrate.
- *Photography software,* such as Adobe Photoshop, allows you to work with photographs, scanned images, or other files (such as graphics files taken from the web). You can manipulate these images to make them fit your document or to make them more appropriate for your audience and purpose. But don't change the items so much that you change the meaning.
- *Presentation software,* such as Microsoft PowerPoint, lets you create slides, computer presentations, and overhead transparency sheets. Some types of presentation software, such as Macromedia Director, are designed to create complex multimedia presentations that include sound and video.

- *Project management software,* such as Microsoft Project, makes it easy to create Gantt charts or organizational tree charts.
- *Spreadsheet software,* such as Microsoft Excel, creates pie charts, bar graphs, line graphs, and so on from the data in a spreadsheet.
- *Word-processing programs,* such as Corel WordPerfect or Microsoft Word, include simple image editors ("draw" feature) and other tools for working with visuals. More sophisticated page layout programs, such as Adobe InDesign, also provide ways for you to work with visuals.

Using Colour

Years ago, it was expensive and difficult to use colour in anything but the most important documents. Adding colour often meant adding cost, because each change of colour involved cleaning the printing press, using new ink, and then cleaning the press again for a different colour. Smaller colour projects, such as overhead transparencies, were often coloured by hand. However, today, colour computer screens and inexpensive colour printers can make full-colour projects relatively easy and inexpensive, especially for small documents. Colour is an effective tool in a visual, because it helps focus reader attention and makes the document more visually interesting. Colour can also help you organize your visual. It can help you orient your reader and emphasize certain areas of your visual or document. Yet too much colour or the wrong colour combinations can be worse than no colour at all. Ugly colours, lack of contrast, disturbing background colours (e.g., black or red), and jarring combinations can turn your readers away. Moreover, while colour can greatly enhance how audiences understand technical data, technical communicators need to understand the basics of how people perceive colour. For more information on colour, visit http://precisionintermedia.com/color.html.

Figure 8.26 illustrates an effective use of colour on the website for Staples, an office supplies retailer. Staples uses red on its storefront signs, and the webpage continues this theme. The company logo is white type on a bright red background. The rest of the website integrates red and white, drawing the reader's eye to key locations. Other text and features are in blue, which complements the red and stands out against the white background. The page does not overuse any one colour.

When using colour, remember the following guidelines:

- **Use colours consistently.** A particular colour should mean the same thing throughout the visual or the document.
- **Use colours selectively.** Too many colours create "visual noise." Don't mix too many colours, and use colours to help organize the page. Avoid using light colours on a light background: darker print provides more contrast with a light background.

Figure 8.26 A Website That Uses Colour Effectively.
Source: Courtesy of Staples. www.staples.ca.

- **Consider audience and purpose.** Certain audiences and situations may call for certain colours. For example, if your document addresses university students, you might wish to use the school colours. Also, not all audiences will see colour as you do. Approximately 8 percent of males and 0.4 percent of females have trouble distinguishing between colours (Cooper, 2008). Whenever possible, test your colour choices on audience members.

- **Consider intercultural issues.** Colours have different meanings in different countries. In many parts of Asia white is the colour of mourning, but in Canada, it symbolizes innocence and purity.

- **Consider the medium.** It is cheaper and easier to add colour to a webpage or presentation than to use colour on a glossy brochure. Consider how your document will be published before making colour choices.

Avoiding Visual Noise

Too many visuals and too much clutter create "visual noise." People understand visuals easily, but not if the chart, graph, or other visual is so crowded or disorderly that it cannot be understood. Called "chartjunk" (Tufte, 1990, p. 34) and "gratuitous graphics" (Levy, et al., 1996), these bells and whistles end up overshadowing readable, credible visual information. The result, according to studies by Noam Tractinsky and Joachim Meyer, is a gap between the information and the presentation, and this gap is widening with the introduction of new presentation technologies (1999, p. 398).

In addition, visuals that look fine in one format may appear crowded in another. For instance, what looks great on a website may look crowded or out of proportion on a print page. When creating visuals, use a minimalist approach. Keep your designs simple and elegant. Don't use too much clip art, too many colours, or too many images. Test your visuals to be sure they make sense to your audience. If your organization has an in-house graphics designer, ask that person's opinion.

Visuals and Ethics

Technical communicators have a responsibility to present information accurately. Although you are perfectly justified in presenting data in the best light, you must avoid misrepresentation. Any one set of data can be contorted so that it supports contradictory conclusions. In addition, even though your numbers may be accurate, your visual display could be misleading. For example, by altering the placement of the values along the y-axis of a graph, you can make a huge leap seem like a tiny blip. With currently available computer software, it is easy to create misleading visuals. For example, when bar charts use pictures (see "Pictogram" earlier in this chapter), the relative size of the bar and type of picture might convey a particular bias (Kostelnick & Roberts, 1998, p. 292). As well, a deep colour on one bar and a light colour on another might prevent a reader from seeing all the data equally. See Figure 8.27 for an example of a distorted graph.

Graphs can also be confusing or misleading if the axes are not labelled. Readers assume that an axis begins at zero, but this may not always be the case. Image labels can also be confusing if they are too small for readers to see or, worse yet, are missing. In addition, photographs and other images can easily be manipulated using software. Copyright (see Chapter 10) is also a consideration, because an image you obtain on the web is likely protected by copyright and cannot be used or altered without permission.

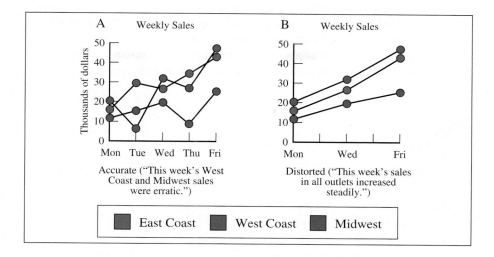

Figure 8.27 An Accurate Line Graph and a Distorted Version. Selective omission of data points in graph B causes the lines to flatten, implying a steady increase rather than an erratic pattern of sales, as more accurately shown in graph A.

Aim for Fairness and Accuracy. Label the axes of charts and graphs. Indicate the source of your data. Use colour appropriately and evenly. If your visual accompanies text, indicate how this visual supports the textual information.

Without getting bogged down in needless detail, an accurate visual includes all essential data. Figure 8.27 shows how distortion occurs when data that would provide a complete picture are selectively omitted. Graph A accurately depicts the numeric relationships measured from the value scale. In graph B, too few points are plotted to give an accurate picture of sales trends.

Decide carefully what to include and what to leave out of your visual display.

Cultural Considerations

Although groups such as the ISO have tried to standardize a wide range of visual information across cultures, you will not always use ISO symbols for your visuals. Visual communication does have global appeal, but charts, graphs, tables, and other visual forms are not universal; in other words, "the world told is different from the world shown" (Kress, 2003, p. 1). Not all cultures read from left to right, so a chart intended to be read left to right that is read in the opposite direction could be misunderstood. Colour is also a cultural consideration. Representations of images that might be used in a computer icon or diagram may be culturally offensive if they portray sensitive images, such as certain animals (the cow in Hindu culture) or gender roles (women with bare heads in certain Arabic cultures).

Checklist for Visual Communication

- Does the visual serve a legitimate purpose (clarification, not mere ornamentation)?
- Is this the best type of visual for your purpose and audience?
- Is the level of complexity appropriate for the audience?
- Is the visual titled and numbered?
- Are all patterns in the visual identified by label or legend?
- Are all values or units of measurement specified (milligrams per litre, millions of dollars)?
- Is colour used tastefully and appropriately?
- Do the visual relationships represent the numeric relationships accurately?
- Are all data sources cited?
- Has written permission been obtained for reproducing or adapting a visual from a copyrighted source in any type of work to be published?
- Is the visual introduced, discussed, interpreted, integrated with the text, and referred to by number?
- Is the visual easy to locate?
- Is the visual uncrowded, uncluttered, and free of "visual noise"?
- Is the visual ethically acceptable?
- Does the document respect users' cultural values?

Exercises

1. Find an article in a newspaper, journal, or magazine that does not include the visuals necessary to support the communication purpose or meet the audience's needs. Analyze the article, and identify where visuals would be helpful. Make a list of the visuals you would recommend to the article's author or the publication's editor.

2. From the list you drew up in Exercise 1, select two proposed visuals and create them using the graphics component of a word-processing program or graphics software. In a presentation to your class, explain how additional visuals would improve the usability of your article, and show the visuals you created.

3. **FOCUS ON WRITING**. In printed materials and websites, find an example of each of the kinds of visuals discussed in this chapter (diagram, table, pie chart, simple bar chart, deviation bar graph, etc.). Critique each visual. Does it convey the information effectively? Would a different type of visual be more effective? Is visual noise distracting? What would you do to make the visual more effective or more appropriate to audience and purpose? Write up your findings as a short memo to your instructor.

4. Obtain an instruction manual for a piece of technology with which you are familiar. Before looking at the manual, list the visuals you think might be included in the manual and consider the role each of those visuals would play in making the manual usable. Then compare your list with the visuals that are actually in the manual and analyze the differences between the manual and your list:

   - For visuals that are in the manual and on your list, compare the role in the manual and the role that you defined.
   - For visuals in the manual but not on your list, evaluate the role and effectiveness of the visuals. Do you agree with the decision to include those visuals in the manual? Why or why not?
   - For visuals not in the manual but on your list, evaluate the role that you defined and the effectiveness of that segment of the manual as it exists without the visual. Do you agree with the decision not to include those visuals in the manual? Why or why not?

 The Collaboration Window

Return to the teams you worked in for the collaborative exercise at the end of Chapter 2 and examine the audience and purpose statements you created for the survival guide for incoming students. List the topics you are likely to include in the guide. Then list the visuals that you believe would effectively support the purpose of each section of the guide. As a team, present your plans to the class, explaining the rationale for each proposed visual.

The Global Window

The International Organization for Standardization (ISO) is devoted to standardizing a range of material, including technical specifications and visual information. If you've ever been in an airport and seen the many international signs directing travellers to the restroom or to the smoking area (or informing them not to smoke), you have seen ISO signs. Go to the ISO website at www.iso.ch to learn about ISO symbols. Prepare a short report and presentation for class explaining how these symbols are developed. Show some of the symbols and explain why these work for international communication.

MyCanadianTechCommLab

Go to MyCanadianTechCommLab at www.mycanadiantechcommlab.com for additional online exercises and problems.

CHAPTER **9**

Ethical Issues in Technical Communication

Chapter Objectives

By the end of this chapter you will be able to:

1. Understand the importance of ethics when communicating both orally and in print.

2. Understand the different kinds of ethics.

3. Differentiate between legal obligations and ethical obligations when writing.

4. Avoid the most common types of ethical errors associated with writing (i.e., suppressing knowledge from the public, exploiting cultural differences).

5. Understand how technical communications are affected by ethical issues and how to respond to ethical situations that may arise.

Carac Allison, London, Ontario

Carac Allison earned an undergraduate degree in English from York University in Toronto. His first job was at the Financial Aid office at the University of Western Ontario. In 1998, along with two other staff members, Carac helped the university transition from using paper applications to using online applications and databases for adjudication.

After four years in the Financial Aid office, Carac created the Registrar's Web Team and began providing IT solutions for Admissions, Records, the Centre for New Students, and Financial Aid. More IT professionals were hired to accommodate the demands of students using the Registrar's website, as well as the needs of staff and faculty members.

By 2006, the Web Team's scope had grown to include the entire Vice Provost's portfolio. Today, Carac works with a programming staff of eight and is responsible for five major service websites. "People are surprised when I tell them that my degree is in English and not Computer Science. But what I've come to understand is that 80 percent of my job is communication: drafting emails, writing technical documents, preparing presentations, managing meetings, and supporting my staff. The IT field is constantly changing. The experience I've gained in communicating is what I rely upon."

Ethics, Technology, and Communication

Technical communication does not occur in a void. It happens in the world of human beings, politics, and social conditions; a world in which we regularly face ethical dilemmas that pit our sense of what is right against a decision that may be more efficient, profitable, or better for the company.

Ethical questions often revolve around topics related to technology. For example, a new computer chip that secretly collects personal information about a person's web-surfing habits presents a privacy dilemma. Should users be allowed to choose whether to give out this information? Some people would say yes, and in Canada, there is federal and provincial legislation that puts some limits on using private information. Even so, the decision is usually less a legal one than an ethical one. The communication about this product (for example, a press release announcing it or a user's manual that accompanies the computer) plays a central role in this ethical dilemma. Should the technical writer include this information, exclude it altogether, or de-emphasize it by using a small font?

These are not simple questions. Taking an ethical stance requires a personal decision on your part about how to balance your ethical and moral beliefs with the realities of the job. It requires you to consider the effects of your decisions on the users of your product, on your company, on society, and on your job. Sometimes standing your ground on an ethical issue may mean losing your job or suffering retaliation from co-workers.

Examples of Ethical Issues in Technical Communication

The Walkerton tragedy (see www.cbc.ca/news/background/walkerton) and the tainted blood scandal (see www.cbc.ca/news/background/taintedblood and www.thecanadianencyclopedia.com/index.cfm?PgNm=TCE&Params=A1ARTA0009152) help illustrate the relationship between ethics and technical communication.

The Walkerton Tragedy

The Case. In May 2000, people in the town of Walkerton, Ontario, became ill after drinking from the town's water supply. Symptoms included fever, urinary tract infection, and kidney problems. Between May 15 and May 21, over 2300 people became sick.

The Communication Situation. Although the Walkerton Public Utilities Commission stated that they had found no problem with the water supply, tests of the water revealed the opposite. The commission's supervisor Stan Koebel and his brother Frank Koebel, who worked as a water supervisor, both insisted that the water supply was fine to drink. Memos that both had written during the six-day period, as well as tests they had run, indicated the same thing.

The Aftermath. Only after a town doctor advised people to stop drinking the water did the number of sick people stop increasing. Upon investigation, the Ontario Clean Water Agency declared that the water supply had been mismanaged for years, and that many entries made by the Koebel brothers had been falsified. Seven people died, and it was estimated that the cleanup would cost upwards of $150 million.

The Tainted Blood Scandal

The Case. By the 1980s, human immunodeficiency virus (HIV) was a well-known threat, as was hepatitis C. However, it was not until the late 1980s that the Canadian Red Cross Society (CRCS) began screening donated blood for both viral threats. Aside from Canadian donors, the CRCS received much of its donated blood from prison inmates and from areas known to have a large population of people diagnosed with HIV. By the late 1980s, approximately 2000 people had been infected with HIV, and approximately 30 000 people had been infected with hepatitis C after receiving transfusions with blood supplied from the CRCS. In fact, approximately 95 percent of hemophiliacs who received blood from the CRCS before 1990 became infected with hepatitis C.

The Communication Situation. In 1993, Justice Horace Krever was sanctioned to run the newly created Commission of Inquiry on the Blood System in Canada. By 1997, Krever's findings concluded that the tainted blood got into the CRCS blood bank because no policy had been implemented to deal with the threats of HIV and hepatitis C, despite the fact that both the government and the CRCS knew of the situation.

Organizational Role. The relationship between provincial and federal governments and the CRCS was not well defined, and each institute believed the other institute was responsible for addressing the problem. Krever found that the government had refused to implement testing systems used in the United States because of the estimated cost (around $20 million).

Written Communication. Krever's commission discovered that key documents had been destroyed. These documents not only acknowledged the situation but also supported decisions that would lead to the infection of thousands of Canadians.

Aftermath. After the Krever commission report was published, the CRCS was no longer in charge of blood services. Instead, the CRCS was eventually replaced by Canadian Blood Services. While financial compensation was offered to many victims who had received blood between 1986 and 1990, those who were infected before 1986 have not been compensated. Approximately 20 000 people have received no compensation.

In your own communication, you will often face ethical decisions—about how much information to include, how much to leave out, how to word an issue, or how to shape the information for users and consumers. In the end, communication is never neutral. It always comes with some type of consequence.

Types of Ethical Choices

Throughout history, people have tried to define universal principles of ethics to provide a basis for ethical decision making. The following are three of these theories.

- **Kant's categorical imperative.** Immanuel Kant (1724–1804) argued that certain ethical situations dictate certain actions. Kant suggested that "codes of conduct and morality must be arrived at through reason and be universally applicable to all societal environments at all times." Kant emphasized the individual's responsibility and the intention of the act, not its consequence (Fink, 1988, p. 7).
- **Utilitarianism.** Associated with John Stuart Mill (1806–1873), the ethical principle known as utilitarianism asserts that "ethical conduct should aim at general well-being, creating the greatest happiness for the greatest number of people." Unlike Kant, Mill argued that the outcome, not just the intention of an act, determined how people judge the ethics of a behaviour (Fink, 1988, p. 7).
- **Ethical relativism.** Taken to its extreme, ethical relativism suggests that any act may be ethical, depending on the particular ethical, religious, and cultural stance of the individual or group. A more moderate approach to relativism would suggest that acts must be weighed not against some fixed set of standards, as in Kant's notion, but in the context of the culture and individual circumstance. More recently, some would argue, Canadian culture in particular has gravitated toward a relativistic position regarding ethical behaviour.

Such broad ethical principles, however, rarely provide sufficient guidance for the countless ethical decisions technical communicators face today. Kant's codes of ethics or Mill's utilitarianism might have been useful in their historical periods, but today, most philosophers and ethicists agree that in a complex world, it is more effective to consider the particular situation and to develop standards appropriate for that situation.

For technical communication, you might consider an approach based on *reasonable criteria* (standards that most people consider acceptable), which take the form of obligations, ideals, and consequences (Christians, Tackler, Rotzoll,

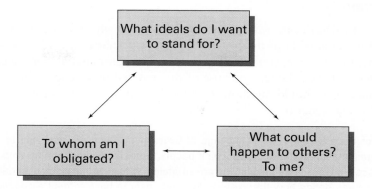

Figure 9.1 **Reasonable Criteria for Ethical Judgment.**

Brittain-McKee, & Woods, 2005; Ruggiero, 1998, pp. 33–34). *Obligations* are the responsibilities you have to everyone involved:

- obligation to yourself to act in your own best interest and according to good conscience
- obligation to stand by the clients and customers to whom you are bound by contract—and who pay the bills
- obligation to your company to advance its goals, respect its policies, protect confidential information, and expose misconduct that would harm the organization
- obligation to co-workers to promote their safety and well-being
- obligation to the community to preserve the local economy, welfare, and quality of life
- obligation to society to consider the national and global impact of your actions

When the interests of these parties conflict—as they often do—you have to decide where your primary obligations lie.

Ideals are the values that you believe in or stand for: loyalty, friendship, compassion, dignity, fairness, and whatever qualities make you who you are. *Consequences* are the beneficial or harmful results of actions. Consequences may be immediate or delayed, intentional or unintentional, obvious or subtle. Some consequences are easy to predict, some are difficult, and some are impossible. Figure 9.1 depicts the relations among these three criteria.

Legal versus Ethical

Given the criteria just discussed, you can see that just because certain actions are legal does not necessarily mean that they are ethical. The copyright, plagiarism, and privacy examples listed here illustrate this point.

Copyright

Chapter 10 describes certain circumstances under which you may use copyrighted material without the copyright holder's permission. Under the fair use doctrine, for example, you are allowed to use certain materials for educational purposes. But even though your use of the material may be legal, in some circumstances you should question the ethical implications of that use. Consider the following scenario:

> For a class called "The Language of Cyberspace," you are assigned to do a presentation on the ways in which people form communities on the web. You locate a website for people who are struggling with a certain medical condition, and you notice how the users of this site seem to have formed a community among themselves, discussing specific personal aspects of their condition and seeking advice from each other. You make overhead transparencies of some of these web discussions, telling yourself that you don't need permission because you are using only a portion of the material and you are using it for educational purposes. You use these transparencies in a class presentation.

Even though this use is legal, is it ethical? Your obligation to your co-workers (fellow students) and to the community should remind you to consider that the people who logged on to this website never expected their names and personal information to be put up on an overhead in front of a class. What if one of the users turns out to be the friend of a classmate, and that classmate never knew about the friend's medical condition?

In this case, you should have considered not only the legal aspects of your decision but also the ethical ones. Your obligation to yourself to act in good conscience might lead you to ask how to avoid causing possible embarrassment to the users of this site, either by selecting a different site for your presentation (one that does not use names) or by changing or omitting the names of the users before placing your material on a transparency.

Plagiarism

Plagiarism is using someone else's words and ideas without giving that person proper credit. Even when your use of a source may be legal, you may still be violating ethical standards if you do not cite the information source.

Assume that you are writing a class report on genetically modified plants. In your research, you discover a very good paper on the web. You decide that parts of this paper would complement your report quite nicely. Under copyright and fair use guidelines, you can reproduce portions of the paper without permission. And with the web, it is very easy to cut and paste them into your paper. But does this legal standard and the technical ease with which you can do it mean that you can use someone else's material freely, without giving that person credit? Even though it might be legal under fair use guidelines to reprint the material without notifying the copyright holder, using someone else's material or ideas without giving that person credit is plagiarism.

Plagiarism is a serious infraction. Students can be suspended or expelled from school. Researchers can lose their jobs and their standing in the academic community. Most important, plagiarism is serious because it violates several of the reasonable criteria for ethical decision-making discussed earlier in this chapter. Plagiarism violates your obligation to yourself to be truthful, and it violates your obligation to society to provide fair and accurate information. It also violates your obligation to co-workers—in this case, other students and researchers. Especially in the age of the internet, when it's easy to use material from websites, you need to consider the ethics of the situation.

Privacy

Chapter 10 describes privacy issues in technical communication, especially in light of the capability of web users to collect personal information over the internet, and the conflicts between Canadian, American, and European approaches to personal privacy. Because one of your ethical obligations should be to society (to consider the national and global impact of your actions), privacy is high on the list of ethical issues to consider.

If you are designing a website, for example, should you create a page that asks users for their name, address, and other personal information? If this were a business discussion, you might automatically say yes. Because it is an ethical context, you would need to ask about your obligations to society. A privacy statement such as the one in Figure 10.4 (page 210) might be one way to address both the business and ethical sides of the question. Another solution is to make sure users have a way to remove their names from your database at any time.

Additional Ways in Which Actions Can Be Unethical

Besides plagiarism or violations of copyright and privacy, your actions can be unethical in other ways. As you read this section of the chapter, consider these situations in relation to the reasonable criteria listed in Figure 9.1. Note that most of these situations relate to workplace issues. Figure 9.2 illustrates how workplace pressures can influence ethical values.

Yielding to Social Pressure

Sometimes you may have to choose between doing what you know is right and doing what your employer or organization expects. Suppose that just as your company is about to unveil its new pickup truck, your safety engineering team discovers that the reserve gas tanks (installed beneath the truck but outside the

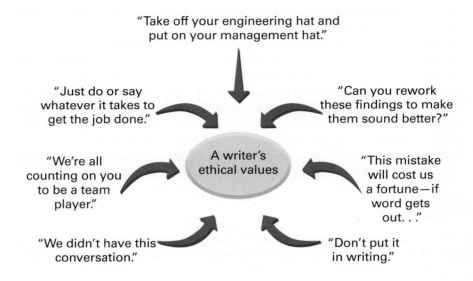

Figure 9.2 **How Workplace Pressures Can Influence Ethical Values.**

frame) may, in rare circumstances, explode on impact from a side collision. You know that this information should be included in the owner's manual or, at a minimum, in a letter to the car dealers, but the company has spent a fortune building this truck and does not want to hear about this problem.

Companies often face contradictory goals of production (producing a product and making a profit on it) and safety (producing a product but spending money to avoid accidents). When production receives first priority, safety concerns may suffer (Wickens, 1992). If you find yourself in such a work environment, you need to rely on your own ethical standards. In the case of the reserve gas tanks, you may determine that your obligation to society overrides your obligation to yourself or your company. If you make this choice, prepare to be fired for taking on the company.

Mistaking Groupthink for Teamwork

Some organizations rely on teamwork and collaboration to get a job done; technical communicators frequently operate as part of a larger team of other writers, editors, designers, engineers, and production specialists. Teamwork is important in these situations, but teamwork should not be confused with *groupthink*, which occurs when group pressure prevents individuals from questioning, criticizing, or "making waves" (Janis, 1972). Group members may feel a need to be accepted by the team, often at the expense of making the right decision. To some extent, the tainted blood scandal discussed earlier in this chapter illustrates groupthink in action. Although employees of the CRCS knew that they were cutting corners, no one took action for fear of losing their job.

Suppressing Knowledge the Public Needs

Pressures to downplay the dangers of technology can result in censorship of important information. For example, high-level employees at major North American tobacco companies apparently knew for years about the harmful effects of cigarettes and other nicotine-related products (chewing tobacco, cigars, and so on). Yet U.S. lawsuits in the late 1990s proved that many managers and other company decision-makers went to great lengths to suppress this information. Should these employees have come forward and admitted what they already knew—that cigarettes cause cancer and other diseases and that nicotine is very addictive? The answer is yes, so long as they were prepared to suffer the consequences. You will need to ask if your obligation to the company takes priority over your greater obligation to your fellow citizens. What about your obligation to yourself to be truthful and to act in good conscience? Again, being aware of your own ethical stance is critical in these situations.

Exaggerating Claims About Technology

Organizations that have a stake in a particular technology may be especially tempted to exaggerate its benefits, potential, or safety. Assume that you are a technical writer working on the manual and brochure for an uninterrupted power supply, a device that allows computers and other electronic devices to have power even if the main power goes out. Your company manufactures several models of these power supplies. The low-end model will maintain power for five minutes after the main power goes out; the high-end model for 40 minutes. To emphasize the potential of the product, your manager asks you to use only the 40-minute figure, thereby exaggerating what the other model can do. How would you approach this ethical dilemma? Would you simply do what you were told, or would you find a way to raise the issue with your team and your manager? Your choice will most certainly be affected by your ethical values.

Exploiting Cultural Differences

Cross-cultural communication carries potential for ethical abuses. Based on its level of business experience or its particular social values, a given culture might be especially vulnerable to manipulation or deception. Some countries, for example, place greater reliance on interpersonal trust than on lawyers or legal wording, and a handshake can be worth more than the fine print of a legal contract. If you know something about a culture's habits or business practices and you use this information unfairly to get a sale or make a profit, you are ignoring your obligations to yourself and your community.

Types of Technical Communication Affected by Ethical Issues

Certain forms of communication have specific features worth considering in an ethical context.

Graphics

As noted in Chapter 8, graphics are powerful tools for technical communication, and this power can be used in many ways. Graphs, charts, icons, and other images can provide quick, efficient displays of complex information, but they can also be manipulated to distort information. For example, a line graph that does not have clearly labelled axes might make a financial trend look better than it really is. Other design features, such as the size or shape of graphical images, can also be misleading. For example, Figure 9.3 misrepresents the data that it is trying to convey. Whereas the graph (Figure 9.3a) effectively conveys the average monthly cost to rent a two-bedroom apartment, the pie chart (Figure 9.3b) seems to suggest that the costs of living in Halifax and Regina are roughly the same. However, if you take the time to read the actual rental costs listed in Figure 9.3a, you will see that Halifax apartments cost 20 percent more than Regina apartments. These differences are far larger than the pie chart in Figure 9.3b implies.

One study found that technical communicators most frequently rate ethics based on the results of the communication: "the greater the likelihood of deception and the greater the injury to the reader as a consequence of that deception, the more unethical is the design of the document" (Dragga, 1996, pp. 262–263).

Webpages and the Internet

The power of a webpage to convey information is obvious, and this topic has been discussed elsewhere in this book. To be thoroughly ethical, you need to consider the speed of the internet, its global reach, and a webpage's ability to combine sound, colour, images, text, and interactivity. These features all have the potential to manipulate and distort information. Imagine a website for a herbal remedy that may be helpful for anxiety. This herbal remedy may not have government approval, and it may even have harmful side effects. But you could set up a promotional website that looks extremely scientific and factual. Logos from quasi-scientific organizations might give the page a sense of professional credibility. Statistics, charts, and links to other websites might all give this the appearance of a valid medical site. Yet as a communicator, you need to question the possible outcome for users and the overall risks to society of setting up such a site.

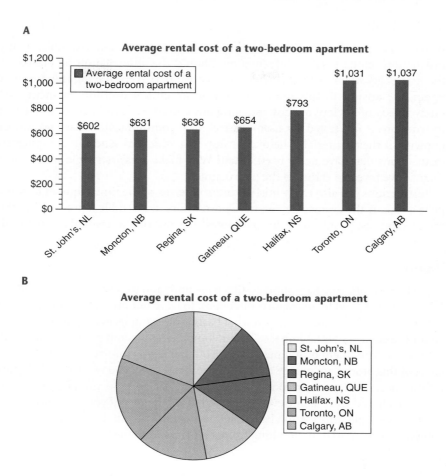

A

Average rental cost of a two-bedroom apartment

B

Average rental cost of a two-bedroom apartment

Figure 9.3   **Distorted Bar Graph and Pie Chart.**
Source: Created by author, based on Canada Mortgage and Housing Corporation's data (CMHC)
"Average Monthly Rent in Privately Initiated Rental Apartment Structures of Three Units and
Over," 2007. All rights reserved. Reproduced with the consent of CMHC. All other uses and
reproductions of this material are expressly prohibited.

Memos and Emails

As noted earlier, the Walkerton crisis involved information conveyed in the form
of memos. Memos and emails may seem innocuous enough, but the messages
they convey can present serious ethical choices. A memo that contains misleading information or that deliberately conceals important facts represents a breach
of ethics. Communicators should be aware that information in a memo often has
serious ethical implications.

Instructions

Instructions entail a variety of ethical considerations. For example, many instructions contain safety information. Should this information be placed on the first page, where it might deter some consumers from buying the product? Again, the answer to this question rests on an ethical decision balancing the safety needs of society against the company's need for profit. Also, if a set of instructions is not tested for usability, technical communicators have no way of knowing if their material is helpful or not. Is it ethical to send out complicated instructions that have never been tested? Why make a user struggle when a test might have revealed errors in the instructions?

Instructions can also easily mislead users in terms of the time required to complete a task. If the average person needs two hours to assemble a product but the instructions say, "Ready to use in 30 minutes," this information would be unethical.

Reports

Reports must often be kept short to fit a page limit and to be efficient for readers. For conciseness and focus, reports often have to leave out minor information. But who decides what is minor, and on what basis? For example, in preparing a report about the environmental impact of your company's pulp and paper manufacturing process, you might be tempted to leave out damaging information, such as the effect of this process on nearby rivers and streams. Even if you want to include this information, your team or your manager might disagree. So you face an ethical decision. Should you include everything? What will happen if you do or don't? On what basis should information be left out or included? If you do decide to defy the company, be prepared for anything from a reprimand to the loss of your job.

Proposals

Proposals present specific plans to get something done. A sales proposal, for example, might present your company's plan to design a website for a local community organization. Because you are probably bidding against other companies, you want to project the best image and offer the best service for the best price. So you may be tempted to stretch the truth about the time required to complete the job. Is this ethical? On the one hand, such projects usually exceed the deadline, and if you tell the truth while your competitor lies, you might lose the job. On the other hand, dishonesty is likely to damage your company's reputation (and your own). Other ethical questions raised by proposals include costs and materials to be used.

Oral Presentations

In giving an oral presentation, you have the complete attention of your audience. People are listening to you as an expert on the subject, and this face-to-face situation elicits trust between presenter and audience members. Whereas a printed document leaves the writer "invisible," oral presentations create an intimate atmosphere between speaker and listener. In a position of relative power, the speaker can convey accurate information in a fair and balanced manner or can use this trust to manipulate the audience by stirring up emotions without warrant. For example, if your purpose is to present technical background on a proposed waste incinerator in your community, you should offer the facts as best you can, rather than playing to the audience's confusion or naiveté.

Responding to Ethical Situations

To ensure that your communication is ethical, consider the reasonable criteria discussed earlier and shown in Figure 9.1. In addition, many professional organizations have created their own codes of ethics for the particular situations that people in those professions face. For example, in Ontario, engineers follow the code of ethics set out by Professional Engineers Ontario (PEO), while nurses follow the Canadian Nurses Association (CNA) code of ethics. While there is no standardized code of conduct in Canada for technical communicators, many practitioners follow the ethical code set out by the Society for Technical Communication. Figure 9.4 presents the ethics code of the STC.

Checklist for Ethical Communication

Accuracy
- Have I explored all sides of the issue and all possible alternatives?
- Do I provide enough information and interpretation for recipients to understand the facts as I know them?
- Do I avoid exaggeration, understatement, sugar-coating, or any distortion or omission that leaves recipients at a disadvantage?
- Do I state the case clearly, instead of hiding behind jargon and generalities?

Honesty
- Do I make a clear distinction between what is certain and what is probable?
- Are my information sources valid, reliable, and relatively unbiased?
- Do I actually believe what I'm saying, instead of being a mouthpiece for groupthink or advancing some hidden agenda?
- Would I still advocate this position if I were held publicly accountable for it?
- Do I inform people of the consequences or risks (as I am able to predict) of what I am advocating?
- Do I give candid feedback or criticism, if it is warranted?

Figure 9.4   **Ethical Guidelines for Technical Communication.**
Source: Reprinted with permission from the Society for Technical Communication, Arlington, VA.

Fairness

- Am I reasonably sure this document will not harm innocent persons or damage their reputations?
- Am I respecting all legitimate rights to privacy and confidentiality?
- Am I distributing copies of this document to every person who has the right to know about it?
- Do I credit all contributors and sources of ideas and information?

Sources: Brownell and Fitzgerald (1992), p. 18; Bryan (1992), p. 87; Johannesen (1983), pp. 21–22; Larson (1995), p. 39; Unger (1982), pp. 39–46; Yoos (1979), pp. 50–55.

Exercises

1. Find the professional code of ethics for your major or career. Divide into groups of three or four students, each of whom has a different major. Compare your professional codes, noting similarities and differences. Discuss why each code seems appropriate for that profession.

2. **FOCUS ON WRITING.** One of your company's vice presidents has asked you to help the company develop an updated code of ethics. Developing the official code of ethics will require months of research and collaboration with attorneys, consultants, editors, managers, and other stakeholders. In the meantime, the V.P. has asked you to develop a brief but practical guide for ethical communication that will serve as a practical reference for all employees until the final code of ethics has been approved. It will also lay out the key components to be included in the official code.

   Using the material in this chapter and the web resources listed here, prepare a two-page memo to outline your brief guide to ethical communication. Your purpose is to explain clearly how to avoid major ethical pitfalls in corporate communication.

   - **www.apegs.sk.ca**
     Monthly publications, statistics, feature stories, and legal information for the Association of Professional Engineers and Geoscientists of Saskatchewan.
   - **www.engineering.com/Library/ArticlesPage/tabid/85/articleType/ CategoryView/categoryId/7/Ethics-Case-Studies.aspx**
     Case studies in engineering ethics from the Engineering.com website.
   - **www.professionalethics.ca/cdn.html**
     Links to ethical information on professional groups such as the Canadian Medical Association (CMA) and the Institute of Electrical and Electronics Engineers, Canada (IEEE), as well as international ethics, compiled by philosopher-ethicist Chris MacDonald.

3. In groups of two or three, locate a piece of technical communication (or use one provided by your instructor) and evaluate its ethical stance. Is the information presented in such a way that ideas or facts are exaggerated or suppressed? Are any cultural issues exploited? Share your thoughts in class and explain how your team would revise the information.

4. Write a memo comparing two websites that represent opposite sides of a controversial issue, and focus on the word choice and the evidence used, such as statistics, academic research, and visual design, to convince the reader of a particular point of view. Make sure you find groups that represent opposing stances; for example, People for the Ethical Treatment of Animals (www.peta.org) and Canada Beef Inc. (http://canadianbeef.info). In your memo, discuss the ethical implications of each website's communication strategy.

The Collaboration Window

In groups of two or three, locate another piece of technical communication, but this time actively search for one that seems to take an ethical stance in how it presents its information. If you can, contact the author or one of the writers of this piece and ask how this person made his or her decisions. If you cannot contact the author, speculate on the organizational dynamics, legal issues, and personal choices this person made. How would members of your team go about making the same decisions?

The Global Window

FOCUS ON RESEARCH.
Counterfeiting, sometimes known as "intellectual property piracy," has become a major point of tension between Canada and many developing nations. Counterfeit products ranging from computer chips and pharmaceuticals to cigarettes and cell phones now flood markets in Asia and South America, and many may even be found on the streets of Toronto and other Canadian cities.

Beginning with the web resources listed here, do some research to learn more about the problems of counterfeit products. What are the advantages and disadvantages, both economically and politically, of trying to crack down on unauthorized copycat products? Why do some countries do little to police such piracy while others, including Canada, view it as a major priority?

Write a brief report to analyze the ethical, economic, and political issues that influence the global debate on counterfeiting, and present your findings in a brief oral presentation to your class.

- **http://newswire.ca/en/releases/archive/December2010/01/c9137.html**
  An article on how to avoid purchasing counterfeit items from online marketplaces.

- **http://cacn.ca**
  The Canadian Anti-Counterfeiting Network's webpage includes case studies, links, and frequently updated news.

- **www.bloomberg.com/news/2011-05-05/ebay-lvmh-apple-septwolves-lime-wire-intellectual-property.html**
  An article on how businesses and industries are fighting back against counterfeiting.

MyCanadianTechCommLab

Go to MyCanadianTechCommLab at www.mycanadiantechcommlab.com for additional online exercises and problems.

CHAPTER 10

Copyright and Privacy

Chapter Objectives

By the end of this chapter you will be able to:

1. Differentiate between copyright, plagiarism, and patent or trademark law.

2. Determine what material is copyrighted and what is not, and how to find the copyright holder and acquire permission.

3. Understand the concept of privacy and how it works when applied to electronic resources.

Sri Raghu, Vancouver, British Columbia

Sri Raghu entered the field of technical writing after completing his bachelor's degree in Business Administration, majoring in Marketing and Computers. In order to understand technology better, he did a post-graduate diploma in Information Technology. He also completed a certification course in Business English Communication from the British Council and Cambridge University. "A decade ago, technical writing for the IT industry was an emerging career option and provided enormous growth potential for aspiring technical writers," says Sri.

He started his career working in two small German IT companies creating documentation for ERP and CRM solutions. He then moved to Infosys Technologies, a 70 000-person company with offices in 30 countries and employees of 40 nationalities. As part of Infosys, he created user documentation for enterprise applications, digital video solutions, and defence applications.

"It is important to develop good process knowledge, apart from language, technology, and domain expertise," says Sri, who achieved the Capability Maturity Model Level 5 (CMM 5) for his project. Sri is based in Vancouver and works as a documentation consultant providing technical writing, process consulting, and content management system (CMS) implementation services for IT companies.

Why Technical Communicators Need to Understand Copyright and Privacy

Technical communicators rarely create every word, image, or sound from scratch. Often just the right diagram, image, sound, or wording can be found in some other material. You have probably had this experience when preparing a project for a class or for work. You begin researching on the web and find the perfect piece of clip art. Or you are looking through a trade magazine or newspaper, and there it is—exactly the right chart for the "implications" section of your report. Or maybe you need a diagram for an upcoming presentation, and you find one in a book. Can you use these materials without permission? What if you scan the image into your computer and modify it first? What if the project is strictly for school? Didn't you hear somewhere that use of material for educational purposes requires no permission? What if the project is for your company? These are copyright issues and should make you pause before you copy.

Along with copyright concerns, privacy is an issue for technical communicators. If you are working on a project that involves a website, you may face the decision of whether to collect personal information from site visitors. Can you collect this information and use it legally without permission? If you are writing a manual, are you allowed to use demographic data about the organization's customers?

Many organizations have legal departments to help you answer these questions. However, if you are a student or a freelance communication consultant or are rushing through a project without time to seek advice, you need to know the basics. It's especially important to understand copyright and privacy in the age of electronic technologies. Although such concerns existed before the web, they are heightened by the speed and power of these new technologies. Technical communicators are prime users of these technologies and must be aware of not only the technical aspects but also the legal ones.

SECTION ONE: COPYRIGHT

Copyright—An Overview

"Copyright law," says one expert, "is essentially a system of property." However, unlike physical property (such as your car, your home, or your land), "the province of copyright is communication" (Strong, 1993, p. 1). In other words, copyright is the legal system that gives owners rights over their communication products. These products can include books, musical recordings, photographs, drawings, letters, and memos. Any time an idea can be fixed in a tangible medium, that communication product can be copyrighted.

Copyright law originated in England in part to protect the printing trade. The Canadian government established copyright because, if properly enforced, it can enhance and expand "the creation and availability of knowledge" (Gervais, 2005, p. 318). Authors and other creators have an incentive to create new works, such as a new novel or a piece of music, because they know that for a limited time, they will own the copyright to their work and others will be legally prohibited from copying it. When the copyright expires, the work enters the *public domain* (more on this later in the chapter). Public domain material is accessible to everyone. This access to information is important in a democracy.

Remember that you can't copyright ideas, just expressions of ideas. According to Digital Copyright Canada, "The fact is that Copyright only applies to the presentation of ideas, not the ideas themselves.... The intent of Copyright is to encourage the creation of works so as to enrich society as a whole. Copyright law recognises that works are not created in a vacuum but rather they draw on ideas from other works" (Digital Copyright Canada, 2008).

Naturally, the lines can get a bit blurry, and courts often determine the details of a case. But in general, the thing to remember is that you copyright the expression of an idea when the expression becomes fixed in a tangible medium. For example, if you have an idea for a diagram of the brain and you create an original diagram (by hand or with a drawing program such as Adobe Illustrator), you hold the copyright to this diagram but not to the idea of the structure of the human brain or other diagrams of the brain.

How Copyright Infringement Differs from Plagiarism

Although copyright infringement and plagiarism are frequently confused, they are not the same. You can plagiarize someone else's work without actually infringing on the copyright. Plagiarism (representing the words, ideas, or perspectives of someone else as your own) is primarily an ethical issue, whereas copyright infringement is a legal and economic issue. (For more on plagiarism, see Chapter 9.)

How Copyright Law Differs from Patent or Trademark Law

Copyright law is part of a broader set of laws that deal with *intellectual property*. Intellectual property is the ownership of creative expressions, inventions, and designs. Copyright is the arm of intellectual property law designed to deal with creative works. The two other types of intellectual property law, that are not discussed at length in this book, may interest you at some point in your career.

Patent Law. Patent law governs mechanical inventions, machines, and processes. In many engineering and science organizations, as well as research universities, patent specialists make sure that a new invention or process is filed with the patent office.

Trademark Law. Trademark law governs icons, symbols, and slogans. Organizations file for trademark to protect their unique logos, such as the Coca-Cola name or symbol or the Nike "swoosh." The label ™ is used to indicate trademark.

How Individuals and Companies Establish Copyright

People establish copyright by first creating an original expression of an idea: a brochure, novel, poem, photograph, diagram, or other tangible work. Since the enactment of Canada's copyright in 1924 and the numerous modifications since then, the law states that anything you create is automatically copyrighted the moment the item becomes fixed in a tangible medium. In other words, the moment you type, write on paper, photograph, draw, or record something, you (or your company) automatically own the copyright.

You can help remind people of the copyright by adding this information somewhere on the product itself:

© 2011 Daniel P. Olsen

© 2011 Central Geology Corporation

To gain full legal protection, you can register the material with the Canadian Intellectual Copyright Office. Should you or your company need to sue for copyright infringement, this registration provides extra evidence.

Even if an author does not add the © symbol, the work is automatically copyrighted. In other words, nearly everything you see in print or on the computer is copyrighted.

What Rights a Copyright Holder Can Claim

Only the copyright holder has the right to reproduce the material, create a derivative work, distribute the work, or display or conduct a public performance of the work. The copyright holder can give permission—limited or full—for others to use the work. So, for example, if you were interested in using the drawing of an anti-collision light power supply presented in Figure 10.1, you would need to contact the copyright holder, in this case, the Society for Technical Communication (STC). The drawing was reproduced from the front cover of an issue of the STC's journal.

When You Can and Cannot Use Copyrighted Material

All original works are copyrighted once they are fixed in a tangible medium. Any time you download, copy, scan, or otherwise reproduce an item, you may be infringing on someone's copyright. Whether or not you knew the item was copyrighted is immaterial.

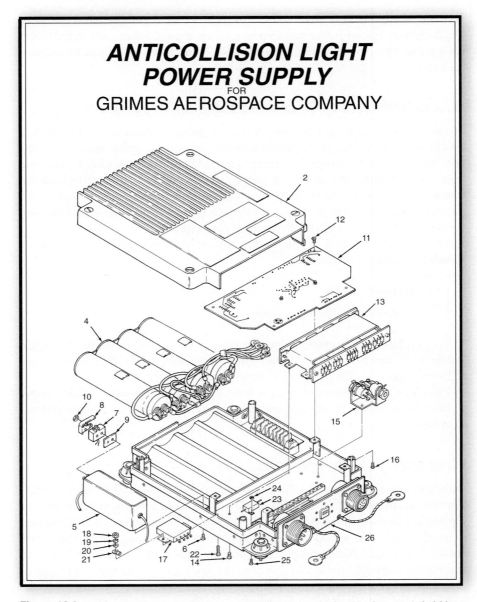

Figure 10.1 **A Diagram Protected by Copyright.** The copyright for this diagram is held by the Society for Technical Communication.
Source: Reprinted with permission from the Society for Technical Communication, Arlington, VA.

You can use a copyrighted work without infringing if you obtain permission from the copyright holder. The holder might grant limited permission—for example, to use the material one time in one publication only—or might grant unlimited rights.

You can also use material without permission when the materials are in the *public domain*. Copyright holders can place their materials in the public domain; if they do not do so, all materials will eventually become public after the term of protection has expired. It is common on the web, for example, to find websites labelled "Public Domain Clip Art Files." These images are no longer copyrighted by the original owners. In Canada, the copyright on print material expires 50 years after the death of the author, measured from the end of the current year. The copyright on photographs begins at the end of the year the photograph was taken, and ends 50 years later. For the complete *Canadian Copyright Act*, go to http://laws-lois.justice.gc.ca/eng/acts/C-42/FullText.html.

Note: In Canada, government publications cannot be adapted or translated without permission from the Crown Copyright & Licensing division, but they can be reproduced. For more information on these regulations, go to http://publications.gc.ca/site/eng/ccl/aboutCrownCopyright.html#permission_not_required.

Fair Use Doctrine. An important but sometimes overlooked legal right to use copyrighted material without seeking permission is the doctrine of *fair use*. Copyright was never intended to be a one-sided policy favouring only copyright holders. The Government of Canada established copyright as a balance between the rights of copyright holders and the needs of the public. On the one hand, authors, artists, and other creators need incentives to produce their works. Because they hold the rights to their works for a limited time, they gain financially from their efforts. But if copyright holders were allowed total control of their materials, the public would have very limited sources of information.

So the government established the doctrine of fair use as a way to balance creators' rights with public access. Fair use states that under certain conditions, it is fair and legal to use copyrighted works without obtaining the copyright holder's permission, as long as the source is clearly identified. Courts ask four questions to establish whether a use is fair (see Figure 10.2). They tend to look favourably on cases in which

- material is being used in an educational setting;
- material has been published;
- only a small part of the material is being used; and
- use of the material will not affect the market value of the original.

For this reason, classroom use has generally been considered fair. Instructors and students rarely require permission to use material in a school project (but they must acknowledge the source, otherwise they are engaging in plagiarism). However, if you are a consultant or an employee of a for-profit organization, the fair use doctrine may not apply.

Recently, copyright's balancing act has tipped toward the copyright holder. For example, if you go to the library or a copy shop to make copies, you may see an ominous warning sign above the machine. These signs rarely mention fair use. Many products, such as software, come with strictly worded statements

- **What is the *purpose* of the use?**

  Commercial or educational? If commercial (and thus for profit), courts will view it less favourably than if your use is strictly educational.

- **What is the *publication status* of the material?**

  If the material has been published, it will be viewed more favourably than if it has not been published. For example, your use is more likely to be considered fair if it is from a published magazine rather than from a series of unpublished letters.

- ***How much* are you using?**

  If you are using only a small part of a text or work, this use will be viewed more favourably than if you are reproducing a large part or the entire work.

- **What will be the *economic impact* of your use on the original work's owner?**

  If your use of the work will not damage the potential market of the original, this use will be viewed more favourably than if it would cause damage.

Figure 10.2 Guidelines for Determining Fair Use of Copyrighted Material.
Source: Adapted from Patry (1985), p. vii.

about what will happen if you make a copy. But these statements never mention that under the fair use doctrine, you have a legal right to make copies under certain conditions.

When Your Company Owns the Material

When you create technical communications as an employee—from manuals to standard operating procedures to webpages—you are creating copyrightable material. Don't think, however, that *you* own the copyright. Under what is called the *works-for-hire doctrine,* companies in most circumstances automatically own the copyright to all materials created by their full-time employees. If you are a consultant instead of a full-time employee, the company may ask you to sign a contract stating that you will automatically give it the rights to products that you produce for them. For example, if you are doing freelance writing for a nursing magazine, the publisher will probably ask you to sign your rights for that story over to the corporation that owns the magazine.

Documenting Your Sources

Even if you receive permission to use someone else's ideas or material or if your use qualifies as fair use, you must document the source of this material. You can document your sources by including an in-text reference, a caption, or a statement (if you use the material during an oral presentation). For instance, if you use some copyright-free clip art in a paper for school, you don't need permission, but you should still credit the artist or company by adding a caption that includes the name of the artist or company and the location where you found the material. For more on documenting sources, see Appendix B.

Electronic Technologies and Copyright

Copyright law is at a crossroads. The laws governing copyright are very clear: all items fixed in a tangible medium are copyrighted and you need to request permission to use these items unless they are in the public domain or meet requirements for fair use. Yet current technology encourages just the opposite. Copying, scanning, making transparencies, downloading and sharing files—all these tasks that technology has made easy, both in the workplace and on the internet, are potential violations of someone else's copyright.

As a technical communicator, you will be increasingly surrounded by technology that invites you to take files, clip art, images, sounds, and other tangible works and use them in your own material. Beware of this temptation. The laws governing copyright are under considerable debate, with some people claiming that these laws are no longer relevant, given today's technology. But until this debate is settled, the law still holds.

Photocopiers and Scanners

Copiers were one of the first technologies to raise serious questions about how to work with copyright in an electronic age. Most copy shops have reacted conservatively, in part due to lawsuits that accused them of violating copyright by making copies of articles and publishing these as student coursepacks. For this reason, you often see strongly worded copyright warnings posted above photocopiers.

Copying something without the copyright holder's permission is often an infringement. But remember that the fair use doctrine allows you to make copies for educational purposes. Even in a workplace setting, if you make some copies to distribute at a meeting, you are exercising the educational aspect of fair use. But if you wanted to make a copy of a diagram or illustration for use in your company's annual report, you would need the copyright holder's permission. In 2004, the Supreme Court of Canada ruled that the Law Society of Upper Canada was not infringing on copyright laws by photocopying court decisions and other legal resources, citing that "research must be given a large and liberal interpretation in order to ensure that users' rights are not unduly constrained" and this "is not limited to non-commercial or private contexts" (Canada News Wire, 2008, p. 1).

The same guidelines apply to scanners. Scanning an image is a violation of copyright unless your use qualifies as fair (see Figure 10.2) or you have permission. However, scanners and image software (such as Adobe Photoshop) allow you to take the scanned image and manipulate it, often to the extent that no one would ever recognize it as the original. Is this a copyright violation? It could be. But what if no one can tell? This becomes a question not just of law but also of your own ethical standards, as discussed in Chapter 9.

The Web as a Marketplace of Ideas and Information

The web is often billed as an information marketplace and, indeed, you can find endless images, sounds, information, and photographs on almost any topic by searching a few websites. The web is part of the internet, and the internet has always been based on the idea of open information. In the early 1980s, when the internet was still young, researchers and students used the technology to share ideas. The web continues this tradition. On almost any website, you can click on "download source" and obtain the HTML source code for that webpage. You can also obtain the graphics, logos, diagrams, images, and more with a few simple clicks.

But this technology thus encourages people to take copyrighted material without ever considering the original work's legal status. In fact, observers have speculated that the internet might spell the death of copyright law as we know it. However, what seems to be happening right now is that copyright law is being reconsidered—and sometimes strengthened—in light of this technology. So even though the web might encourage certain behaviour, it is still a good idea to keep copyright law in mind when you use material from the internet.

Using Material from the Internet

Perhaps you have located a bar chart on the web that you'd like to use in your report. It is technically very easy to cut and paste or download the bar chart and insert it in your document. But is it legal? You notice that the chart has no copyright symbol (©). But remember—all expressions fixed in a tangible medium are copyrighted. The © symbol is not necessary. Therefore, downloading the chart and using it in your document could be a copyright infringement. You should first consider whether your use is covered by the fair use doctrine (see Figure 10.2). Is your report for commercial or educational purposes? Has the material already been published? (Webpages count as publishing.) How much of the material will you use, and how will your use affect the original? If in doubt, ask permission.

But what if instead of using the bar chart in your printed report, you create a link to it from your company's webpage? Is providing a link to another site equivalent to copying or reproducing that site? This and similar questions related to internet technologies are hard to answer. If you're worried about a possible lawsuit, check with an attorney who specializes in intellectual property.

Locating Copyright-Free Art

You can safely use copyright-free images, sounds, graphics, or photographs, and many websites offer such items. Although these items were copyrighted at one time, either the copyright holder decided to place the materials in the public domain or the copyright has expired. The internet encourages this kind of sharing, and you can often find exactly what you need on a copyright-free page. Usually, the author or owner will ask that you credit the source, and you should honour this request. For example, if you use a copyright-free text from the University of Toronto Libraries' Book Online webpage, you would add the following phrase:

> Copyright-free text from University of Toronto Libraries' Book Online database, http://link.library.utoronto.ca/booksonline

or something similar. Often the owner will ask you to use a particular phrase.

Email and Electronic Messages

Remember the recent email message you received from a classmate, your boss, or your mother? That message is copyrighted by the person who created it. So if you forwarded this message to a friend, technically, you have infringed on the owner's copyright. The same is true for a posting to a listserv, bulletin board, or other electronic discussion site.

Copyright law will probably bend at some point to accommodate this use of technology. However, if you wish to use an email message or list posting as part of a project, particularly a research or company project that will receive wide distribution, ask the copyright holder's permission (unless your use complies with the fair use doctrine as explained in Figure 10.2).

The posting of an email message beyond where the original author intended to post it also raises privacy concerns, which are addressed in the next section.

CD-ROMs and Multimedia

The more media you work with, the harder the questions about copyright and intellectual property become. If your company plans to produce a CD to accompany a new product, that CD may combine images, music, film clips, and text. Each item will require careful checking to ensure that the proper legal issues have been addressed. Working with multimedia creates a labyrinth of complex legal issues that require close consultation with an intellectual property attorney.

For more information about copyright, see the Canadian Intellectual Property Office website at cipo.ic.gc.ca and the Canadian Copyright Licensing Agency at accesscopyright.ca.

SECTION TWO: PRIVACY

Privacy—An Overview

Like copyright, privacy is a concept people may not consider until it is too late. For example, new technologies make it easier to accumulate data about consumers, and until those data are misused, people rarely stop to think about how much of their personal information resides in numerous databases.

Privacy is a legal concept. According to the Canadian Charter of Rights and Freedoms, under Section 8, every Canadian is protected against an unlawful search and seizure. This is just one interpretation of the idea of privacy. The rapid expansion of electronic communication and copying devices is now spreading concerns about abuse of a different type of privacy—privacy related to information. For this reason, the Canadian government has taken steps to protect privacy with regards to electronic communication.

Computer Technologies, Privacy, and Technical Communication

Canada's detailed privacy legislation governing information privacy is called the *Personal Information Protection and Electronic Documents Act* (PIPEDA). As an updated version of the 1995 Canadian Standards Association Model Code for the Protection of Personal Information, PIPEDA was designed to define and cover all areas of privacy affected by modern technology.

Since PIPEDA became law in 2001, it has expanded to include the health and commercial sectors, and the legislation in some provinces (such as Quebec, British Columbia, and Alberta) is also sector-specific. PIPEDA conforms to the European Union's requirements for privacy. However, it does not conform to privacy law in the United States. The Office of the Privacy Commissioner has ruled that PIPEDA has no jurisdiction over the personal information of Canadians collected by organizations located outside of Canada. This means that American databases can collect information about Canadians.

Although PIPEDA has been in effect for years now, it faces constant scrutiny from organizations such as the Canadian Internet Policy and Public Interest Clinic (CIPPIC) to keep up with the changes within the technological and business communication fields. As Jennifer Stoddart, the Privacy Commissioner of Canada, notes, "[A decade ago], the Information Highway was a catchphrase; now it is a reality. The trickle of personal information crossing borders has become a torrent. Meanwhile, emerging technologies such as location tracking devices are raising new risks for privacy" (2007).

Technical communicators must have a good understanding of PIPEDA. It requires organizations that collect individuals' personal information to obtain consent to collect, use, or disclose their information to others. The Act defines personal information as "information about an *identifiable* individual, but does not include the name, title or business address or telephone number of an employee of an organization" (emphasis added). This definition is important for technical communicators or organizations that transfer information to a third party for processing. The organization that had the original consent for the collection, use, and disclosure of the information continues to bear responsibility for protecting the privacy of that information while in the hands of the third party.

For example, if a Canadian university or college sends information about a student to another Canadian post-secondary institution, the originating school is required to protect the information while the information is in the hands of the other school. The protection could be as simple as including a confidentiality statement on the student's file or providing provisions that limit the third party's use or disclosure of the information.

Technical communicators are often at the forefront of such privacy issues, because they are involved in designing manuals, software interfaces, webpages that collect personal data, video training tapes, and other products that require the use of personal data or images.

Privacy in the United States. Although U.S. citizens frequently talk about their right to privacy, this right is not actually stated in the U.S. Constitution. American privacy law is based on court cases, state law, some federal laws, and constitutional issues, such as the Fourth Amendment ban against search and seizure. In many respects, the rights of Americans to personal privacy are considerably less than privacy rights of Canadians and Europeans.

In October 2001, in response to the terrorist attacks of September 11, 2001, the U.S. Congress passed the *Patriot Act*, a far-reaching set of laws that allowed the government wide access to information about citizens. In general, it gave the government the right to seize or subpoena electronic information from companies and public institutions, including private information about private citizens. By 2006, the Act was reauthorized to give government officials the same tools and resources to fight terrorism that they can use against criminals.

However, despite the U.S. government's claim that the Act has stopped terrorists from attacking America, critics state that the civil liberties of citizens have been weakened. Specifically, the Act allows the FBI and government officials to eavesdrop on emails, telephone calls, and business and personal communications without a court order. Many critics also point out that the Act can be used for "sneak and peek" warrants for crimes other than suspected acts of terrorism. They maintain that the enhanced information-sharing system created from information collected by the FBI could lead to a database of information on citizens who were not the subject of any criminal investigation.

The *Patriot Act* also has implications for Canadian technical writers. Many Canadian companies outsource their information and communication services to U.S. companies. Once information is transferred to the United States, it immediately becomes subject to American laws. Thus, the U.S. government could require those companies to hand over personal information about Canadian citizens.

According to Canada's Privacy Commissioner, companies that outsource information for processing to the U.S. should inform their customers or clients that their information may be available to the U.S. government or its agencies under a lawful order made in that country. This practice would allow Canadians to choose whether to deal with companies that outsource information to U.S. companies. However, this practice is not law in Canada. Lawyers Wendy Gross and Michelle Kisluk warn that "such an approach could become a logistical nightmare for the organization if clients permit the organization to provide them with services, but refuse to allow... certain pieces of their personal information to be disclosed to U.S.-linked companies" (2005).

Privacy in Cyberspace

Webpages can raise important privacy concerns. If you are part of a technical communication team designing a company website, you will need to answer certain specific questions related to the privacy of those who visit your site. Many business-related websites post a separate page that explains how the company handles the private information of customers and visitors. This practice helps reduce fears about using the internet for business.

Shopping Online

A study by Statistics Canada reported that Canadians spent $15.1 billion on online purchases in 2009, up from $12.8 billion in 2007 (Statistics Canada, 2010a). Online shopping has become a regular part of life around the globe. Most large stores have both online and physical sites, and many stores, such as Amazon.ca, are completely online. As a technical communicator, you could be involved in projects that require you to work on e-commerce sites, and you will need to make judgments about the usability, privacy, and safety issues associated with these sites. Your end users may have the following questions about your sites.

Is Online Shopping Safe? One question users often have is whether online shopping is safe. Many technical methods are used to ensure data privacy, but to the end user, these methods may not be clear or understandable. Concepts such as "data encryption" do not make sense to the average online shopper. But security icons, such as a padlock in the locked position (normally in the lower right-hand corner of the screen), provide a visual cue for the user. Online financial sites such as Collective Point of Sale Solutions (see Figure 10.3) also provide secure methods and do so in ways that are understandable to users. Despite assurances from companies that it is safe to use credit cards for online shopping, a survey by VISA Canada showed that 94 percent of Canadians polled believed that using a credit or debit card in-store is safe, while only 63 percent believe the same about online shopping (Thomas, 2011).

Is Online Shopping Private?   When you help create a webpage, you need to decide if this page will automatically collect information about the users who connect to it. Your team or company may wish to do this, but you should think

Figure 10.3 Collective Point of Sale Solutions Ltd. Collective P.O.S. is one of a number of web-based services that provides merchants with secure ways to exchange funds and shop online. *Source:* www.collectivepos.com. These materials have been reproduced with the permission of Collective Point of Sale Solutions Ltd. Copyright 2011 Collective Point of Sale Solutions Ltd. All rights reserved.

about having an overall privacy policy for the website. In Canada, companies place such privacy statements as links on their websites, as in the example in Figure 10.4. Such a statement lets users know how their information will be used and what choices they have, including information on whether the site uses cookies. As a technical communicator, you may be asked to help write such a privacy statement. Privacy statements, outlining the company's approach to consumer privacy, should be readily available on the website and should be written in plain language, not legalese.

Global Privacy Issues

The web has made it difficult for Canadian companies to ignore international issues. When you create a webpage and place it on the internet, almost anyone from anywhere in the world can access the page. Despite countless benefits, this

Figure 10.4 **A Privacy Statement from the MyPictureBook Website.**
Source: Courtesy of MyPictureBook.

broad reach across international borders also raises concerns about privacy. Different countries and regions have different laws, viewpoints, and practices about issues that a Canadian web developer might take for granted. Privacy is one of these issues.

In Canada, collecting personal data is common practice. When you shop for groceries, you may use a scannable card to collect store points or travel points. This loyalty card is not there to save you money or send you on a vacation: it allows the store or card-issuing company to collect information about the types and brands of items you purchase. Card companies often sell this information to other companies. For example, if you regularly buy a certain brand of cat food, the card company may sell your name, and the names of others like you, to marketers who sell pet items.

The same scenario is true for most Canadian direct mailing services. If you make purchases through a catalogue, that company is allowed to sell your name and address to other companies unless you have requested otherwise. As most of us know, this process can generate lots of junk mail. The same process is now in full swing on the web. Each time you enter personal information on a website when making a purchase, chances are that unless stated clearly otherwise on the website, your name, address, and record of visits to that website will be used for marketing purposes and possibly sold to other companies. Cookies and other web technologies simplify this sort of data collection.

In Canada, some information is open to all companies that wish to buy it, while other information (such as a criminal record) is accessible only to law enforcement, except in extenuating circumstances. You can refuse to give your personal information or ask to have it removed from a mailing list. You can also file your name with a special service that will attempt to take your name off most mailing lists (but the process is never perfect). And under certain laws, especially when your credit history is involved, you have a legal right to correct misinformation. But the burden is on you to take action.

In Europe, however, companies are not allowed to collect information without your permission. They must also provide a clear mechanism for you to change or remove your information. The European Union's *Data Privacy Act* turned this policy into law. Anyone doing business with a country in the European Union must follow this law. However, with the introduction of PIPEDA, Canadian privacy laws can now assure the European Union that the personal information of European citizens will be protected by Canadian organizations.

In short, the laws and habits of Canadian citizens are not always appropriate guidelines for designing webpages with a global reach. To accommodate non-Canadian visitors to your website, work with the company's lawyer or with colleagues in marketing or international sales. Consider formulating a specific privacy policy for your company websites.

Privacy and Documentation

Technical communication and privacy also intersect in documentation. When you prepare manuals, quick reference cards, brochures, and help screens, you may want to include testimonies from customers or examples of how customers use the product. But before you can use such information, you need written permission from the individual customers or companies involved. The same is true if you use any photographs of customers using your product. Although you or your company may hold the copyright to such items, you still need to ask permission so that you are not violating the individual's or company's right to privacy.

Privacy and Videotapes

Technical communicators are often involved in the preparation of training tapes. These tapes are used by company trainers, marketing and sales staff, or customers to help people learn to use a new product or service. For example, if you work for a company that makes gardening equipment, your company may create both a manual and a training video to accompany a Rototiller. Customers could read the manual or watch the video to learn how to operate and maintain their new machine.

As part of the training video, you may wish to use footage taken when your marketing team was out visiting customers. Or you may have other footage of employees in the company using the equipment. Even though your company may own the copyright to this material, it is still important to obtain permission from the people in the video (employees or customers) to use the footage in a training video.

Checklist for Copyright and Privacy

Using Copyrighted Work

- Does your use of this material explicitly meet all fair use criteria?
- If you do not meet fair use criteria, do you have the owner's written permission to use this material?
- As an employee, are you aware that your company owns any work you produce for your employer?
- Have you clearly documented all sources, regardless of whether you have received permission or have met fair use criteria?
- Have you received permission to use any material electronically, including email?
- When in doubt, have you obtained legal counsel?

Respecting Privacy

- Are you aware of the privacy implications of the specific product you're working on?
- Have you obtained permission to use a person's image or personal quotation in any type of document or video?

- For electronic collection of personal data, have you considered the legal issues involved? Are you aware how PIPEDA affects your decisions?
- Are you vigilant in protecting your company's trade secrets and other proprietary information?
- When in doubt, have you obtained legal counsel?

Exercises

1. Interview a professional in your field to determine how copyright law affects his or her work and company. Consult with the company's legal department if possible. Report your findings in a memo to your instructor.

2. In groups of two or three, discuss two possible situations in which someone else's material might be used for a new purpose—for example, a diagram from a magazine could be scanned and used in a brochure. Given the details of the situations you describe, decide if the material is being used according to fair use guidelines.

3. **FOCUS ON WRITING**. Technical communicators can now find many sources of graphics, sounds, and photographs on the web. But which ones can be reproduced and which cannot? How do you know when you need permission to use an image or graphic in a brochure or on a website? And how do you go about requesting such permission?

   For the first part of this assignment, use a search engine to locate sources of images and graphics on the web, beginning with the websites listed here. Explore these sites to determine which offer copyright-free images and which do not. Compile a list of your findings and create a handout (or a website) to share this list with your class.

   Second, develop a set of guidelines based on information you find on the sites listed here. These guidelines should explain how to assess whether or not a particular image requires permission to be reproduced. Share these guidelines with your class and discuss how to use images and documents found on the web while respecting the copyrights and intellectual property of others.

   - **www.pbase.ca**
     Canada Stock Photos, a webpage that contains hundreds of photos of various subjects.

- **www.clip-art.com**
  Links to dozens of sources for clip art and animation files.

- **www.cpsr.org**
  Homepage of Computer Professionals for Social Responsibility.

- **www.cipo.ic.gc.ca**
  Homepage of the Canadian Intellectual Property Office.

The Collaboration Window

Form groups according to your major and plan a brochure (or some other form of technical communication) using copyrighted materials. Write up a process by which you would obtain the materials (public domain, request permission). Share your findings with the rest of the class.

The Global Window

Copyright and privacy are subject to the laws of a country or region. The internet and other technologies complicate matters because data can easily travel around the world without regard for borders. The World Intellectual Property Organization (WIPO) is an international group that considers the global implications of intellectual property issues. You can learn more about WIPO by visiting its website at www.wipo.org.

If you can, talk to a communication professional who deals with international audiences. Ask about any difficulties the person has encountered with copyright or privacy. Review the WIPO website with this professional and ask how the information on this site might affect the way she or he would write, design, and distribute a document.

MyCanadianTechCommLab

Go to MyCanadianTechCommLab at www.mycanadiantechcommlab.com for additional online exercises and problems.

Technical Communication Situations and Applications

CHAPTER 11
Everyday Written Communication Situations 217

CHAPTER 12
Presentation Skills 253

CHAPTER 13
Product-Oriented Communication Situations 273

CHAPTER 14
Complex Communication Situations 304

Communication Situations

The four chapters in Part Two describe a variety of communication situations and include information about approaches and formats that are, in most cases, appropriate for these situations. Depending on your particular profession, company, and unique communication situation, these categories may not always be a perfect fit. Ultimately, all situations are unique, and your choices should be driven by a clear and thorough understanding of your audience, purpose, and the company or organization. For example, a situation that calls for a long report in one company might be handled by a memo or short report in another. One organization might produce all of its user documentation in printed books, while another might place all of this information on a website. And in some companies, email is the preferred method of communicating, while in others, a combination of email and paper memos is the norm.

Moreover, in actual workplace applications, the categories in these chapters usually overlap. As described here, they are meant to allow you to practice discrete forms of writing and communication: writing a definition or description, writing a memo, writing a set of brief instructions. But on the job, you may need to write a memo that contains some specifications and some description, or you may need to write a short report that contains some documentation and proposes a set of actions for the company to take.

Use these four chapters as opportunities to practice and explore. In class, discuss any experiences you may have had on the job or during an internship that differ from what you read in this book. Consider creating a class website that lists the most common communication situations you and your classmates encounter, and then list the types of documents you most frequently work on.

Here are the situations described in the next four chapters:

Everyday Situations. Some situations require correspondence that takes place on a regular basis in most organizations (such as email or memos).

Presentation Skills. Certain situations require you to present your ideas clearly to an audience using technology.

Product-Oriented Situations. Other situations require you to describe, explain, document, or market a technical product or service.

Complex Situations. Still other situations require more complex approaches, which may include long reports or proposals.

Each chapter ends with a set of exercises. The website for this textbook (www.mycanadiantechcommlab.com) contains links to sample documents online as well as exercises related to different document types.

No matter what the circumstance or the document, certain guidelines always apply:

- Perform a thorough audience and purpose analysis.
- Create your product with usability in mind.
- Carefully select a visual format and medium.
- Consider copyright issues.

CHAPTER 11

Everyday Written Communication Situations

Chapter Objectives

By the end of this chapter you will be able to:

1. Write an email or a memo using the appropriate language.

2. Know how to write a professional letter, résumé, and short report with the appropriate language and format.

Ursula McCloy, New Hamburg, Ontario

Ursula McCloy graduated from the University of Waterloo with a Master of Arts in English Literature, specializing in eighteenth-century novels and narrative theory. Although she originally intended to work as a writer, researcher, or program assistant in a museum environment, an acquaintance at a software company asked if she would take a short contract doing simple copy edits for a developers' reference guide, a job that she found challenging and that she enjoyed mastering despite having no technical background.

From there, her first full-time job at a software company turned into a permanent career. Initially the sole writer, she was responsible for each step in the documentation process: quoting, designing, implementation, and delivery. Eventually, she became involved in areas such as graphics, marketing, websites, user interface design, and quality assurance. As the staff grew, she took on a role training new writers and managing the team. Her motivation to work in this field comes from the opportunity to undertake a variety of different tasks and expand her skills beyond the traditional realm of documentation. "How could anyone get bored at their job, when every day there is a new chance to learn and grow and work on something new?"

Email

Email has become a major form of business and technical communication, surpassing much of what used to be accomplished with paper letters and memos. Unlike paper, email can be used to address, quickly and efficiently, an individual, a group within an organization, or a group of interested users from outside the organization. It can reach thousands of readers in a matter of seconds, and these readers can continue forwarding the email message to others. Diane Domeyer notes that email is used so frequently because it provides "historical context…, including the ability to maintain a record of conversations and obtain project updates from coworkers and business colleagues" (Cywinski, 2008). Although paper documents can be photocopied and redistributed, few people take the time to do so. But with email, all it takes is one or two simple keystrokes, and the message has been forwarded.

Email is extremely useful in situations where people are in different time zones or have different working schedules. You can send an email at 2:00 a.m. if you are a night owl, and your early-bird colleague can read it in the morning. Email is useful if you want an electronic paper trail to track the communication—useful for helping you remember details about a project and for legal reasons, too.

Audience and Purpose Analysis

Unlike paper documents, email does not provide you with much control over the final audience. You may intend for your note to reach only a small group of people, but because email is so easily forwarded, your audience could turn out to be much larger. People also tend to be more casual and off-the-cuff in an email, sometimes more so than they would be in person; therefore, audience consideration becomes crucial. Suppose, for example, that after a long week of work on a particularly tough engineering design project, you send a quick email message to another manager. In your message, you complain about one of the engineers not holding up his end of things. You quickly press "Send" and head out the door. On Monday, at a status meeting, you are surprised to find that your message was forwarded to several other engineers, and they're talking about it! Clearly, your original message was not intended for them, but either by accident or on purpose, someone forwarded it along.

So be sure you understand a cardinal rule about audience, purpose, and email: Always assume that your message will go far beyond its original recipient, and don't send anything via email that isn't appropriate for a wider audience or that would make you uncomfortable if used for a different purpose.

Types of Email

Email messages usually follow the same basic format as a memo with a memo-style heading (Subject, Date, From, To), but they often use salutations (Dear

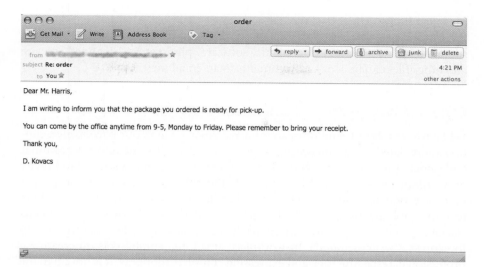

Figure 11.1 An Email Message.
Source: Thunderbird screenshot courtesy of Modzilla.

Laura) and closings (Thanks, Sam) like a letter. Email can be used for a variety of purposes and situations: to exchange information, share ideas, schedule meetings, and collaborate on work projects (see Figure 11.1).

Typical Components of Email

Most email messages have the following parts.

Header Information. This information includes the standard fields from a memo (Subject, Date, From, To). Also, depending on the email program, the header may include more detailed information, such as the following:

- *Host server:* The computer that generated the message
- *Time of receipt:* The exact time the computer received the message
- *Return path:* An email address the computer can use if the message bounces (fails to reach its destination)
- *Message ID number:* A number that the network uses to track the individual message.

The header also includes a list of other recipients who received the message as a courtesy copy ("cc").

Message Body. The text of the message.

Attachments. Formatted documents, software, photographs, scanned images, and other files can be sent as attachments to an email message.

Style and Netiquette of Workplace Email

When we write to a friend or in an informal environment, our emails often contain abbreviated words, misspellings, typos, and a lax attitude towards grammar and punctuation. There is often a highly informal tone and emphasis on brevity over completeness. Workplace email, on the other hand, should use proper grammar, punctuation, and spelling. Other items which should be avoided are text-style abbreviations like "LOL," "imho," and the like, as well as emoticons (facial expression pictorially represented by punctuation and letters, usually used to express a writer's mood). In workplace email, the emphasis is on creating a professional, respectful tone and expressing complete thoughts. It is not up to the reader to decipher an email message; rather, the central message and points must be clear, and to the point. An email that is too casual (for example using words like "cool" or "random" and emoticons) or is incomplete undermines the writer's professionalism and hurts his or her credibility.

Usability Considerations

Keep It Short. Readers are impatient and don't want to scroll down through long screens full of information. So keep email messages brief and to the point. If you need to, put larger related files of information on a webpage or use an attachment, which readers can read at their leisure.

Break Up the Information. Unbroken text is hard to read on the screen. So don't write one long block of text with no paragraph breaks. Keep paragraphs short, and use numbered lists, headings, and bullets to break up the message.

Include Links to Websites. Include links to other relevant websites when necessary, rather than including all the content.

Don't Send Huge Attachments Without Checking First. Not all email browsers are capable of handling attachments (formatted files, photos, images). Also, if recipients have slow internet connections or pay by the minute for their connection, they will be annoyed by large attachments that take forever to download. Before sending an attachment, ask what file types the recipient's equipment can handle and if his or her browser can accept attachments.

Pay Attention to Spelling and Formality. Email users lean toward an informal writing style. Even though many email programs contain spell-checkers, people rarely use them. Yet a correctly spelled message is more credible than a sloppy one. Also, when composing a message for someone you don't know or someone in a position of authority, begin with a formal salutation ("Dear Professor May").

Avoid Flaming. *Flaming* refers to email that is unnecessarily angry and makes extreme personal attacks. Because email users are not communicating face-to-face, they sometimes use email to let off steam. Always read over your message, especially in a tense or delicate situation, before sending it. Strive for messages that are informative and useful, not emotionally charged.

Don't Use All Caps. Words in all capital letters are hard to read. And in email, they have a special meaning: All caps is the equivalent of shouting. So don't shout unless you mean to.

Use Emoticons Sparingly. Smiley faces, made from a colon, dash, and right-hand parenthesis :-) or from downloaded icons, are used to convey humour. Use these and other emoticons infrequently, and don't use them in a formal message or in a message to someone you don't know.

Figure 11.2 shows a workplace email. The text is clear and concise, and the email conveys a professional tone. Figure 11.3 shows an email that ignores the usability considerations mentioned above. Although the writer and recipient are close friends as well as employee and supervisor, this email should never have been written in the workplace. Not only does the message have legal implications in terms of the writer's job performance and future with the company, but it also violates another employee's confidentiality. In addition, it is much too informal for a workplace document.

Checklist for Email

Netiquette

- Do you check and answer your email daily?
- Have you checked your distribution list before mailing, to verify that the message reaches only intended recipients?
- Do you avoid flaming?
- Have you chosen an alternative medium for any formal correspondence?
- Before sending a long attachment, have you checked with the recipient?

Ethical, Legal, and Interpersonal Implications

- Have you avoided writing anything you couldn't say face-to-face?
- Have you avoided humour and wisecracks?

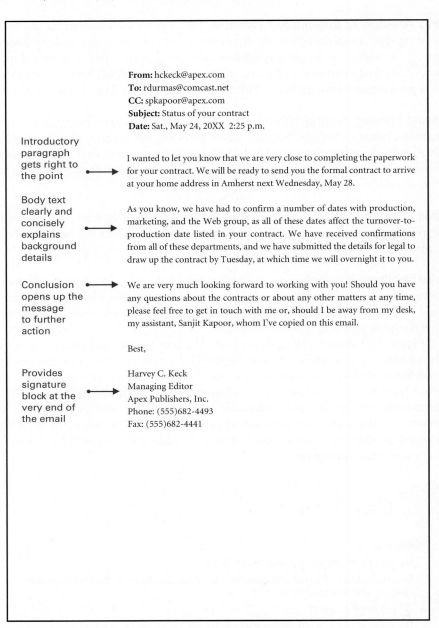

From: hckeck@apex.com
To: rdurmas@comcast.net
CC: spkapoor@apex.com
Subject: Status of your contract
Date: Sat., May 24, 20XX 2:25 p.m.

Introductory paragraph gets right to the point

I wanted to let you know that we are very close to completing the paperwork for your contract. We will be ready to send you the formal contract to arrive at your home address in Amherst next Wednesday, May 28.

Body text clearly and concisely explains background details

As you know, we have had to confirm a number of dates with production, marketing, and the Web group, as all of these dates affect the turnover-to-production date listed in your contract. We have received confirmations from all of these departments, and we have submitted the details for legal to draw up the contract by Tuesday, at which time we will overnight it to you.

Conclusion opens up the message to further action

We are very much looking forward to working with you! Should you have any questions about the contracts or about any other matters at any time, please feel free to get in touch with me or, should I be away from my desk, my assistant, Sanjit Kapoor, whom I've copied on this email.

Best,

Provides signature block at the very end of the email

Harvey C. Keck
Managing Editor
Apex Publishers, Inc.
Phone: (555)682-4493
Fax: (555)682-4441

Figure 11.2 A Workplace Email.
Source: Gurak and Lannon, *Strategies for Technical Communication in the Workplace* (2010).

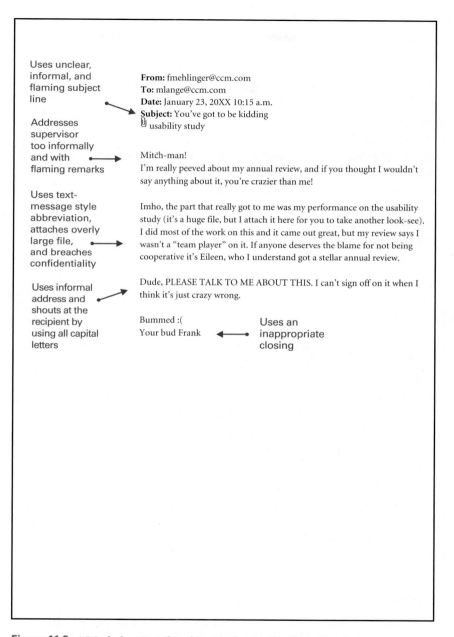

Uses unclear, informal, and flaming subject line

Addresses supervisor too informally and with flaming remarks

Uses text-message style abbreviation, attaches overly large file, and breaches confidentiality

Uses informal address and shouts at the recipient by using all capital letters

From: fmehlinger@ccm.com
To: mlange@ccm.com
Date: January 23, 20XX 10:15 a.m.
Subject: You've got to be kidding
📎 usability study

Mitch-man!
I'm really peeved about my annual review, and if you thought I wouldn't say anything about it, you're crazier than me!

Imho, the part that really got to me was my performance on the usability study (it's a huge file, but I attach it here for you to take another look-see). I did most of the work on this and it came out great, but my review says I wasn't a "team player" on it. If anyone deserves the blame for not being cooperative it's Eileen, who I understand got a stellar annual review.

Dude, PLEASE TALK TO ME ABOUT THIS. I can't sign off on it when I think it's just crazy wrong.

Bummed :(
Your bud Frank

Uses an inappropriate closing

Figure 11.3 A Workplace Email Lacking Professional Style and Netiquette.
Source: Gurak and Lannon, *Strategies for Technical Communication in the Workplace* (2010).

- Have you avoided using email for confidential information?
- Have you avoided using the workplace network for personal correspondence?
- Before forwarding an incoming message, have you obtained permission from the sender?

Readability
- Is there a clear subject line?
- Do you refer clearly to the message to which you are responding?
- Are sentences and paragraphs short?
- Do you avoid paragraph indentations and ALL CAPS?
- Are formal salutations and closings used, when appropriate?
- Are emoticons used sparingly?
- Have you included a signature section?
- Have you proofread carefully?

Memos

 People in almost every profession use memos to communicate business or technical information within the company, to outside vendors, to clients, or to other relevant parties. Today, the paper memo is rapidly being replaced by email. Even so, paper memos are often called for, especially if the situation is more formal or the discussion is somewhat lengthy. Use a memo when you need to:

- transmit information to a group
- make a short evaluation or recommendation
- distribute minutes from a meeting
- provide follow-up on a discussion

Different organizations have different standards and practices for memos. For example, at some companies, memos are used only to convey formal information and are always written on letterhead. Other, less formal information is sent via email.

Audience and Purpose Analysis

To determine the length, content, tone, and approach of a memo, pay attention to the various audience members who will receive it. Some companies use standard memo distribution lists: a list for all managers, a list for all software developers, and so on. The purpose of your memo should be clear: Is it to inform your audience? To persuade people? To convince them to take action? The organization and writing style of the memo should match this purpose.

Types of Memos

Memos cover every conceivable topic. See Figure 11.4 for one example. Common types are described next.

Memo of Transmittal. Like a letter of transmittal, a transmittal memo accompanies a package of material, such as a report, a manuscript, or a proposal. The transmittal memo introduces the material, explains what is enclosed, and offers short comments or information not provided in the document itself. Transmittal memos may be as simple as a sentence or a bulleted list describing what is enclosed.

Meeting Minutes. Memos are often used to transmit minutes from a meeting. If the minutes go beyond two pages, the memo is probably not the best format, and you might want to opt for a short report instead.

Brief Report. The memo format is often used as the basis for very brief reports. Instead of writing a longer, detailed report, the writer will create a short, concise version, using the basic template of a memo structure. You will learn more about short reports later in this chapter.

Typical Components of a Memo

Memos differ across organizations and professions, but most paper memos contain the following parts.

Name of Organization. Most paper memos are printed on company letterhead, so you won't actually need to insert the name or address of the organization.

The Word Memo or Memorandum. This heading can be centred or set flush with the left margin.

To, From, Subject, Date. These four fields are set flush with the left margin, followed by a colon:

To:	Julian Barker
From:	Riley O'Donnell
Subject:	Internal price list
Date:	16 January 2012

Sometimes, the word *Re* is used in place of *Subject*. Also, these fields may occur in a different order, depending on the particular situation. In some companies, the order may be Date, To, From, Subject.

GREENTREE BIONOMICS, INC.

MEMORANDUM

TO:	D. SPRING, PERSONNEL DIRECTOR
FROM:	M. NOLL, BIOLOGY DIVISION
SUBJECT:	NEED TO HIRE MORE PERSONNEL
DATE:	1/16/2012
CC:	E. BRAGIN, CHEMISTRY DIVISION

With 26 active employees, Greentree has been unable to keep up with scheduled contract. As a result, we have a contract backlog of roughly $500,000. To increase our production and ease the workload, I recommend that we hire three general lab assistants.

I have attached a short report outlining the cost benefits of these hires. Could we meet sometime next week to discuss this in detail? I will contact you on Monday.

Figure 11.4 Sample Memo. This memo informs employees about a workplace hiring situation.

Memo Body. The body copy should be set in a few short paragraphs. Use lists to display prices, specifications, or other features. Use the direct approach pattern (see Figure 11.8 on page 236) whenever possible, and get to the point quickly.

Typist's Initials and Distribution and Enclosure Notations. If you are typing a document for someone else, then you will need to include your initials following the body of the text. Distribution and enclosure notations are described under the "Letters" section of this chapter and are used in a similar manner with memos.

Usability Considerations

Distribute the Memo to All the Right People. With email, this is easy because you can send it to an electronic list of names. With a paper memo, however, each copy needs to be placed in a mailbox or mailed in an envelope. You may need to ask for assistance with this task; the office administrator often has preaddressed labels you can use.

Place Important Information to Draw Attention. Don't bury the important information in a large block of text midway through the memo. Use the key point in the subject line, and follow the top-down approach if possible, presenting the important information clearly in the first paragraph (see Figure 11.8).

Keep It Short and to the Point. Unless you are writing a short report in memo format (see "Short Reports"), keep your memo as brief as possible, limiting it to one page if you can.

Check Spelling, Grammar, and Style. Run the spelling and grammar checkers, but also proofread or ask a colleague to proofread the memo.

Make Sure All Appropriate Parties Receive a Copy. No one appreciates being left out of the loop, so be sure to include everyone who should be informed.

Letters

Although many people use email in place of letters, traditional paper letters are still an important part of technical communication. Letters are used to address a single individual, a committee, or an organization. Letters can be short or long, depending on the context. Letters also tend to be more formal than memos, email, spoken communication, or voice mail messages, because letter writers tend to be more careful than they would be with electronic communication. A letter takes time to write, print, and proofread, and in that time, a writer may decide to make a few changes or perhaps to not even send the letter at all. In contrast, email is quicker to compose and send.

Use a letter when you need to:

- explain something you've enclosed, such as your résumé, a report, or a manuscript
- inquire about a product, service, or organization
- complain about or praise a product or service
- request technical information

Different professions have different standards for letter writing. In most engineering and science professions, letters are generally short and to the point. In certain circumstances, a longer letter may be required to provide the appropriate amount of information.

Audience and Purpose Analysis

To determine the length, content, tone, and approach to a letter, pay attention to audience and purpose. Imagine, for example, that you are a technical writer working on a new website, and you order updated font software. After installing the software, you discover that it does not perform as promised. The company from which you purchased the software has a strict no-refund policy on opened software. You are rather angry about the situation, so you decide to write a letter to the software manufacturer.

Who will be the audience for this letter? What is the primary purpose of your correspondence? Too often, people in this situation don't consider that their actual purpose is to obtain a refund, not to express anger. Consider the following opening:

> When I learned that your software does not perform as promised, and when I could not return it to the store, I was furious. How could you sell such a defective product?

Instead of making the recipient defensive, try to establish common ground and show that you are a reasonable person seeking a reasonable solution:

> I have always been a loyal user of your company's products, so I was disappointed that this software did not perform as stated in your marketing material. Because CompCity does not allow software returns, I ask that you refund the price. I will be glad to send the product back to you.

Along with your choice of words and tone, consider the following:

- Address your letter to the correct person or persons.
- Understand how that person will feel about your request. If the person receives hundreds of letters a day, for example, he or she might feel short-tempered and might appreciate a friendly—but determined—tone.
- Make sure other interested parties receive copies of the letter.

Types of Letters

There are many types of letters, including the following.

Letter of Transmittal. The transmittal letter accompanies a package of material, such as a report, a manuscript, or a proposal. Usually more formal than a transmittal memo and addressed to a recipient outside your organization, the transmittal letter introduces the material, explains what is enclosed, and provides any additional comments or information not offered in the document itself. Transmittal letters often include a sentence describing what is enclosed, such as

> This package contains a 12-page proposal, a price list, and my business card.

Make sure you address your transmittal letter to the correct person.

Cover Letter for a Job Application. One type of transmittal letter is the cover letter that accompanies a résumé and job application (see Figure 11.5). The purpose of a job application cover letter is to explain how your credentials fit this particular job and to convey a sufficiently professional persona for the prospective employer to decide that you warrant an interview. Another purpose is to highlight some specific qualifications or skills. For example, you may have "C++ programming" listed on your résumé under the category "Programming Languages." But for one particular job application, you may wish to accentuate this item. You could do so in your cover letter:

> You will note on my résumé that I am experienced with C++ programming. In fact, I am not only a skilled C++ programmer, I have also taught evening programming classes at Metro Community College.

Make sure the first paragraph of your cover letter states the position you are applying for, especially if you are applying to the Human Resources Department. For example, you could begin as shown on page 230:

> Please consider my application for a junior management position at your Chicoutimi resort.

Inquiry Letter. You may need to inquire about a product, service, set of specifications, or other item. As with most technical communication, keep your inquiry letter short and to the point. Follow the direct approach (see Figure 11.8 on page 236), and state clearly at the outset what you are requesting and why. Make sure you provide multiple ways for the recipient of the material to reach you: email, fax, phone, surface mail.

Word-Processing Templates. When discussing letters, it's important to note that most word-processing software (such as Microsoft Word) allows you to select

203 Elmwood Avenue
Toronto ON M3M 2B8
April 23, 2012

Sara Costanza, Director
Human Resources
Liberty International, Inc.
Montreal QC H3H 2B8

Dear Ms. Costanza:

Please consider my application for a junior management position at your Chicoutimi resort. I will graduate from Ryerson University on May 30 with a Bachelor of Commerce in Hospitality and Tourism Management. Dr. H. V. Garlid, my nutrition professor, described his experience as a consultant for Liberty International and encouraged me to apply.

For two years I worked as a part-time desk clerk, and I am now the desk manager at a 200-unit resort. This experience, combined with earlier customer relations work in a variety of situations, has given me a clear and practical understanding of customers' needs and expectations.

As an amateur chef, I know of the effort, attention, and patience required to prepare fine food. Moreover, my skiing and sailing background might be assets to your resort's recreation program.

I have confidence in my hospitality management skills. My experience and education have prepared me to work well with others and to respond creatively to changes, crises, and added responsibilities.

Should my background meet your needs, please phone me any weekday after 4 p.m. at (613) 326-2419.

Sincerely,

James D. Purdy

Enclosure

Figure 11.5 **Sample Cover Letter for a Job Application.**

from templates or predesigned letter formats. These templates usually provide fields for you to insert your name, your company name, and your message. Some templates provide background artwork or other decorative features. As tempting as it may be to simply choose a template, make sure the one you use is appropriate for your audience and purpose. If not, either use a blank document, or modify the template to suit your needs. Figure 11.6 shows a typical word-processing template.

Typical Components of a Letter

Most letters have the same basic components. Many organizations have set formats they follow for writing letters, so depending on where you work, these parts may appear in different locations on the page. But in general, a letter contains the elements listed here.

Heading and Date. If your stationery has a company letterhead, simply include the date two lines below the letterhead at the right or left margin. In Canada, you may chose to use the more common ISO 8601 format when writing dates; for

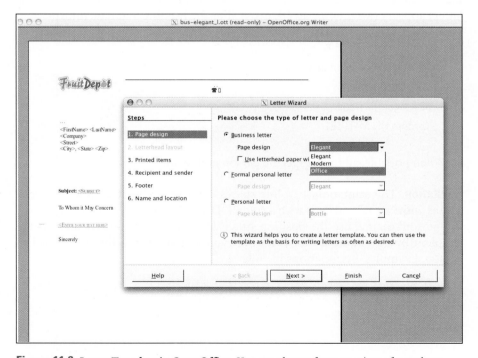

Figure 11.6 Letter Template in OpenOffice. You can choose from a variety of templates designed for different situations, or even customize one to fulfill your needs.
Source: OpenOffice.

example, 2012-12-31 for December 31, 2012. Yet many Quebec organizations follow the European format of day-month-year (for example, 31/12/2012) due to the strong cultural links to France. Other organizations, particularly ones that deal with American organizations, will follow the U.S. style of month-day-year (e.g. 12/31/2012). These differences in style can create confusion. The important thing is to keep the date consistent with both your audience and the standard adopted by your organization.

On blank stationery, include your return address and the date (but not your name):

> 154 Sea Lane
> Harwich ON K1B 2F5
> 2012 June 12

Use Canada Post's two-letter provincial abbreviations (e.g., ON for Ontario, QC for Quebec, BC for British Columbia) in your heading, in the inside address, and on the envelope.

Inside Address. The inside address (the address to which you are sending the letter) appears two line spaces (returns) after the heading and date information, flush against the left margin:

> Dr. Ann Mello, Dean of Students
> York University
> 30 Mogul Hill Road
> Toronto ON M4N 3E1

When possible, address a specific person and include his or her title.

Salutation. The salutation, two line spaces (returns) below the inside address, begins with "Dear" and ends with a colon ("Dear Ms. Smith:"). If you don't know the person's name, use the position title ("Dear Manager:"). Only address the recipient by first name if that is the way you would address that individual in person. Examples of salutations include

> Dear Ms. Martinez:
> Dear Managing Editor:
> Dear Professor Lee:

Remember not to use sexist language, such as "Dear Sir" or "Dear Madam." Instead, use the position title ("Dear Sales Manager:").

Body Text. Typically, your letter text begins two line spaces (returns) below the salutation. Workplace letters typically include:

- a brief introductory paragraph identifying you and your purpose
- one or more body paragraphs containing the details of your message
- a conclusion paragraph that sums up and encourages action

Keep the paragraphs short whenever possible. If the body section is too long, divide it into shorter paragraphs or place some items in a list (see Figure 11.7).

Complimentary Close. The closing, two line spaces (returns) below the last line of text, should parallel the level of formality used in the salutation and should reflect your relationship to the recipient (polite but not overly intimate). The following closings are listed in decreasing order of formality:

> Sincerely, Very truly yours, *or* Sincerely yours,
>
> Respectfully,
>
> Cordially,
>
> Best wishes, *or* Warmest wishes,
>
> Best regards, *or* Regards,

Align the closing flush against the left margin.

Signature. Type your full name and title on the fourth and fifth lines below the closing, aligned flush left. Sign your name in the triple space between the closing and your typed name.

> Sincerely,
>
> *Meredith M. Curtin*
>
> Meredith M. Curtin
>
> Principal Researcher

Specialized Components of a Letter

Some letters also have specialized parts, such as the following.

Attention Line. Use an attention line when you write to an organization and do not know your recipient's name but are directing the letter to a specific department or position. Place the attention line flush with the left margin two line spaces (returns) below the inside address.

LEVERETT LAND & TIMBER COMPANY, INC.

creative land use
quality building materials
architectural construction

January 17, 2012

Mr. Thomas E. Muffin
Clearwater Drive
Vancouver BC V5L 2K3

Dear Mr. Muffin:

I have examined the damage to your home caused by the ruptured water pipe and consider the following repairs to be necessary and of immediate concern:

Exterior:
Remove plywood soffit panels beneath overhangs
Replace damaged insulation and plumbing
Remove all built-up ice within floor framing
Replace plywood panels and finish as required

Northeast Bedroom—Lower Level:
Remove and replace all drywall, including closet
Remove and replace all door casings and baseboards
Remove and repair windowsill extensions and moldings
Remove and reinstall electric heaters
Respray ceilings and repaint all surfaces

This appraisal of damage repair does not include repairs and/or replacements of carpets, tile work, or vinyl flooring. Also, this appraisal assumes that the plywood subflooring on the main level has not been severely damaged.

Leverett Land & Timber Company, Inc., proposes to furnish the necessary materials and labour to perform the described damage repairs for the amount of six thousand one hundred and eighty dollars ($6,180).

Sincerely,

J.A. Jackson

Julia A. Jackson, President
JAJ/ob
Enc. Itemized estimate

Phone: 604-555-9879   Fax: 604-555-6874   Email: llt@yonet.com

Figure 11.7 Sample Business Letter.

> Glaxol Industries, Inc.
> 232 Rogaline Circle
> Vancouver BC V1F 3S6
>
> ATTENTION: Director of Research and Development

Subject Line. Typically, subject lines are used with memos, but if the recipient is not expecting your letter, a subject line is a good way of catching a busy reader's attention.

> SUBJECT: *New patent for hybrid wheat crop*

Place the subject line below the inside address or attention line. You can underline the subject to make it more prominent.

Distribution and Enclosure Notations. These items typically go at the bottom of the page. If you distribute copies of your letter to other recipients, indicate this by inserting the notation "cc." This notation once stood for "carbon copy," but since carbon paper has been replaced by photocopying, it is now said to stand for "courtesy copy."

> cc: J. Hailey, S. Patel

Similarly, if you enclose any items, you can note this at the bottom of the page:

> Enclosures: Certified cheques (2), KBX plans (1)

Usability Considerations

Organize for the Situation. You can choose between two basic organizing patterns. The first is *direct* organization, in which you begin with the most important information (your request or the conclusion of your ideas) and then give the details supporting your case. The second is *indirect* organization, in which you start with the details and build toward a request or conclusion.

Figure 11.8 illustrates each approach. A direct approach is usually better, because readers can get right to the main point. But when you have to convey bad news or make a request that needs a sales pitch first, it's often better to build your case first and then make your claim or request toward the end. When complaining about a faulty product, for example, a direct approach would probably be better, because the customer service person, who could easily receive hundreds of letters each day, will get to the point quickly. But for a letter requesting a raise in your consulting fee, an indirect approach is more appropriate.

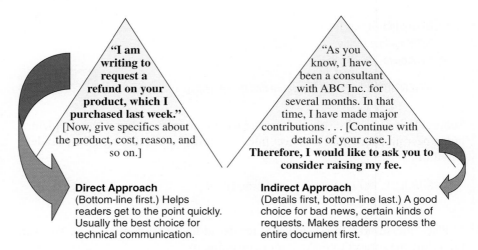

"I am writing to request a refund on your product, which I purchased last week." [Now, give specifics about the product, cost, reason, and so on.]

"As you know, I have been a consultant with ABC Inc. for several months. In that time, I have made major contributions . . . [Continue with details of your case.] **Therefore, I would like to ask you to consider raising my fee.**

Direct Approach
(Bottom-line first.) Helps readers get to the point quickly. Usually the best choice for technical communication.

Indirect Approach
(Details first, bottom-line last.) A good choice for bad news, certain kinds of requests. Makes readers process the entire document first.

Figure 11.8 Deciding on Your Writing Approach. It is appropriate to use a direct approach most of the time, but use an indirect approach when you have negative information to convey. If you do use the indirect approach, keep your information short and to the point so your reader does not need to read a long narrative to get to the point.

Address the Letter Properly. A letter that is addressed to the wrong person will not be very effective. Before sending a letter, spend time researching the name of the person to whom you should send it.

Use Language at an Appropriate Technical Level. If your letter is too technical, recipients will not understand it. But if your letter is too simplistic, you may insult or bore your reader. Learn all you can about your audience's level of expertise so you can choose appropriate language.

Include All Necessary Information. If you are writing to ask for an updated version of your software but you forget to include the current version number, the recipient will not be able to help. If you are lucky, that person will try to reach you and ask for more information. But quite possibly, your letter will be moved to the "get back to this" pile, and you may never receive a reply. Provide all the details your recipient will need.

Check Spelling of Proper Nouns. Make sure you spell the name of the recipient, the company, and the product correctly. If the company is known as "Electronics, Inc.," don't use "Electronic Corp." And it may sound obvious, but be sure you've spelled your own name correctly, too!

Clearly State the Main Point. Whether you use a direct or indirect organizational pattern, state your main point clearly and directly. If you want a refund on a product, *make sure* you say, "I am writing to request a refund" or something equally direct.

Avoid Puffed-Up Language. Avoid the stuffy, pompous, and tired phrases some writers think they need to make their letters sound important. Here are a few of the old standards with some clearer, more direct translations:

Avoid	**Use instead**
As per your request	As you requested
In accordance with your request	As you requested
Contingent upon receipt of	As soon as we receive
Due to the fact that	Because
Please be advised that I	I

In the legal profession (and others), certain phrases such as these are known as "terms of art" and connote a specific concept. If you are writing a letter about a legal issue, you may not be able to avoid terms of art phrases. But for all other letters, strive for a simple, clear style.

 Checklist for Letters

Content
- Have you identified the name and position of your recipient?
- Is the letter addressed to the correct and specifically named person?
- Does the letter contain all of the typical components?
- Does the letter have all needed specialized components?
- Is the letter's main point clearly stated?
- Is all the necessary information included?

Arrangement
- Does the introduction immediately engage the reader and lead naturally to the body section?
- Is the direct or indirect pattern used appropriately?
- Does the conclusion encourage the reader to act?

Style
- Is the language at an appropriate technical level?
- Is the tone conversational (free of puffed-up language)?
- Does the tone reflect your relationship with the recipient?
- Are spelling and grammar correct?

Résumés

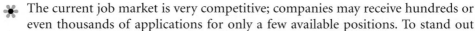

The current job market is very competitive; companies may receive hundreds or even thousands of applications for only a few available positions. To stand out from the competition, you must have a résumé that is attractive to potential employers. Attractive résumés look good, read easily, and provide information the employer needs in order to determine if the person should be interviewed. Employers initially spend only 15 to 45 seconds looking at a résumé; during this scan, they are looking for qualifications that fit their needs. Therefore, a good résumé is one that responds to the needs of the potential employer.

Audience and Purpose Analysis

Each résumé you send should be tailored to the wants and needs of the potential employer. If most recent work experience is considered most valuable by an employer, it should be listed first, rather than education or personal information. Since each employer and employment situation is different, your résumé will change as you apply for different jobs or gain new skills and experiences. The purpose of each résumé is to impress your potential employer enough for you to be scheduled for an interview or for your application to be passed along in the employment process.

Typical Components of a Résumé

There are several basic components to a résumé: contact information, career objectives, education, work experience, personal data, personal interests, and references.

Contact Information. Be sure to provide current information where prospective employers can reach you. If you are between addresses, be sure to provide both sets of information and check each regularly. Much business communication is now done via email or phone, so be sure that both your email address and your phone number are accurate.

Career Objectives. This is your opportunity to spell out to your prospective employer what kind of job you want. Your objectives project an image of who you are to your potential employer. To give a distinct and positive image, you need to be specific about your goals and avoid vague statements (see Figures 11.9 and 11.10).

Education. When listing your education, begin with your most recent school and work backward. You need to include the name of the school, degree completed, year completed, and your major and minor (if applicable). If your grade point average or class rank is favourable, list them. In addition to degrees, be sure to list any coursework that might be relevant to the position you are applying for.

Don Philip Weerasinghe

Current Address:
18 Marion Crescent
Markham, ON
Canada
(905) 123-4567
dweerasinghe@yahoo.ca

Permanent Address:
1234 Willowbrook Road
St. Albert, AB
(403) 555-5555

OBJECTIVE   Cooperative Education position related to manufacturing

EDUCATION   **B.S. Mechanical Engineering**, Expected graduation date: May 2012
                    Minor: Statistics
                    The University of Western Ontario, London, ON
                    GPA: 3.0/4.0

COMPUTER   **Software:**   **Languages:**
SKILLS   AutoCAD   MiniTab   Fortran   PowerC
                    TK solver   Mathematica   Visual Basic   C++

EXPERIENCE   **Retail Sales Assistant Manager**, Harberg's Family Value Mart Markham, ON
                    Fall 2010–present
                    • Work 20 hours per week.
                    • Assist clients with clothing selections.
                    • Responsible for in-store marketing.
                    • Assist Manager with staff training.

                    Self-employed, Lawn care business, St. Albert, AB   Summer 2008 and 2009
                    • Solicited business through cold calls and visits.
                    • Developed business marketing strategy.
                    • Increased customer base through referrals for quality work.
                    • Performed necessary equipment maintenance and repairs.
                    • Covered all expenses and yielded net profit of $6000.

                    Server, Cuisine of India, North York, ON 2006–2008, High school
                    and summers
                    • Trained on and used excellent customer service practices in
                      fast-paced, work environment.
                    • Participated in corporate program to increase sales; achieved all sales goals.
                    • Worked 30 or more hours per week in summers; worked 10 hours
                      per week during school year.

ACTIVITIES   Student Engineers Council (WEC), Membership Committee Chair, 2005–2006
                    Big Brother, Big Sister Program of London, 2008–2010
                    York Region Youth Tutors, 2002–2006
                    High School Senior Band, 2004–2007

HONORS   Dean's Honor Roll, 2009, 2010
                    Ontario Distinguished Scholar, 2002
                    Scholar Athlete Award, 2001–2002

AVAILABILITY   January 2010 preferred; also available August 2010

Figure 11.9 Sample Entry-Level Résumé.

Nadine Wolf
222 Harriet Avenue, Calgary, AB H8C 4-M4
Phone: (403) 444-4444
Email: nwolf@umn.edu

Objective   To obtain a position as an Environmental Educator/Naturalist working at a Nature Centre
using my skills in alternative teaching techniques and conservation promotion.

Education   **Bachelor of Science**, Natural Resources and Environmental Studies
University of Calgary
- Emphasized major in Environmental Education
- Minor in Recreational Resource Management
- Maintaining three jobs while attending school full time

Related   **Tour Guide**, Bell Museum of Natural History-
Experience   University of Calgary   September 2006-Present
- Lead several educated guided tours that are one to two hours each day for preschool to
  sixth graders from diverse schools and played relative indoor activities games
  to increase their knowledge
- Teach kids about the natural history of Alberta & promote conservation
- Care for and handle 13 reptiles and 5 amphibians
- Supervise and engage visitors with knowledge and information by using the objects,
  materials & resources available in the Touch and See Room

Youth Program Leader, Ann Sullivan School-YMCA-
Calgary, Alberta   September 2006–Present
- Manage 15 third graders in an after school Beckons Program
- Plan, create and implement 45 minutes of curriculum activities each day
- Encourage positive behavior while being an enthusiastic role model
- Supervise the kids during snack and academic time

Environmental Education Intern, Carpenter Nature Centre-
Calgary, Alberta   June 2006–August 2006
- Learned and implemented community environmental educational curriculum
- Taught and observed summer programs held for preschool to seventh graders
- Experienced the world of a naturalist through day-to-day routines
- Cared for and handled the many different animals every day in the summer
- Learned and gained knowledge about bee keeping while conducting bee keeping
  once a week with a Naturalist at the nature centre
- Designed and constructed an interactive display on geology and dendrology for the
  interpretative centre

Volunteer   **Primary Leader**, Centre for Outdoor Adventure-
Experience   University of Calgary, Alberta   May 2006–Present
- Plan, prepare, and lead outdoor adventure trips with college participants on weekends
- Created advertisement online and with flyers to promote trip programs

Outreach Primary Leader, Calgary Inner City Outings-
Calgary, Alberta   May 2004–Present
- Lead 8-12 year-old at-risk youth on outdoor activities to increase their understanding
  of nature
- Plan & create outings ideas for future trips, what to teach and where to go
- Conduct safe wilderness experiences and promote the ideal of conservation to the youth

Program Helper, Ginew/Golden Eagle Program-
Calgary, Alberta   September 2003–2004
- Helped Native Indian youth strengthen and develop life skills
- Participated in cultural activities to help youth increase their self-esteem
- Developed activities that promoted knowledge for healthy life choices

Certifications Canadian Red Cross Adult CPR/AED & First Aid   October 2007
Fifteen Passenger Van Training at the University of Calgary

Figure 11.10 Sample Résumé with "Experience" Grouped Into Two Sections.
Source: Adapted from University of Minnesota, St. Paul Campus Career Center.

Work Experience. List your most recent job first and then earlier jobs. Include the dates you were employed, the employers' names, and their contact information; also be sure to describe your exact job duties and any promotions and honours received. If it is to your advantage, specifically state why you left each job. In addition, include military experience and relevant volunteer work.

Personal Data. By law, you are not required to reveal your sex, religion, race, age, national origin, disability, or marital status; however, if this information is relevant for a particular job class, you may wish to include it.

Personal Interests. List any hobbies or interests that are relevant to the position that you are applying for. Also list any work-related skills, such as foreign languages, computer skills, and other abilities.

References. List three to five people who have agreed to provide strong assessments of your qualifications. These people must know about your job search, know you well, and be able to speak concretely on your behalf. Your references should not be family members but rather former employers, professors, and community figures.

Organization of a Résumé

The organization of your résumé should emphasize your strongest skills and experiences. Your experiences will dictate the organization of your résumé. If you wish to show a pattern of job experience, you should use *reverse chronological organization*. This organization lists your most recent experience first and then moves backward in time toward your earlier experiences. If you have gaps in your job record, you should use *functional organization,* which allows you to focus on skills, abilities, and experiences instead of on employment chronology. *Combined organization* is often used when résumés are to be electronically scanned; this method combines highlighting specific job skills with reverse chronological ordering.

Online Résumé Services

A variety of online sources can help you get your résumé written and placed in a database for potential employers to see. Web services like Monster.ca give you a variety of options when it comes to posting your résumé on the web. You can use a service's own template to create a résumé tailored to its system, upload your own electronic résumé, or copy and paste your résumé into the service's system. The social networking site LinkedIn (www.linkedin.com) is also a good choice. Unlike Facebook, which is designed to keep in touch with friends, LinkedIn is specifically designed for professional networking. With so many employers searching the web for future employees, an online service is a good way to get your résumé seen by potential employers.

New Types of Résumés

In today's information age, there are various new types of résumés, each addressing a different audience. Besides the standard print résumé, there is the scannable résumé, the résumé made from a template, and the electronic résumé.

Scannable Résumés. Many companies feed résumés through an optical scanner that then stores the résumés electronically in a database. Such a system allows an employer to search literally thousands of résumés using keywords. In order to prepare such a résumé, nouns should be used as keywords, and you should list all of your skills, credentials, and job titles. Since the résumé is stored electronically, it can be longer than a print résumé.

Résumés from a Template. Programs such as Microsoft Word provide electronic templates that can be filled in with an individual's own personal data. Such programs organize the information put into the template, and the organization can be easily changed as the template is shifted.

Electronic Résumés. A résumé can be submitted electronically via email to a potential employer. This type of résumé can be an electronic copy of a print résumé or can take the form of a hyperlinked résumé. A hyperlinked résumé allows pieces of your portfolio, your personal statement, writing samples, and other information about you to be directly accessed on the web.

Checklist for Résumés

Content
- Is all of your contact information accurate?
- Is your career objective clear?
- Do you put your strongest characteristics forward?
- Do you accurately describe your previous jobs?
- Have you included all necessary contact information for your previous employers?

Form
- Is the type of résumé appropriate for the job you are applying for?
- Does the organization of your résumé put your best characteristics forward?
- If you have a scannable résumé, does it use keywords effectively?
- If your résumé has hyperlinks, are they all functioning?

Overall
- Is everything spelled correctly? Is your résumé free of grammatical errors?
- If you have a print résumé, is it on quality paper?
- Is your résumé uncluttered and tasteful?
- Does your résumé read easily?

Short Reports

Reports present ideas and facts to interested parties, decision makers, and other audiences. Technical professionals rely on short reports as a basis for informed decisions on matters as diverse as the most comfortable office chairs to buy or the best recruit to hire for management training. Unlike long reports, short ones (two to five pages) do not contain a lot of detail. For example, a long report describing the geologic conditions of an area might include an appendix with detailed comparisons of topsoil, groundwater, and other conditions. A short report would summarize this information in a brief table or, depending on the audience's prior knowledge, omit this information altogether.

Short reports are appropriate in a variety of situations. When the purpose of your communication is to inform an audience, offer a solution to a problem, report progress, or make a recommendation, you may wish to use a short report. Short reports often use a memo-like structure, starting with a memo-style header and breaking the text up into chunks separated by headings, but they contain more information than the typical memo.

Audience and Purpose Analysis

Do your best to determine who will read this report. For instance, even if the report is addressed to team members, it may be sent on to other managers, the legal department, or sales and marketing. If you can learn about the actual audience members in advance, you can anticipate their needs as you create the report.

Also, before you start the report, be clear about its true purpose. For example, you may be under the impression that the report is intended simply to inform your colleagues about the new technical specifications for a component part. But after you interview some audience members and begin researching the content, you learn that what your audience really wants is a report that makes recommendations. Should your company invest in these new parts, or should it continue with the parts it currently uses? Recommending is different from informing. It requires you to weigh the evidence, examine the data, and decide what you think is right.

Types of Short Reports

Short reports come in many types, depending on the situation. Common types include the following.

Recommendations. Recommendation reports interpret data, draw conclusions, and make recommendations, often in response to a specific request. The recommendation report in Figure 11.11 is addressed to the writer's boss. This is just one example of a short report used to examine a problem and recommend a solution.

Trans Globe Airlines

MEMORANDUM

To: R. Ames, Vice President, Personnel
From: B. Doakes, Health and Safety
Date: August 15, 2012
Subject: **Recommendations for Reducing Agents' Discomfort**

In our July 20 staff meeting, we discussed physical discomfort among reservation and booking agents, who spend eight hours daily at automated workstations. Our agents complain of headaches, eyestrain and irritation, blurred or double vision, backaches, and stiff joints. This report outlines the apparent causes and recommends ways of reducing discomfort.

Causes of Agents' Discomfort
For the time being, I have ruled out the computer display screens as a cause of headaches and eye problems for the following reasons:

1. Our new display screens have excellent contrast and no flicker.
2. Research findings about the effects of low-level radiation from computer screens are inconclusive.

The headaches and eye problems seem to be caused by the excessive glare on display screens from background lighting.
      Other discomforts, such as backaches and stiffness, apparently result from the agents' sitting in one position for up to two hours between breaks.

Recommended Changes
We can eliminate much discomfort by improving background lighting, workstation conditions, and work routines and habits.

Background Lighting. To reduce the glare on display screens, these are recommended changes in background lighting:

1. Decrease all overhead lighting by installing lower-wattage bulbs.
2. Keep all curtains and adjustable blinds on the south and west windows at least half-drawn, to block direct sunlight.
3. Install shades to direct the overhead light straight downward, so that it is not reflected by the screens.

Figure 11.11 Sample Recommendation Report in Memo Format.

Workstation Conditions. These are recommended changes in the workstations:

1. Reposition all screens so that light sources are at neither the front nor the back.
2. Wash the surface of each screen weekly.
3. Adjust each screen so the top is slightly below the operator's eye level.
4. Adjust all keyboards so they are 27 inches from the floor.
5. Replace all fixed chairs with adjustable, armless secretarial chairs.

Work Routines and Habits. These are recommended changes in agents' work routines and habits:

1. Allow frequent rest periods (10 minutes each hour instead of 30 minutes twice daily).
2. Provide yearly eye exams for all terminal operators as part of our routine health care program.
3. Train employees to adjust screen contrast and brightness whenever the background lighting changes.
4. Offer workshops on improving posture.

These changes will give us time to consider more complex options such as installing hoods and antiglare filters on terminal screens, replacing fluorescent lighting with incandescent, covering surfaces with nonglare paint, or other disruptive procedures.

cc. J. Bush, Medical Director
     M. White, Manager of Physical Plant

Figure 11.11 (*Continued*)

Progress Reports. Many organizations depend on progress reports (also called status reports) to track activities, issues, and progress on various projects. Some professions require regular progress reports (daily, weekly, monthly), while others may use these documents on an ad hoc basis, as needed to explain a specific project or task. Managers often use progress reports to evaluate projects and decide how to allocate funds. Figure 11.12 shows a progress report.

Meeting Minutes. Many team or project meetings require someone to record the proceedings. Minutes are the records of such meetings. Copies of these minutes are usually distributed to all team members and interested parties. Often organizations have templates or special formats for recording minutes. Meeting minutes are often distributed via email.

Typical Components of Short Reports

Cover Memo-Style Heading. Many short reports begin with a brief cover memo explaining what the report contains.

Headings for Major Sections. Use headings for the major sections. Headings allow readers to scan the report quickly before launching into the text itself, and they provide a road map for the entire document.

Body Text. Use a standard font, and keep body text brief and to the point.

Bulleted Lists and Visuals. Use numbered or bulleted lists if the content warrants it. Lists help readers skim the document and order the information. But too many lists can be confusing, so use lists sparingly to make certain key points visible.

Usability Considerations

Use Effective Page Layout and Document Design. The longer the document, the more navigation tools you should include to help readers find what they need and stay focused on the material. Even a short (two- to three-page) report of solid, unbroken text (no font changes, no headings) can quickly become hard to read. Use headings, numbered lists, page numbers, and font changes to increase readability.

Perform Your Best Research. Make sure you've gathered the right information before you begin writing the report. For the recommendation report in Figure 11.11, the writer did enough research to rule out one problem (computer display screens as the cause of employee headaches) before settling on the actual

Subject: **Progress Report: Equipment for New Operations Building**

Work Completed

Our training group has met twice since our May 12 report in order to answer the questions you posed in your May 16 memo. In our first meeting, we identified the types of training we anticipate.

Types of Training Anticipated

- Divisional Surveys
- Loan Officer Work Experience
- Divisional Systems Training
- Divisional Clerical Training (Continuing)
- Divisional Clerical Training (New Employees)
- Divisional Management Training (Seminars)
- Special/New Equipment Training

In our second meeting, we considered various areas for the training room.

Training Room

The frequency of training necessitates having a training room available daily. The large training room in the Corporate Education area (10th floor) would be ideal. Before submitting our next report, we need your confirmation that this room can be assigned to us.

To support the training programs, we purchased this equipment:

- Audioviewer
- LCD monitor
- Videocassette recorder and monitor
- CRT
- Software for computer-assisted instruction
- Slide projector
- Tape recorder

This equipment will allow us to administer training in a variety of modes, ranging from programmed and learner-controlled instruction to group seminars and workshops.

Figure 11.12   **Sample Progress Report in Memo Format.**

Work Remaining

To support the training, we need to furnish the room appropriately. Because the types of training will vary, the furniture should provide a flexible environment. Outlined here are our anticipated furnishing needs.

- Tables and chairs that can be set up in many configurations. These would allow for individual or group training and large seminars.
- Portable room dividers. These would provide study space for training with programmed instruction and allow for simultaneous training.
- Built-in storage space for audiovisual equipment and training supplies. Ideally, this storage space should be multipurpose, providing work or display surfaces.
- A flexible lighting system, important for audiovisual presentations and individualized study.
- Independent temperature control, to ensure that the training room remains comfortable regardless of group size and equipment used.

The project is on schedule. As soon as we receive your approval of these specifications, we will proceed to the next step: sending out bids for room dividers and having plans drawn for the built-in storage space.

cc.   R. S. Pike, SVP
      G. T. Bailey, SVP

Figure 11.12 (*Continued*)

problem (excessive glare on display screens from background lighting). Research may include interviewing people, using the library, searching for information on the internet, and taking informal surveys (see Chapter 5).

Use Visuals as Appropriate. Insert visuals as needed. In a short report, you don't want to bog readers down with excessive graphic information; just a few well-chosen graphs, tables, or charts can help clarify your point (see Chapter 8).

Address the Purpose. Remember the purpose when you create the report. If your purpose is to recommend, don't take a neutral stance and simply state the facts. If your purpose is to show progress, make it clear at the outset what progress has been made. Use the direct approach (see Figure 11.8)—for example:

> Our goals for this month were to finish the Alpha project and begin planning the Beta project. We have exceeded these goals, and this report will describe our current progress.

Use Appropriate Headings. Use headings that make sense to your readers. The memo in Figure 11.11 is essentially an overview of a problem followed by a recommended solution, and the headings ("Cause of Agents' Discomfort" and "Recommended Changes") make this clear.

Write Clearly and Concisely. Get to the point quickly. Use a brief introductory paragraph that states your case or conclusion. Don't bog your reader down with unnecessary background or history sections.

Checklist for Memos and Short Reports

Ethical, Legal, and Interpersonal Considerations
- Is the information specific, accurate, and unambiguous?
- Is this the best report medium (paper, email, phone) for the situation?
- Are all appropriate parties receiving a copy?

Organization
- Is the important information in an area of emphasis?
- Is the direct or indirect pattern used appropriately to present the report's bottom line?

Format
- Does the memo have a complete heading?
- Does the subject line forecast the memo's content and purpose?
- Are paragraphs single-spaced within and double-spaced between?

- Do headings announce subtopics, as needed?
- If more than one reader is receiving a copy, does the memo include a distribution notation (cc:) to identify other readers?

Content
- Is the information based on careful research?
- Is the message brief and to the point?
- Are tables, charts, and other graphics used as needed?
- Are recipients given enough information for an informed decision?
- Are the conclusions and recommendations clear?

Style
- Is the writing clear and concise?
- Is the tone appropriate?
- Has the memo/report been carefully proofread?

Exercises

The website for this textbook (www.mycanadiantechcommlab.com) contains links to sample documents online as well as exercises related to different document types.

1. **FOCUS ON WRITING.** People regularly contact your organization (your company, agency, or college department) via email, letter, or your website to request information. To answer these many inquiries, you decide to prepare a frequently asked questions (FAQ) list in response to the 10 most asked questions about products, services, specific concentrations within the major, admission requirements, or the like. In addition to being posted on your website, this list can be sent as an email attachment or mailed out as a hard copy, depending on your readers' preferences.

   After analyzing your specific audience and purpose and doing the research, prepare your list in short report format, paying careful attention to the usability considerations in Chapter 4.

2. **FOCUS ON WRITING.** Your boss or college dean wants recommendations about whether to begin electronic monitoring of email correspondence and internet use at your company or your school. A few of your audience's major questions: What are the pros and cons? What are the ethical considerations? Should we do it routinely? Should we do it selectively? Should we rule it out? Is more inquiry needed? Should we allow the entire organization to share in the decision?

Do the research, and prepare a recommendation memo that makes your case reasonably and persuasively (review Chapter 9 for ethical considerations).

3. Write a letter to a business about one of its products following the format described in this chapter. Exchange letters with another student, and check each other's letters using the rules from this chapter. Rewrite and send the letter; if you get a response, share it with the class.

4. Divide into groups of four. Each group member chooses a job advertisement online or in a newspaper and tailors his/her résumé to the job description following the rules outlined in this chapter. Collect all the ads and the résumés from the members. Then, as a group, try to match each résumé with the corresponding job ad.

5. Write a letter to your school administration outlining something that you like or don't like and feel needs to be addressed by the administration. Follow the guidelines described in this chapter.

The Collaboration Window

Writing, especially in the workplace, is not done in isolation. Even when you are the main author of a memo or report, you will work with others to gather information, analyze findings, learn about user tasks, and so on. First, with your field or major in mind, choose one form of communication described in this chapter (letter, memo, short report), and analyze how you will need to work with others in your field when composing such a document. Second, research what additional steps you will need to take to adapt your document in order to post it on a website. You can research what's involved in converting printed documents to web presentation by exploring some of the links you found at http://w3 schools. com/html/default.asp, an interactive website that takes you through the process of building a website step-by-step.

Once you have determined how you will need to work with others at each stage of the document development process, summarize your conclusions in a brief descriptive memo or email to your professor.

The Global Window

Interview a person whose work takes him or her to one or more countries outside Canada, and ask the person to describe for you which types of documents are used in which situations in those countries and settings. For example, is a paper letter always considered formal? Is letterhead paper the same size around the world? In Canada, email seems to be replacing the paper memo. Is this true in other countries as well? If you have trouble locating someone to interview, try asking your instructor for the name of someone who hires interns from your program. You could also ask your instructor for the names of faculty members who travel abroad.

MyCanadianTechCommLab

Go to MyCanadianTechCommLab at www.mycanadiantechcommlab.com for additional online exercises and problems.

Presentation Skills

By the end of this chapter you will be able to:

1. Understand the unique benefits and expectations of face-to-face communications.

2. Understand the various types of presentations.

3. Identify the elements of a presentation's introduction, body, and conclusion.

4. Develop strategies for dealing with nerves and keeping the audience's attention.

5. Use visuals and non-verbal communication effectively.

6. Organize and prepare for presentations and meetings.

Karen Campbell, Vancouver, British Columbia

Karen Campbell started her own technical writing business after working in the IT industry for ten years, doing everything from writing code to selling computer networks. She wanted a new career where she could work on a project-by-project basis; that, combined with her enjoyment of learning new things and helping others to understand, made technical writing a natural choice.

Karen has been an independent technical writer for over ten years and has found that the self-employed lifestyle that her business KC Concepts Inc. offers, with its variety and flexibility, suits her perfectly. From the beginning, she has combined technical and marketing writing, though not always together. While she has written several technical manuals and sales brochures, her favourite projects involve both technical information and persuasive writing, including sales proposals, white papers, business plans, and web content. She enjoys working in a variety of areas but admits that if she had an easily-defined specialty, this would make her services simpler. "Even though I have a sales background, I still find marketing the hardest part of being self-employed. Most of my business is from repeat customers and referrals so I strive to keep each client happy."

Effective Presentations

In addition to being good writers and designers, technical communicators need to present their ideas effectively in person. The skills required include stage presence, excellent research, and strong organization. As a technical communicator, you may be asked to make oral presentations at meetings in your department or company (status reports, team meetings, procedure updates), at professional conferences or meetings, to your community, or in the classroom.

Unlike writing, oral presentations are truly interactive. Face-to-face communication is arguably the richest form, because you can give and receive information using body language, vocal inflection, eye contact, and other physical features. In addition, there is room for give-and-take, which does not happen with traditional written documents. Oral presentations allow you to see how your audience reacts. You can get immediate feedback, and you can change or amend your ideas on the spot.

Most professionals use presentation software such as Microsoft PowerPoint or Mac Keynote when giving a presentation. But despite the colours and easy-to-use templates such products offer, you are still responsible for putting together a presentation that is well researched and professionally delivered. Howie Jacobson, director of voice at Bregman Partners, cautions against using technology if you are not prepared. Technology should not be treated as a bandage to cover a weak presentation because it won't work. In fact, technology increases the complexity of a presentation, which makes it harder for inexperienced presenters to get their main message across (Rivera, 2001, p. 34–35).

Analyzing Audience and Purpose

Research an audience's attitudes about, biases toward, and personal experiences with your subject, and see if you can find out exactly who will be attending and what their role is within the organization. Professional speaker Joan Detz suggests learning about the demographic makeup of your audience beforehand, such as the age range, gender ratio, average educational background, work situations, and income levels (2007). For example, a person's role in the organization will affect how he or she listens to your topic. Managers may care about the bottom line, while designers may care more about how much time they will have to work on the interface. Oral presentations also require you to consider the feelings of the group as a whole. When you are speaking to a live audience, people's attitudes and ideas can rub off on others. If one person raises an issue with your topic, others might be reminded that they, too, are interested in this issue. The next thing you know, your audience will become a group, not a collection of individuals.

In defining the purpose of your presentation, understand how your audience will use the information you are presenting. Do people need this information to perform tasks? What do they need to know immediately? How can you make the best use of this time with them, and should you save certain items for email, memos, or web discussions? Is your purpose to inform, persuade, or train?

Is your presentation part of a larger context, such as a conference? Customize your audience and purpose analysis to address these questions, which are specific to oral presentations.

Types of Presentations

Certain types of oral presentations are common in science, business, and technical communication.

Informative Presentations

When your audience needs factual information about products, procedures, technical topics, or other items, give an informative presentation. Informative presentations often occur at conferences, product update meetings, briefings, and lectures. In an informative presentation, your goal is to be as impartial as possible and to provide the best information you can locate.

Training Sessions

Training sessions teach audience members how to perform a specific task or set of tasks. Training can cover areas such as how to ensure on-the-job safety, how to use a specific software application, or how to exit a capsized kayak. Some technical communicators specialize in training.

Persuasive Presentations

The goal of a persuasive presentation is to change an audience's opinions. For example, an engineer at a nuclear power plant may wish to persuade her peers that a standard procedure is unsafe and should be changed. In a persuasive situation, you need to perform adequate research so that you are well informed on all sides of the issue.

Action Plans

Action plans are a more specific form of persuasive presentations. Action plans are appropriate in situations where you want your audience to take a particular course of action. If you wanted to convince other engineers about a design flaw and wanted the company to take specific action about it, you would give an action plan presentation that outlined the problem, presented a specific solution, and persuaded the audience to take the sort of action needed to implement the solution.

Sales Presentations

Sales presentations blend informative and persuasive elements. The speaker usually presents information about a product or service in a way that persuades the audience to buy it. Technical sales presentations need to be well researched. For example, at many high-tech companies, technical sales representatives are scientists or engineers who understand the product's complexities and have a knack for effective communication.

In addition to making presentations in front of live audiences, you may be asked to present via interactive television, satellite, or a live connection via the internet. The more technology involved, the more complicated the presentation, so be sure you have technical experts to assist you. In particular, make sure your overhead slides or computer presentations show up in these electronic formats.

You may also be asked to give a presentation in another person's absence; for example, if a speaker suddenly falls ill or his flight gets snowbound in the airport. In these cases, get as much information as possible from the original speaker.

Typical Components of Presentations

Presentations can be as individual as the presenter. But because audiences need to follow your points and arguments, most presenters organize their presentations around standard components.

Introduction

The introduction to a presentation is your chance to set the stage. For most presentations, you have three main tasks:

1. To capture your audience's attention by telling a quick story, asking a question, or relating your topic to a current event or something else the audience cares about;
2. To establish your credibility by stating your credentials or explaining where you obtained your information; and
3. To preview your presentation by listing the main points and the overall conclusion.

An introduction following this format might sound something like this:

> How many times have you searched for medical information on the web, only to find that after hours online, you can't locate anything useful? If you're like most Canadians polled in a recent survey, you may feel that you are wasting time when it comes to web-based medical information. My name is Travis Armstrong, and I've been researching this topic for a term paper. Today, I'd like to share my findings with you by covering three main points: how to search for medical information, how to separate good information from bad, and how to contribute to medical discussions online.

Body

With a print document, readers who get confused or want to know the scope of the document can look back at the headings, table of contents, or previous pages.

But oral presentations do not have these features. Therefore, you must give your audience a well-organized presentation that is interesting and easy to follow. Structure the material in small chunks. To signal that you are moving from one main point to another, use transition statements such as, "Now that I've explained how to separate good information from bad, let me tell you how you can contribute to medical discussions on the internet."

Conclusion

Your conclusion should return full circle to your introduction. Remind your audience of the big picture, restate the points you've just covered, and leave listeners with some final advice or tips for locating more information. You can also distribute handouts during this time.

Time Constraints

Most presentations have a time limit. If you are presenting at a conference on a panel of three or four people, you may be asked in advance to limit your talk to 15 minutes. If you are presenting at a one-hour meeting, you should consider the amount of time people are able to concentrate and remember to save time for questions. Exceeding your allotted time (usually no more than 20 minutes in most business settings) is inconsiderate of your audience and the other speakers. Practise your presentation and make sure it fits the time allowed.

Sample Outline for a Presentation

A typical presentation will have an outline that resembles this general framework:

TITLE

Introduction
- Ask questions (How many times have you searched... ?)
- Introduce myself
- Outline main points
  - Searching
  - Separating good from bad
  - Contributing to discussions online

Body
- Searching for medical information
- Separating good from bad information
- Contributing to discussions online

Conclusion
- Restate my main points
- Give sources for more information and handout

Skills for Effective Presentations

Developing a general outline and framework for your presentation is a good start. But for a presentation to be effective, it needs to be informative, focused, and well presented. As a speaker, you will need to develop the following skills in creating and executing solid presentations.

Plan Your Presentation

When planning your presentation, consider the purpose, audience, presentation space and time, and material organization. Determine whether you want to inform or persuade. Try to condense your purpose to one sentence to help clarify the main topic. Before writing the presentation, research the audience's knowledge and interest levels, culture, motivation, size, and demographic details. When preparing for the presentation space, some information you might find useful includes the number of seats, the available audio/visual equipment, the seating arrangement, and any potential distractions. Furthermore, if you can arrange the time, you should choose the morning, when most people are alert.

When you organize your presentation, determine the fundamental issue that you want to address. Then you can more effectively identify the main points (two to five) you want to discuss and include logical transitions so the audience can follow along. You can also develop a list of questions that your talk will address. Some ways to organize your talk include the following:

- Topical
- Chronological
- Process Sequence
- Problem/Solution
- Cause/Effect
- Compare/Contrast

Work in a Group

When working in a group, spend time planning the talk together. You can divide the responsibilities among each member of the group. The structure of the presentation should include smooth transitions between each member's talk. One member could conduct the introduction and another member could cover the conclusion.

Follow a Presentation Sequence

Your presentation begins before your actual talk. A few minutes before beginning your presentation, you can build a rapport with audience members by mingling and learning names. This additional time will give you the opportunity to feel comfortable in the room, reinforce or reassess your analysis of the audience, relax your voice, and calm your nerves.

The most critical part of a presentation is the first few minutes. After you introduce yourself (and co-presenters), your company, and give any acknowledgments, you need to capture the audience's attention with a rhetorical question, surprising statistic or fact, or anecdote. Then you should provide your audience with an outline to help them follow your ideas. If your purpose is to inform, you should announce clear parameters for content. If your purpose is to persuade, you need to identify the problem and solution.

When you are ready to begin discussing your main points, make a smooth transition from the introduction to the body of the presentation. Remember to guide the audience throughout the presentation. Introduce each of your main points with a transition from the previous point. Announce what you are going to discuss before elaborating on the details. Provide supporting evidence and relevant examples for each main point. Then include intermediate conclusions to indicate that you have finished one point before introducing the next one.

In your conclusion, remind the audience of what you discussed and its significance, and finish with a call to action or give the audience something to remember. To reinforce your central argument, keep the conclusion brief and end with a strong, confident voice. Finally, thank the audience and proceed to the question/discussion period.

Learn to Manage Your Nerves

Being well prepared is the best way to manage your nerves. Always plan the presentation in advance, prepare for worst-case scenarios, prepare back-up visuals and handouts, bring an extra light bulb, and rehearse in front of a mirror, with a recorder, or with a practice audience.

Try breathing deeply and slowly before the presentation to help you relax. During the presentation, you should try to engage the audience quickly. This will help you feel more comfortable with the group.

Keep the Audience's Attention

Announce your central idea at the beginning of the presentation when the audience is most alert. State this central idea clearly at the beginning and repeat it at the end of the presentation to reinforce it. Provide background information to peak the audience's interest and give the audience some context for your topic. Remember to speak clearly at a moderate pace, but speak at a slower pace when discussing major points, complex ideas, and conclusions. Then, after each part of your presentation, summarize with an intermediate conclusion. This pause will allow the audience to absorb the details from each section and retain the significant information.

Be Prepared to Deal with Difficult Questions

You should always try to maintain control of the presentation. Guide the discussion by addressing minor issues but limiting the time you spend on them. When rehearsing the presentation, try to anticipate the possible reactions and questions from the audience.

When an audience member asks a difficult question, you can ask for clarification. For example, rephrase the person's question in your own words or ask the person to rephrase the question. You can delay your answer with a comment such as *That's a good question* or *I'm glad you asked that question*—or a quick discussion with the person about the implications of the question. If the question is negative, you can also agree with it but offer an alternate perspective. If the question is about information that you don't know or aren't sure about, offer to get back to the person with the answer the next day.

Work on Your Presentation Look and Style

To improve the audience's response to your ideas, you need to establish your credibility with the group. Some methods that establish your credibility include checking spelling and grammar in your presentation materials, wearing appropriate clothes, cleanliness and neatness of the presentation area, and sincerity during the talk and the question/discussion period.

You also need to concentrate on your body language. Effective speakers make eye contact and smile throughout the presentation. Relax your shoulders as you stand up straight, and turn your body to face the audience. If you are using a screen, place the screen at a 45-degree angle to the audience while you stand in the centre of the stage. Continue to make eye contact with your audience, even if you are referring to a visual. Move forward to emphasize a point and move to one side to indicate a transition to another point. Although some gestures can help, do not over-gesture because it can be distracting. Practise in front of a mirror or an audience to ensure that you do not put your hands in your pockets, sway or pace excessively, fidget, or use verbal fillers such as *um*, *uh*, or *like*.

For the audience to follow your ideas, make sure you speak loud enough, use a conversational tone that includes pauses, and articulate each word. Emphasize verbs and descriptions of important processes to draw attention to them. Showing enthusiasm during your talk will help convey your message and encourage questions and discussion from the audience.

If you are using a microphone, take the time to adjust it so you feel comfortable. Be aware of possible feedback and wires, know where the on-off switch is, and keep your mouth close to the microphone so the audience can hear you.

Using Visuals

Visuals can enhance a presentation because they focus the audience's attention, reinforce information, illustrate examples, and involve the audience in your ideas. Visuals can also increase the audience's retention of information.

A general rule about using visuals is to bring back-ups in other media types. Technology can break down, and you need to be prepared to carry on, no matter what happens.

Computer Projection Software

Most presentations use visuals of some sort: overhead transparencies, flip charts, or computer projection software. Keep in mind that the more technology you use, the more prepared you must be for technological breakdown. Used properly, computer software can make presentations interesting and enjoyable because they allow the use of colour, graphics, clip art, and images from the web.

Animation and presentation software makes computers an ideal tool in presentations. When including text, follow these general guidelines:

- Use five bullet points or fewer per slide so you do not overwhelm the audience.
- Use keywords and phrases, and choose graphs over charts. Maximize the font size (18 point or larger), and use smaller fonts for secondary points.
- Use images and contrasting shades or colours to help the audience follow your ideas, but do not include distracting images.
- Always test out your file with the equipment in advance, as computers can sometimes be unreliable and difficult to set up at a presentation.

PowerPoint, Keynote, and Similar Presentation Software

With presentation software such as PowerPoint or Keynote, you can produce professional-quality slides and then show them electronically. Created in 1987, PowerPoint began as a black-and-white program for Macintosh computers, and has since been used by more than 400 million people. Here is a sampling of the tasks you can do with PowerPoint and Keynote design and display features:

- Create slide designs in various colours, shading, and textures.
- Create drawings or graphs and import clip art, photographs, or other images.
- Create animated text and images—for example, you can use bullets that flash one at a time on the screen or bars and lines on a graph that are highlighted individually, to emphasize specific characteristics of the data.

- Create dynamic transitions between slides, such as having one slide dissolve toward the right side of the screen as the following slide uncovers from the left.
- Amplify each slide with speaker notes that are invisible to the audience.
- Sort your slides into various sequences.
- Precisely time your entire presentation.
- Show your presentation directly on the computer screen or large-screen projector, online via the web, as overhead transparencies, or as printed handouts.

For a step-by-step guide to getting started on PowerPoint, select "Auto-Content Wizard" from the opening screen. There you can find ideas for slide content and schemes for organizing your presentation.

The Presentation Software Debate

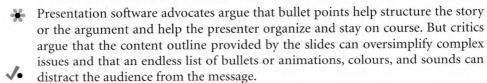

Presentation software advocates argue that bullet points help structure the story or the argument and help the presenter organize and stay on course. But critics argue that the content outline provided by the slides can oversimplify complex issues and that an endless list of bullets or animations, colours, and sounds can distract the audience from the message.

As an example of how over-reliance on presentation slides can cloud the thinking process, consider the following scenario:

> On February 1, 2003, the space shuttle *Columbia* burned up upon re-entering the earth's atmosphere. All seven people aboard died. The *Columbia* had suffered damage during launch when a piece of insulating foam had broken off and damaged the wing.
>
> While the *Columbia* was in orbit, NASA personnel tried to assess the damage and recommend a course of action. It was decided that the damage did not seem serious enough to pose a significant threat, and re-entry proceeded on schedule. Suggestions from lower-level employees that the shuttle should fly close to a satellite that could photograph the damage for a clearer assessment were overlooked and ultimately ignored by the decision makers.
>
> The Columbia Accident Investigation Board (2003) concluded that a PowerPoint presentation to NASA officials had played a role in the disaster: Engineers had presented their findings in a series of confusing and misleading slides that had obscured errors in their own engineering analysis. Design expert Edward Tufte points out that one especially crucial slide was so crammed with data and bullet points and so lacking in analysis that it was impossible to decipher accurately (pp. 8–9).

Here are the Board's findings:

> **COLUMBIA ACCIDENT INVESTIGATION BOARD FINDINGS**
>
> As information gets passed up an organization hierarchy, from people who do analysis to mid-level managers to high-level leadership, key explanations and supporting information is filtered out. In this context, it is easy to understand how a senior manager might read this PowerPoint slide and not realize that it addresses a life-threatening situation.
>
> At many points during its investigation, the Board was surprised to receive similar presentation slides from NASA officials in place of technical reports. The Board views the endemic use of PowerPoint briefing slides instead of technical papers as an illustration of the problematic methods of technical communication at NASA (p. 191).

In the end, technological tools are merely a *supplement* to your presentation; they are no substitute for the facts, ideas, examples, numbers, and interpretations that make up the clear and complete message audiences expect. In addition, they are not a substitute for detailed print documents, such as reports.

Other Visual Aids

One problem with presentation software is that it encourages the speaker to rely too heavily on one type of visual aid. Many people become distracted or even fall asleep during PowerPoint or Keynote presentations because it can be a very passive technology that doesn't require the audience to do anything. Moreover, the speaker doesn't always interact with the program except to move to the next slide, so there's no movement to keep the audience's attention. To encourage more interaction between the audience and the speaker, incorporate other visual aids into the presentation.

Handouts. Handouts can be an effective tool in your presentation toolkit. They allow you to provide the audience with more detailed information about your topic that they can take with them and read later. Handouts are useful from a speaker's perspective because they allow you to keep your slides to a limited amount of written text and can help you keep your slides simple. If you bring handouts to a presentation, consider when you want to give them to the audience. The moment you provide handouts, your audience will look at the handouts and not at you.

Overhead Transparencies. Overhead transparencies are clear plastic pages with images and text printed on them that are projected onto a screen via an overhead projector. Overheads are easy to use and reliable. When possible, choose pictures, figures, and tables over text. Also, they must be legible to everyone in the audience. Always bring an extra light bulb to the presentation as a precaution.

Whiteboards.   In small rooms with small groups, whiteboards are useful for developing ideas during the talk. However, avoid using a whiteboard with a larger audience as it can slow down the flow of a presentation.

Videos.   Videos are very helpful for illustrating system demonstrations because you can pause, rewind, and skip ahead, if necessary. You can continue to speak over a video to clarify some of the details or to highlight certain processes. However, make sure you explain how the video is connected to the rest of your talk so that the video does not take over the presentation. You should also have a back-up video just in case.

When preparing your visuals, keep the text to a minimum. Experiment with capital letters, colours, bold, underlining, or shading to help to make the layout easy to read, and use different font sizes for different types of text (i.e., main headings, subheadings, body, and so on). However, limit the number of slides; one slide every two minutes is an adequate pace.

Dave Paradi, the co-author of *Guide to PowerPoint*, explains how to use colour effectively, which colour combinations to avoid, and which to use to impress your audience. See his article at www.thinkoutsidetheslide.com/articles/choosing_colors_for_slides.htm (Munter & Paradi, 2006).

Presenting the Visuals

When using visuals, guide your audience by including transitions between different aspects of your presentation. While the visual is on the screen, you should focus the audience's attention on the various parts of the visual, and then rephrase your key points to give the audience time to process both the verbal and visual information. Always rehearse your presentation with your visuals so you can get your talk to match the slides. If you write something on an overhead, flipchart, or whiteboard, stop talking for a moment. Then begin speaking once you are facing the audience again.

Microsoft's website offers "how-to" articles and help, such as "Show Me! What Brain Research Says About Visuals in PowerPoint." Go to http://office.microsoft.com and choose "support" from the main menu bar, then choose PowerPoint (or go to http://office.microsoft.com/en-us/powerpoint-help/show-me-what-brain-research-says-about-visuals-in-powerpoint-HA010277194.aspx). Note that these basic principles apply for any presentation software.

Meetings

Most businesses hold regular meetings, during which staff make presentations about current and proposed projects. You should expect to have to make occasional meeting presentations, even as a relatively new employee. Your ability to manage these presentations is taken as a good indication of your leadership ability, so management watches them closely. Follow these steps to ensure that you do well.

Prepare for the Meeting

Research your audience and clarify the purpose of the meeting. Who will be at the meeting? What is their role in the company? What information do you need to provide? Do you have to be informative or persuasive? How much time do you have?

Rehearse a few times before the meeting to practise the speed of delivery, pitch and volume of your voice, and length of the meeting. Also, test out your visuals and the equipment in the room. The more comfortable you are with your material, the more confident and competent you will be.

Organize the Meeting

To keep your co-workers' attention throughout the meeting, you need to tell them the subject of the meeting at the beginning. Present your conclusions or recommendations first, then present the most important information that you want your co-workers to remember, and, finally, recap the key ideas and leave time for questions and comments.

Follow a Plan

Prepare an outline and refer to it during the meeting to keep yourself on schedule and on topic.

Complete the following details for each meeting:

MEETING PLANNER

DATE, TIME, AND LOCATION: _____

    INTERNAL DEPARTMENT(S)/PERSONNEL: _____

    EXTERNAL COMPANY/CLIENTS: _____

    TOPIC: _____

    KEY IDEAS: _____

    VISUALS/HANDOUTS: _____

    AUDIENCE QUESTIONS/COMMENTS: _____

    FORWARD MINUTES TO: _____

    NOTES: _____

On Meeting Day

Go to the room early to set up your visuals and organize your handouts. Make sure that there is a fresh supply of water and glasses. Adjust the lighting and temperature of the room, if necessary. Be aware of the clock—start and end the meeting on time. Following a schedule closely will allow you to cover everything on your agenda while respecting your colleagues' time.

Persuasive Presentations

Persuasive presentations attempt to influence the audience's responses to a restricted set of choices. You should make a persuasive presentation when you want to influence the audience's behaviour or beliefs, or when you want to reinforce an audience's existing behaviour or beliefs. Your presentation should convey your credibility, connect with the audience, and demonstrate logical reasoning.

Ethics

The success of your presentation depends in part on your level of trustworthiness and credibility. When researching your topic, look for solid, credible evidence such as quotes, statistics, examples, and facts to support your assertions. It is important to recognize the difference between facts and truth—*facts* are true statements that have been verified by tests, experiments, and sensory information, whereas *truth* is a commonly held opinion that cannot be supported with facts. Your speech will be more convincing if the audience trusts you. Therefore, if you demonstrate that you are honest, fair, and well informed during your talk, you will establish your credibility with the audience. You should conclude with confidence and answer questions thoroughly to reinforce the impact of your presentation.

To ensure that your material is credible, consider the following questions when preparing your presentation: Have you carefully researched your topic? Have you used credible sources? Have you considered other existing answers to the problem? Have you thought through any negative consequences? Have you anticipated any audience concerns about the issue?

Emotion

It is important to connect your ideas to the audience's needs. When writing your presentation, you need to make sure that you clearly state your message's relevance to the audience. Since your message must always appeal to the audience, you should look at your ideas from the audience's perspective—show that you understand and respect the audience's point of view. Remember to focus on the issues that the audience feels strongly about and emphasize how your ideas will benefit them.

Begin with a strong introduction. You can start by stating a position that is limited in scope, but meaningful to the audience. You may want to give your audience some background information to involve them in your ideas quickly. Try to convince the audience members that if they do what you suggest, they will be rewarded in some way. Throughout the presentation, remain sincere and be receptive to comments and questions. You can use loaded words with either positive or negative connotations to influence the audience's emotions. However, overuse of negatively charged words can be dangerous, so choose your words carefully. Finally, end with a strong argument, summary, or call-to-action statement.

To ensure that you are able to connect with the audience, consider the following questions: Who is affected by the problem? How are they affected? Who stands to benefit if the problem is solved? Who stands to lose? Why is "doing nothing" not an option? Are there social, political, or economic benefits for the audience and for people other than the audience?

Reason

Always support your argument with concrete, specific data. You can use deductive or inductive reasoning. Deductive reasoning begins with a general observation and moves to specifics. If you use deductive reasoning, state your conclusion first and then provide evidence to support your claim. Often, the audience learns more effectively if they know the conclusion first. In contrast, inductive reasoning begins with specifics and moves toward a generalization. If you use inductive reasoning, state the individual facts first and then build up to your conclusion one point at a time. Use inductive reasoning to structure your presentation when you know that the audience disagrees with your position.

To emphasize your ideas, your argument should follow a logical organizational pattern. Take the time to explain your ideas logically, factually, and clearly, and use arguments that make sense for your profession. Remember to justify your ideas using evidence that your audience will understand and trust. Beginning with your research, you should look for reliable sources such as market research, university-sponsored research, and expert opinion and research. During the presentation, you may want to explain the key terms and technical features of the topic carefully, including any graphs, charts, diagrams, and so on. Also, make sure you address counterarguments because showing the audience that you are open to understanding all sides of the issue is key to your presentation's effectiveness. When you discuss the opposition, use credible evidence to prove the opposition wrong. During the conclusion, clearly redefine the topic and restate your most convincing evidence to reinforce your ideas.

Non-Verbal Communication

Effective communication relies on both verbal and non-verbal cues. We often interpret another person's facial expression, tone of voice, and posture for additional information about his/her message. When verbal and non-verbal messages conflict, we typically trust the latter. However, it is crucial to understand that the meaning of non-verbal cues varies with different cultures. This discussion will focus on North American customs.

Facial Expression

Smiling at someone often encourages that person to begin or to continue to talk. Smiling conveys your approachability and interest in the topic. Another sign of encouragement is moderate nodding. Nodding your head up and down suggests that you are actively listening to your colleague. Similarly, making eye contact with the speaker indicates that you are listening. On the other hand, looking elsewhere frequently implies that you are distracted or uninterested in the topic. Finding the balance between staring and avoiding eye contact is central to successful communication.

Tone of Voice

Vocal cues add or detract from the message you want to express. Volume, pacing, emphasis, and pitch are some vocal cues. Listen to your recorded voice to see which vocal cues need improvement. When listening for volume, consider adjusting how loudly you need to speak to be heard and understood in a presentation for a large audience, in a business meeting with ten to thirty people, or in a conversation with a few people. Similarly, speaking too quickly or too slowly affects how well others understand you. Articulating each word will help you achieve the appropriate speed of delivery. Emphasis is equally important in conveying your message accurately. To avoid sounding monotonous or bored, modify the emphasis and pitch (high or low) of different words. Be aware, however, that changing your inflection changes the meaning of the sentence. Remember, keeping your jaw and throat relaxed enhances the quality of your voice.

Posture

Posture is the way you hold your body. Posture can give away your actual feelings about the topic and speaker. In general, slightly leaning forward suggests that you are interested and comfortable with the other person. However, crossing your arms, slouching, stiffness, fidgeting, and turning your body away from the speaker convey disinterest or discomfort with the other person.

Usability Considerations

Maintain Confidence and Project a Professional Persona. Fear of public speaking is very common, even for the most skilled speakers. The best way to avoid nervousness is to perform solid research on the topic, prepare well, and practise. Deep breathing and positive thinking also help with unsteady nerves. The more confident you appear, the more credible your message.

Be Ready to Adapt to Your Audience. Speaking to a live audience means you may need to adapt on the spot. If you start your talk but quickly realize that your audience does not understand some of the technical terms, you need to be ready to stop, explain some of the terms in simpler language, and perhaps even reconsider whether to do certain parts of your presentation at all. The more experience you gain with giving presentations, the better you will become at learning to "read" your audience.

Prepare for Technology Failures. No matter how many disk copies you bring, how fast the internet connection is, or how great the technical support staff is, you always need to be prepared for your technology to fail. Computer presentation software is dynamic and professional, but it does not always work. Overhead projectors are excellent for presenting outlines of your talk, visuals, and other material, but what do you do if the bulb burns out? Always have a back-up plan—paper handouts (and a spare bulb) are a good idea.

Get a Sense of the Physical Layout of the Room. Make sure you know the size and layout of the room before you show up. Is it a conference room or a large lecture hall? The font size you choose for slides to be shown in a conference room may not be large enough for a lecture hall. If you can, visit the space in advance.

Spell-Check Your Slides. Even though most people spell-check documents, for some reason they often forget to spell-check their presentation slides. You don't want the audience distracted by misspellings on the screen when you are speaking.

Use Your Memory and Practise Your Delivery. Don't read your presentation from note cards or from a prepared speech. Instead, seek a style that is professional but natural. Memorize the key phrases or concepts in your presentation, and use these key terms to jog your memory about the other items you wish to mention. Use bullet points on your overheads or slides to help guide you. Practise until you can speak with confidence. You should practise in front of friends or sample audience members and ask for their feedback. (See the checklist for oral presentations.) Alternatively, record or video yourself, and use this to help improve your style.

Checklist for Oral Presentations

Audience
- Have you analyzed the demographic makeup of your audience?
- Have you analyzed the audience's attitudes, biases, and personal experiences with the subject/topic?

Purpose
- Have you defined the purpose of your presentation?
- Have you understood how your audience will use the information you are presenting?

Content
- Have you stated a clear purpose?
- Have you created interest in the topic and shown command of the material, supporting assertions with evidence?
- Have you used adequate visuals appropriately?
- Have you acknowledged opposing views?

Organization
- Have you begun with a clear overview?
- Have you presented a clear line of reasoning, moving logically from point to point?
- Have you used transitions and outlines?

Style
- Have you dressed appropriately?
- Have you shown confidence and enthusiasm?
- Have you used appropriate language and enunciated well?
- Have you practised to keep within the time limit?
- Have you kept the audience involved?
- Have you prepared for difficult questions?

Exercises

1. Make up a scenario related to your current or future career about an oral presentation you may have to make. Make sure you give all related background information about your job. (For example, you are a healthcare retailer who sells medical equipment. You need to present a new type of clamp designed by your company that you hope the hospital administrators and doctors will want to purchase at the workshop they are attending.) Describe what type of oral presentation you would give, do an audience and purpose analysis, and explain what you would use to enhance your presentation. Compare your scenario with those of other students in your class.

2. Prepare a 10-minute presentation to persuade other students to choose your university or college for their post-secondary career. Include at least one visual aid in your presentation.

3. Prepare a self-introduction in the form of an "elevator pitch." The presentation should be no longer than 90 seconds, about the time it would take to get from the ground floor to the top floor of an office building in an elevator. Consider the following items as possible things to discuss in your self-introduction:

   - Consider what your goals are. What do you want to learn more about through networking? This might be a specific job, an industry, or how to apply a skill set.

   - Determine and describe the most relevant pieces of information about yourself. Examples include a recent externship or job in the field; why a course or newspaper article sparked your interest; transferrable skills developed through an event, interaction, or position.

   This is often called an "elevator speech," because you should imagine that you are stuck in an elevator and you need to tell the people around you about yourself before they get off. Think about how you can use this short time not only to introduce yourself, but also to convey something about who you are and what you do.

   Think about "how" you will speak to them. Will you look at them? Will you smile? Will you use gestures? Sometimes how you present is just as important as what you say.

4. **FOCUS ON WRITING.** Prepare a PowerPoint or Keynote presentation on a technical process detailing how a piece of technology works. Use no more than 10 slides and no more than three bullet points per slide. Be sure to follow the guidelines in the chapter. Consult the following resources for more tips:

   - **www.rebooting.ca/crc/crc-home/helpHnts.pdf**

     "Ten Steps to a Winning Presentation"—a concise guide that can be used as a checklist to make sure that your presentation is on the right track.

   - **www.thomaslarock.com/2010/08/top-ten-presentation-mistakes**

     "Top Ten Presentation Mistakes," by Thomas LaRock, offers his insight on the biggest mistakes made during technical presentations.

The Collaboration Window

In the workplace, you will have to speak with a diverse group of people about a myriad of topics. To build your confidence in your conversation skills, work in groups of four or five and choose five unrelated topics to discuss (e.g., balancing home and work life, advantages of cell phones, why voter turnout is so low for municipal elections). Spend five to seven minutes on each topic, and have every group member speak about each topic.

To illustrate the importance of eye contact, gestures, and facial expressions, work in pairs and sit back-to-back with your partner. Then have a conversation for five to seven minutes. What non-verbal information was missed? Did you rely on tone, pitch, and inflection more as both the speaker and the listener?

The Global Window

In this chapter, you have learned some of the key concepts in creating an effective presentation for a Canadian audience. But what about presentations to international or intercultural audiences? Understanding cross-cultural differences is key to getting your message accepted.

In groups, use the internet to investigate some of the challenges of making presentations in other countries. A good website to start your investigation is www.worldbusinessculture.com. Examine topics such as cross-cultural differences in non-verbal communications, teaching or presentation techniques, and organizational culture. As a group, present your findings to the class.

MyCanadianTechCommLab

Go to MyCanadianTechCommLab at www.mycanadiantechcommlab.com for additional online exercises and problems.

CHAPTER 13

Product-Oriented Communication Situations

Chapter Objectives

By the end of this chapter you will be able to:

1. Understand the components of specifications.

2. Differentiate between instructions, procedures, and materials.

3. Understand what is needed for marketing material.

John Mighton, Toronto, Ontario

For the past ten years, John Mighton has coordinated JUMP (www.jumpmath.org), a successful school program designed to help teachers teach math in a way that nurtures the potential in all students. Mighton completed a PhD in Mathematics at the University of Toronto and has lectured in Philosophy at McMaster University. He is currently an adjunct professor in Mathematics at the University of Toronto and is a fellow of the Fields Institute, which focuses on research in mathematical science.

Using the experience garnered from his field, John has written an inspirational book on his experiences called *The End of Ignorance: Multiplying Our Human Potential*, as well as workbooks that deliver the full elementary curriculum in mathematics. Based on his observations of thousands of students, Mighton believes that anyone can learn math. He says: "When students don't progress, I assume it is my fault: I always try to fill in any gaps in students' knowledge before I introduce new ideas, and I also try to provide explanations built in clear and simple steps, with enough examples to allow students to consolidate their understanding."

Specifications

Airplanes, bridges, computer software, and nearly everything else in the modern world are produced according to specifications. Specifications ("specs") prescribe standards for performance, safety, and quality. Specifications describe features such as methods for manufacturing, building, or installing a product; materials and equipment used; and size, shape, and weight. Specifications are often used to ensure compliance with a particular safety code, engineering standard, or government or other ruling. Because specifications define an "acceptable" level of quality, any product that fails to meet these specs may provide grounds for a lawsuit. When injury or death results (as in a bridge collapse or an airline accident), the device is usually checked to be sure it was built and maintained according to the appropriate specifications. If not, the contractor, manufacturer, or supplier may be liable.

Specifications are called for in situations where a technology or procedure must be executed in a precise manner. For example, the Institute of Electrical and Electronics Engineers (IEEE) issues a series of specifications (called "standards") that prescribe the technical format and specs for a range of devices, including circuits, electrical insulation, and telecommunications. Engineers are obligated to follow these standards if they want their products to be both safe and compatible with others in that field. Specifications are also important in situations where many professionals from different backgrounds work together on a project. These specs help ensure that contractors, architects, landscapers, and others have a master plan and use the same parts, materials, and designs. Software developers also follow specifications when creating computer programs.

Audience and Purpose Analysis

Specifications may be written for a wide range of readers, including customers, designers, contractors, suppliers, engineers, programmers, and inspectors. An audience analysis will help you determine who will be reading the specs. If your audience consists primarily of technical experts (such as engineers who use the IEEE standards), you can use specialized language and succinct explanations (see Figure 13.1). But if your audience is a mixed group, you may need to include more detail, or you may need to refer readers to other sources of information (a glossary, website, or attachment).

In terms of purpose, specifications are useful when your audience needs to understand and agree on what is to be done and how it is to be done. In addition to guiding how a product is designed and constructed, specifications can also help people use and maintain a product. For instance, specifications for a colour ink-jet printer (see Figure 13.2) include the product's power requirements, noise emissions, weight, and size of paper. Product support literature for appliances, power tools, and other items often contains specifications so that users can select an appropriate operating environment or replace worn parts. Specifications can

IEEE C62.1-1989 - Description

IEEE C62.1-1989 - revision of ANSI/IEEE C62.1-1984
IEEE Standard for Gapped Silicon-Carbide Surge Arresters for AC Power Circuits
Abstract: IEEE C62.1-1989, *IEEE Standard for Gapped Silicon-Carbide Surge Arresters for AC Power Systems,* describes the service conditions, classifications and voltage ratings, design tests with corresponding performance characteristics, conformance tests, and certification test procedures for station, intermediate, distribution and secondary class arresters. Terminal connections, housing leakage distance, mounting and identification requirements are defined. Definitions are provided to clarify the required test procedures and other portions of the text.
Contents

1. Scope

2. Definitions

3. References

4. Service Conditions
    4.1   Usual Service Conditions
    4.2   Unusual Service Conditions

5. Classification and Voltage Rating of Arresters
    5.1   Voltage Ratings
    5.2   Test Requirements

Voltage Withstand Tests
Power-Frequency Sparkover Test

Figure 13.1 **Sample from an IEEE Standard for Surge Protectors.**
Source: © 1990 IEEE. Reprinted, with permission, from IEEE Standard for Gapped Silicon-Carbide Surge Arresters for AC Power Circuits.

 **Specifications**

Power Requirements

Power Adapter (universal input)

Input Voltage:	100 to 240 VAC (±10%)
Input Frequency:	50 to 60 Hz (±3 Hz)

Automatically accommodates the world-wide range of AC line voltages and frequencies. There is no on/off switch on the power adapter.

Declared noise emissions in accordance with ISO 9296:

Sound power level. LWAd (1B=10dB): 5.5 B in Normal mode.

Sound pressure level. LpAm (bystander positions): 42 dB in Normal mode.

Media Weight

Paper:	16 to 110 lb index (60 to 200 gsm)
Envelopes:	20 to 24 lb (75 to 90 gsm)
Cards:	110 lb index max; 0.012 in max thickness (110 to 200 gsm; 0.3 mm max thickness)
Banner Paper:	20 lb (75 gsm)

Media Handling

Sheets:	up to 100 sheets
Banners:	up to 20 sheets
Envelopes:	up to 15 envelopes
Cards:	up to 30 cards
Transparencies:	up to 25 sheets
Labels:	up to 20 sheets of Avery paper labels
	Use only U.S. letter-sized or A4-sized sheets. Use only paper labels specifically designed for use with HP inkjet printers.
OUT tray capacity:	up to 50 sheets

Media Size

Custom size:	
Width:	3.0 to 8.5 in (77 to 216 mm)
Length:	3 to 14 in (77 to 356 mm)
U.S. letter:	8.5 x 11 in (216 x 279 mm)
Banner	
U.S. letter:	8.5 x 11 in (216 x 279 mm)
U.S. legal:	8.5 x 14 in (216 x 356 mm)
Executive:	7.25 x 10.5 in (184 x 267 mm)
U.S. No. 10 envelope:	4.13 x 9.5 in (105 x 241 mm)
Invitation A2 envelope:	4.37 x 5.75 in
Index card:	3 x 5 in (76 x 127 mm)
Index card:	4 x 6 in (102 x 152 mm)
Index card:	5 x 8 in (127 x 203 mm)
European A4:	210 x 297 mm
European A5:	148 x 210 mm
Banner	
European A4:	210 x 297 mm
B5-JIS:	182 x 257 mm
European DL envelope:	220 x 110 mm
European C6 envelope:	114 x 162 mm
European A6 card:	105 x 148 mm
Japanese Hagaki postcard:	100 x 148 mm

Figure 13.2 **Specifications for a Colour Ink-Jet Printer.**

Source: Hewlett-Packard Development Co. Reprinted with permission.

also be important in technical marketing material (discussed later in this chapter) by helping potential customers see the details of the product.

Types of Specifications

Industry Standards. Many industries issue specifications and standards for products in the field. For example, the IEEE issues standards for electrical and electronic devices.

Government Standards. Government organizations, such as Health Canada and Consumer Product Safety, produce guidelines and standards for a multitude of items. For example, Health Canada regulates the production and sale of food products and vitamin supplements.

Functional Specs. Functional specs are used in the private sector to outline exactly what needs to be done on a project (see Figure 13.3). However, a functional spec does not always indicate how certain parts of the project will be implemented. For example, a functional spec for a software product may indicate that the software should allow users to log in, enter data, and move between screens. Software development teams use this functional spec to guide them as they write and test the computer code.

Internet Specs. The World Wide Web consortium (www.w3c.org) is an industry and university organization that develops common protocols (technical standards) for webpage design and development. These protocols provide standards for web development in areas such as graphics, hypertext markup language (HTML), and other technical aspects that allow the web to function across a variety of platforms, countries, and browsers.

Typical Components of Specifications

As noted, there are many types of specifications. The components of the document will often be dictated by the industry or organization. The IEEE surge protector standard in Figure 13.1 follows the format for all similar IEEE documents. In general, specifications include the following parts:

Brief Introduction or Description. Most specs include some kind of overview section—a one- or two-sentence introduction, an abstract, or a similarly brief description of the document. If your audience is completely familiar with the material, a title can serve this purpose.

List of Component Parts or Materials. Specifications that deal with devices or hardware often list the individual parts. For example, if you purchase a new

Ruger, Filstone, and Grant
Architects

SPECIFICATIONS FOR THE POWNAL CLINIC BUILDING

Foundation

footings: 8" x 16" concrete (load-bearing capacity: 3,000 lbs. per sq. in.)
frost walls: 8" x 4' @ 3,000 psi
slab: 4" @ 3,000 psi, reinforced with wire mesh over vapor barrier

Exterior Walls

frame: eastern pine #2 timber frame with exterior partitions set inside posts
exterior partitions: 2" x 4" kiln-dried spruce set at 16" on center
sheathing: 1/4" exterior-grade plywood
siding: #1 red cedar with a 1/2" x 6' bevel
trim: finished pine boards ranging from 1" x 4" to 1" x 10"
painting: 2 coats of Clear Wood Finish on siding; trim primed and finished
with one coat of bone white, oil base paint

Roof System

framing: 2" x 12" kiln-dried spruce set at 24" on center
sheathing: 5/8" exterior-grade plywood
finish: 240 Celotex 20-year fiberglass shingles over #15 impregnated felt
roofing paper
flashing: copper

Windows

Anderson casement and fixed-over-awning models, with white exterior
cladding, insulating glass and screens, and wood interior frames

Landscape

driveway: gravel base, with 3" traprock surface
walks: timber defined, with traprock surface
cleared areas: to be rough graded and covered with wood chips
plantings: 10 assorted lawn plants along the road side of the building

Figure 13.3 **Specifications for a Building Project.**

power tool, you will probably find a list of parts somewhere in the instruction manual.

Reference to Other Documents or Specs. Often one set of specifications refers to another. For example, a functional spec for a software product may refer readers to an earlier document. If you put your spec on a website, you can easily create links from the new document to the old one.

Usability Considerations

Understand How People Will Use the Document. Will readers use the specs to build something (a bridge, a software product)? If so, they will need detailed information. But what if they need to refer to the specs only on occasion, say, if a part is needed? In this case, a spec can be shorter—for example, a list of parts with order numbers and brief descriptions.

Use the Same Terms to Refer to the Same Parts or Steps. If the specs list indicates "ergonomic adapter" in one section but then uses the term "iMac mouse adapter" in a later section to refer to the same thing, users may become frustrated and confused. Keep terms consistent throughout the document.

Use Adequate Retrieval Aids. Especially in longer documents, some audience members may be interested in only one aspect of the spec. For example, a programmer working on a subset of the entire project may want to look up the technical details for her part of the project. If you use clear headings and a table of contents, people can find the parts they need.

Follow a Standard Format. If the organization follows a standard format for specs, use it. If not, you may want to create a template and suggest that the entire company use it. Standard formats help users find what they need, because each document created with a template will contain similar sections and subsections.

Keep It Simple. People look at specs because they want quick access to items, parts, technical protocols, and so on. These users are not interested in reading a novel. If you can, keep your specs limited to short lists, using prose only as necessary.

Check Your Use of Technical Terms. Make sure your technical terms are standard for the industry. Be sure you have spelled these terms correctly or used the standard abbreviations. Remember that your spell-checker won't find some technical terms, so you may wish to create a new dictionary within your word-processing software just for this project.

When Giving Instructions, Use Active Voice. If the specs require you to instruct your audience, use active voice and imperative mood. For example, "Insert the bolt" instead of "The bolt should be inserted" or "Remove the wiring insulation" instead of "Wiring insulation to be removed."

Checklist for Specifications

- Are the specifications appropriately detailed for the audience?
- Do they address all the tasks required of the user?
- To avoid excessive detail for a mixed audience, do you refer readers to other sources of information?
- Do the specs begin with a brief overview of the document?
- For hardware and mechanism specs, is each part listed and described?
- Are other/earlier specs referred to, as needed?
- Is the terminology for parts or steps consistent throughout the document?
- Are all technical terms standard for the industry?
- Are the specs easy to navigate, with clear headings and other retrieval aids?
- Do the specs follow a standard format whenever possible?
- Is the writing concise and clear, with lists preferred to paragraphs?
- Are all instructions phrased in the active voice?

Brief Instructions

 Surrounded as we are by technology, we are quite naturally also surrounded by instructions. Brief, to-the-point instructions are called for when you want to provide users with information on how to assemble, connect, or use a product. Even a product as simple as a build-it-yourself bookshelf requires clear, simple instructions. Brief instructions often appear as part of a larger set of instructions and procedures to help users get started immediately. Figure 13.4 is an example: it lists six steps users need to connect their drives to their computers. Users can refer to the Quick Install brochure to get started immediately, and they can read the more extensive User's Guide later.

Audience and Purpose Analysis

Consider how much experience your audience has with the technology or task. For example, if someone already owns a Zip drive at work and has purchased a new one for home, that person will need only a brief reminder of how to set up and operate the device. Users who are new to this technology, on the other hand, will need more information.

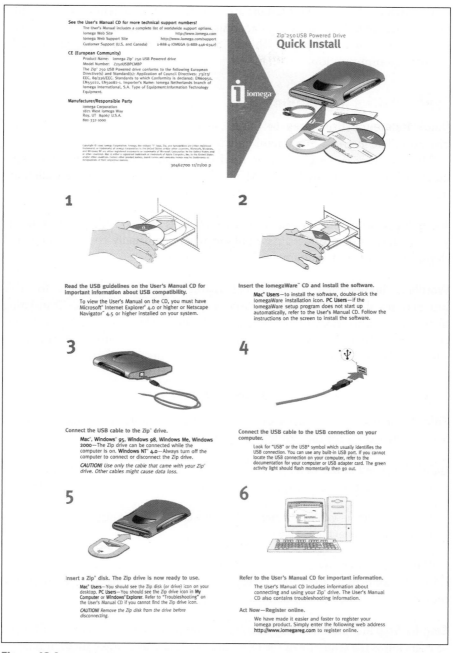

Figure 13.4 A Quick Install Brochure. This quick reference guide is printed as a brochure (shown folded open in this figure). It lists the six steps users need to perform in order to connect their new drives to their computers. Note the use of action verbs (*insert, connect*) and the smart use of diagrams.

Source: Courtesy of Iomega Corp.

In terms of purpose, instructions are usually written to help users perform a task or series of tasks. During your analysis, you need to discover what these tasks are and in what order people should perform them. For more about task-oriented communication, see Chapter 3.

Types of Brief Instructions

Quick Reference Brochures or Cards. Figure 13.4 shows a quick reference brochure. The instructions contain only the basic steps necessary for the task.

The brochure is designed to be used during an installation process. Some quick reference cards, such as ATM instructions you carry in your wallet, are designed to be used repeatedly as needed.

Assembly Instructions. These instruction sheets come with most build-it-yourself devices or products. Assembly instructions usually contain numbered steps, a parts list, and diagrams.

Wordless Instructions. In a global marketplace, it's important to have instructions that can be understood across language barriers. Translating instructions into dozens of languages is expensive and leads to bulky, cumbersome materials. Many companies have turned to wordless instructions, which use diagrams and arrows to explain a procedure (see Figure 13.5).

Typical Components of Instructions

Title. Most instructions, brief or extended, have a short title, such as "Quick Setup Instructions for the Printer." Keep the title brief and to the point.

Quick Overview of the Task. In cases where the instructions will take more than a few steps, you can create a quick overview of the entire process, such as this:

> To use your new SCSI adapter cable, you will first need to install the software and then connect the cable.

You would then divide your instructions into two parts: installing the software and connecting the cable. Overviews help users see the big picture before they embark on the detailed actions.

Step-by-Step Instructions. Most instructions are written in a numbered list format so users know the sequence of the tasks and can remember where they left off.

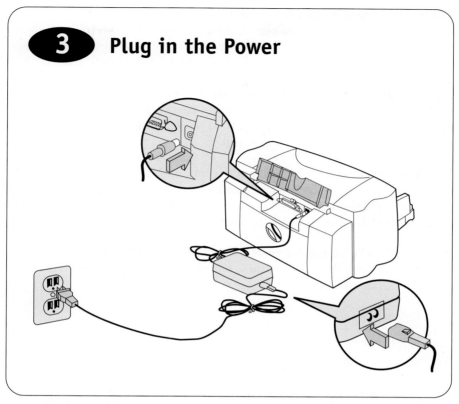

3 **Plug in the Power**

Figure 13.5 **Wordless Instructions.** This example uses a few words but primarily relies on an exploded diagram to explain the procedure.
Source: Hewlett-Packard Co. Reproduced with permission.

Diagrams. Diagrams can be extremely helpful, because they allow users to see the process or the parts to be assembled. Diagrams are especially important when you are creating a document for an international audience.

Follow-Up Information. It is a good idea to provide an address, phone number, website, and email address where users can obtain assistance.

Usability Considerations

Define the Task Your Users Need to Perform. Experts at writing instructions always perform a task analysis, which focuses on tasks users will need to perform in particular situations. For example, the main tasks on users' minds when they open the box for a new computer component, such as a printer, are how to set it up and use it.

Determine the Size of the Final Document. Brief instructions are intended to help users perform tasks quickly. The final document should not be bulky or cumbersome. It should be easy to use and, if possible, printed on a single page. The quick reference brochure shown in Figure 13.4 is a good example.

Use the Same Terms to Refer to the Same Parts or Steps. Readers may be confused by instructions that use terms inconsistently. For example, be sure your instructions don't say to connect the "SCSI printer cable" in one step but then refer to the "peripheral cable" in a later step.

Test Your Instructions. Most technical communication products should be proofread and/or tested by real audience members, and this usability concern is especially important with instructions. You won't know if the instructions work unless you watch a group of users try them out.

Use Imperative Voice and Action Verbs. Imperative sentences leave out the word *you* and begin with the verb. Use these sentences with strong action verbs when listing tasks. For example:

> Connect the cable.
>
> Insert the disk.
>
> Open the hatch.

See Chapter 3 and Appendix A for more information on this subject.

Keep It Simple. Brief instructions should be simple and to the point. Include only the information the user needs to perform that particular task. But direct the user to other sources (online help, website, manual) for further information, if needed.

Procedures

Procedures are documents that provide information, steps, and guidelines for completing a task. Longer than brief instructions, some procedures are used to instruct and train employees. Others are used to meet legal requirements and ensure safety. For example, the Canadian Centre for Occupational Health and Safety (CCOHS) requires employees in certain workplaces (factories, construction sites, hospitals) to follow strict safety procedures. These procedures must be updated according to new laws and policies, and the written procedures must be available for employees to read.

Procedures are also useful in situations where you want to standardize a task. If your company has several employees all performing the same task but doing so with different computers, different software, or different styles, it may be necessary to standardize these procedures so that everyone's work is compatible. A written document, called a standard operating procedure (SOP), becomes the formal explanation of how a particular task is done at that company.

Procedures are also part of the documentation and manuals that accompany new software, hardware, home appliances, and so on. Often these procedures will be written as brief instructions. Other times, they are more elaborate, depending on the audience's technical background, experience, and needs.

Audience and Purpose Analysis

Determine what knowledge your readers already have about the procedure. For example, in a manufacturing plant, many workers may be extremely familiar with the tasks they perform on a daily basis. But if a team that normally works with extruding equipment is asked to take over the mixing machines, those workers will need to be trained according to the standard procedures for that equipment. Your readers in this case would know the basics, because they've worked at the plant for years, but they would need detailed information on the specific machines, amounts of chemicals, and so on.

You may learn that the procedures will be used by multiple audiences, such as long-time employees, new trainees, and so on. In this case, you should consider using the *layered* approach (see Chapter 3): a quick reference procedure for those who need to refresh their memories and a more detailed document for new workers.

In terms of purpose, you need to determine how your readers will use these procedures. Will they use them to assemble a new computer or install software? Will the procedures be used on the factory floor to remind workers of the safest way to perform a task? Can your audience access the procedures on a computer (online help or the web), or do you need to create a paper document? Which medium is likely to be more effective in this situation? Once you know exactly how the procedures will be used, you can make decisions about the document's length, format, level of detail, and medium.

Types of Procedures

Standard Operating Procedures (SOPs). Figure 13.6 illustrates a standard operating procedure for using a special microscope in video-enhanced microscopy. This SOP is for students and researchers who wish to use the equipment. Because the procedure is lengthy, the document is broken into smaller chunks, easily accessible through a hyperlink (note that in a paper document, a table of contents would serve the same purpose). The procedures for each section are written in clear steps using imperative verbs such as *turn on, place,* and *focus.*

Introduction

This Standard Operating procedure applies to the Coherent Innova-90 argon-ion laser housed in Niagara College's High Power Laser Lab (V12). This class-IV laser features either multiline output (up to six wavelengths simultaneously) or single-wavelength with the use of the prism wavelength selector.

Statistics

Manufacturer: Coherent, Inc.
Type: Argon-Ion
Class: IV
Maximum Rated Power: 12 Watts CW
Wavelength Range (in current configuration): 454.5nm to 528.7nm
Cooling: Flowing Water, 2.2 gpm
Power Source: Three-Phase, 208V, 45A per phase

Operating Procedure

Revised 2004/01/16 by M. Csele

STARTING the laser

1. Don safety glasses suitable for an argon laser. These glasses must have an OD of at least 4 at both 488nm and 514nm.
2. Turn the cooling water supply ON. The valve is located behind the laser. Verify water flow if required by observing the output line to the drain (under the table).
3. If not already on, turn the three-phase supply (breakers in the black panel) ON.
4. Turn the LOCK switch on the laser control. The FAULT light and the WATER FLOW light will come on for a moment and should then disappear. If they do not disappear water flow is insufficient and this situation must be corrected before proceeding.
5. Ensure the AUTO START button is selected.
6. Adjust the WAVELENGTH SELECTOR on the control to read '514' if using broadband (multiline) optics. When using single-line optics, adjust the WAVELENGTH SELECTOR to the wavelength in use (note that this only affects output power - if an external power meter is used, this step may be optional).
7. Push the POWER RANGE button corresponding to the desired power range for the experiment (e.g. use the 0.5 Watt range when operation with a 400mW beam output is desired).
8. Ensure that the anticipated path of the output beam is terminated in a beam stop or into the optics of an experiment in progress.
9. Depress the ON pushbutton. The controller will display 'START DELAY' for 30 seconds during which time the cathode will preheat to operating temperature.

Figure 13.6 A Standard Operating Procedure. This document is part of a set of instrument instructions for Niagara College's Department of Technology. This SOP is available on a website, which makes it readily accessible to readers at different physical locations.
Source: Image taken from Niagara College Photonics and Lasers program, www.niagaracollege.ca.

Instructions (Long). Some procedures are written in the form of long instructions. For situations where your audience needs detailed material—a procedure with many parts and steps, such as assembling and starting up a new computer—you would want to create long instructions. These instructions might be turned into a manual (see "Documentation and Manuals" later in this chapter), a website, or a CD-ROM. Figure 13.7 is a portion of a set of long instructions on installing glass block. Note the use of diagrams, bullets, and lettered lists to provide the list of steps and clear illustrations.

Typical Components of Procedures

Title. Create a brief, succinct title that clearly states what this procedure is about; for example, "Setting Up Your New iPad2."

Overview. For longer procedures or those designed for audiences who are new to the task, provide a brief overview of how to use the document and what the document contains.

Mortar I System

The tools required for the Mortar I glass block installation system are a margin trowel, mortar pan, polyfoam brush, sponge, tin snips, screwdriver or power drill, fine tooth saw or miter saw, caulking gun, utility knife, metal file, tape measure, 3/8" to 1/2" striking tool and 2' level.

1. Prepare The Rough Opening

A. Make sure the opening is the correct size. To determine the correct size of the rough opening, add 1/4" to the sum of the nominal block sizes for both the height and width.

Example: Panel (using 8" x 8" block) is four block wide (8 x 4 + 1/4" = 32-1/4") and five block high (8 x 5 + 1/4" = 40-1/4"). Rough opening needs to be 32-1/4" wide and 40-1/4" high.

B. Use a level to make sure the opening is level and plumb.
C. Measure the opening diagonally from corner to corner in both directions, and compare the dimensions to check for squareness. These dimensions should be equal to within 1/8".

Note: If there are any problems with the opening, make adjustments before proceeding.

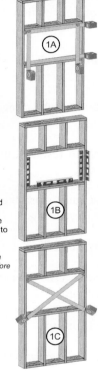

2. Install Perimeter Channel

A. Cut the channel to fit the perimeter of the opening. The channel ends may be cut straight or mitered.

　　a. If cutting the ends straight:
　　　　• Cut the top and bottom channels to the width of the opening.
　　　　• Cut the side channels to the height of the opening minus 1-1/2" so they will fit between the top and bottom channels.

　　b. If mitering the ends, make all cuts at a 45° angle.
B. Cut the top channel in half lengthwise with a utility knife. Score the center groove with the knife and break the channel in half.

Note: *Cutting the top channel in half will allow the top row of blocks to be installed.*
C. Install the bottom channel:

　　• The channel may be installed in the center of the opening, or flush with the interior or exterior side of the opening.
　　• Attach the channel to the opening by inserting #6 x 1" flat head galvanized screws through the predrilled holes in the channel. Insert two screws in each end of the channel.

Note: *If the predrilled holes at the ends were trimmed off when cutting the channel to length, drill new ones at the ends of the cut piece.*

Figure 13.7 Long Instructions for Installing Glass Block. These two pages are part of a 30-page document available as a PDF file from the manufacturer's website. Note the detailed step-by-step information, the use of white space and bullets to organize the information, and the clear, simple illustrations.
Source: Courtesy of Pittsburgh Corning Corporation.

List of Steps. With few exceptions, procedures require audiences to follow explicit steps. Make your steps clear and number them with large enough type so readers can easily return to a particular step if they look away from the document.

Warnings and Cautions. Procedures routinely include advice about avoiding injury or equipment damage. In technical writing, safety information is generally conveyed through the following four types of information, listed in order from least to most serious.

Note: Clarifies a point, emphasizes vital information, or describes options or alternatives.

> **NOTE:** If you don't name a newly initialized disk, the computer automatically names it "Untitled."

Caution: Indicates possible mistakes that could result in injury or equipment damage.

> **CAUTION:** A momentary electrical surge could erase the contents of your working document, so make sure you back up your data.

Warning: Alerts users to potential hazards to life or limb.

> **WARNING:** To prevent electrical shock, always disconnect your printer from its power source before you clean any internal parts.

Danger: Identifies an immediate hazard to life or limb.

> **DANGER:** The red canister contains DEADLY radioactive material. Do not break the safety seal under any circumstances.

You can visually emphasize these items with hazard symbols like these:

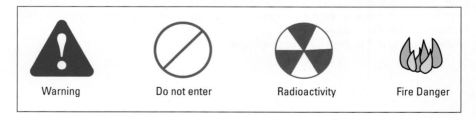

| Warning | Do not enter | Radioactivity | Fire Danger |

Procedure Number and Revision Dates. Many procedures, especially SOPs, are given procedure numbers so that users can refer to a particular document.

Instead of asking for "the SOP about waste disposal" (which could mean one of many documents), an engineer can ask for SOP 35.2. The number before the period (35) indicates the SOP itself, and the number after the period (2) indicates the revision. Many SOPs also list the revision date somewhere on the document itself.

Usability Considerations

Understand the Physical Location Where People Will Use the Information. Will people use the procedures on the factory floor? If so, your materials may need to be in large type to allow for less-than-perfect lighting. You may also need to think about using plastic-coated pages in a binder or other ways to protect the material in certain settings. If users of the document are located in an office, working at a computer, for example, you may want to design a document that stays open easily (by using a comb binding, for example) so that people can read and type at the same time. In other cases, you may want to put the instructions directly on the equipment.

Understand the Purpose and Tasks for this Document. Go back to your audience and purpose analysis and make sure you know how and why your audience will use this document. If workers need to refer to the standard operating procedures while in the middle of a task, they won't want to search for the information. Therefore, headings should be clear, steps should be listed in order, and each page should be visually accessible.

Understand the Technical Expertise of Your Audience. How much background do your users have? Experienced users need only new information, whereas novice users need help getting started. In addition, individual readers may scrutinize the document more carefully, while teams may pass the document back and forth, jumping from item to item. Make sure your document is easy to read and steps are clearly numbered, especially if it is for teams.

Test Your Documents. Make sure you test the usability of your procedures on a small group of users. Procedures often address serious safety issues, so test your document to be sure people are using it as you intended. (See Chapter 3 for more information on usability testing.)

Use Active Voice. For the parts of the procedures that give specific instructions, use active voice and imperative mood. For example, write "Insert the bolt," "Remove the wiring insulation," or "Insert the disk."

Organize Content Chronologically. List the steps in the order you want users to perform them. Number the steps, and refer to individual steps by number, not by content ("Return to Step 4 and repeat this function").

Documentation and Manuals

Documentation and manuals are used in many of the situations and for many of the document types described here and in Chapter 7. Documentation may include brief instructions, procedures, or descriptions. It may also describe processes and provide background on the product. Some documentation comes as a set of manuals. In a large sense, documentation is meant to do what its name implies: to *document* (provide all the supporting information for) a scientific or technical product, suite of products (such as a multimedia system consisting of many pieces of hardware and software), or services.

Documentation is called for when you have a complex product that requires users to have a broad range of information. Often documentation is written in a *layered* format: a large manual with all the technical details for programmers and high-end users, a quick reference card for those who just need reminders of the main keys and tasks, and a "getting started" brochure for people who want to jump right in.

More and more, documentation is published online. If you buy a new computer, it often comes with a thin instruction manual, which contains just enough information to get you started. Once you have the machine up and running, you can access the entire library of information through the system's online help screens. Electronic documentation and manuals can be superior to paper because users can search for terms quickly without paging through an index or table of contents. In addition, online information is often *context-sensitive:* If you need help in the middle of a task (trying to save a file, for example), you can often get help with that task as you are attempting to perform it (see Chapter 3).

Although the term *documentation* refers to many types of documents, our discussion here focuses on manuals.

Audience and Purpose Analysis

Determine the audience's technical background and level of familiarity with the product. Often a company may choose to produce a manual as part of a library of information products to accompany the main product. For example, if your company writes business software for networked computers, your audience may be vast. You may discover that your audience includes the following groups:

- *Network administrators,* who need to know the product's technical specifications;
- *Managers,* who need to understand the bottom-line—business details of the software;
- *Sales representatives,* who need a more detailed understanding of the product so they can use it to generate quotes and keep track of customers.

Your first task would be to determine which of these users requires which type of documentation. Network administrators may need the largest manual, because they will need to troubleshoot an entire range of problems, from user errors to system crashes.

In terms of purpose, learn all you can about how your audience will use the document and what tasks people need to perform. For example, after conducting interviews and studying the daily activities of network administrators, you may discover that they spend 50 percent of their time looking up user errors, 10 percent checking out potential system errors, and 40 percent updating the system and running reports. This analysis should guide you in creating a manual that focuses first on user errors, followed in importance by system updates and reports.

Types of Manuals

A complete manual contains background information, specifications, descriptions, and procedures, all in one document. This type of manual is appropriate for a situation or product that is straightforward—a home appliance, a computer peripheral (scanner or printer), or a simple software application. For more complex products or services, a single document that contained all information would be too large, making it hard for mixed audiences to access. Novices would find leafing through the specifications frustrating, and experts would find all the getting-started information superfluous.

Increasingly common, especially for computer equipment, is a more concise type of manual. Often printed in small-book format, the concise manual might offer computer start-up instructions, brief specifications, and basic operating tips. The more lengthy and helpful information is in the computer software (online help), and users can access this information once they've started up the machine.

Typical Components of Manuals

Overview.   Because manuals are often large documents, it is important to provide your readers with a road map before they get started. An overview section can be brief, and it should outline what the manual contains and how users should approach the document.

Access Points.   Users may only need to find one piece of information in a large manual, so make sure your access points—table of contents (see Figure 13.8), running heads, and index—are well developed and easy to use. Test them to see if users can actually find what they are looking for.

Table of Contents

Introduction   **4**

Preface 4
Hardware Requirements.. 5
Software Installation 6
License Agreement/Disclaimer.. 6

Mode of Operation   **8**

Overview.. 8
Example Circuits.. 8
General Purpose Schematic Driven SPICE 9
Externally Generated Netlists.. 10
Efficiency Report 11
Command Line Switches... 13

Schematic Capture   **14**

Basic Schematic Editing... 14
Label a node name... 17
Schematic Colors 19
Placing New Components 20
Programming Keyboard Shortcuts 20
PCB Netlist Extraction 21
Editing Components 22
    Edit a Visible Attribute... 22
    Specialized Component Editors... 23
    General Attribute Editor 24
Creating New Symbols 26
    Symbol Editing Overview... 26
    Drawing the body 27
    Adding the Pins 27
    Adding Attributes... 28
    Attribute Visibility... 30
    Automatic Symbol Generation 31
Hierarchy 32
    Hierarchy Overview... 32
    Rules of Hierarchy.. 32
    Navigating the Hierarchy.. 33

Waveform Viewer   **35**

Waveform Viewer Overview 35
Data Trace Selection 35
Zooming... 40
Waveform Arithmetic 40
User-Defined Functions.. 47
Axis Control 48
Plot Panes 48
Color Control... 49
Attached Cursors... 50
Save Plot Configurations 54
Fast Access File Format... 55

Figure 13.8 **An Effective Table of Contents.**
Source: Courtesy Linear Technology Corp.

Chapters. In longer manuals, divide the material into chapters. Each chapter contains a logical grouping of information: "Getting Started," "Installing the Printer," "Connecting to the Network," and so on. Order chapters in the sequence you want users to encounter the information. If the manual contains more than 10 chapters, you might group the chapters into sections: "Section One: Getting Started," "Section Two: For Network Administrators," "Section Three: Specifications." Each section would then contain approximately three to six chapters.

Reference Information. No manual can contain everything every user will need. So make sure you provide a web address, email address, and telephone number for users to contact someone if they get stuck or need more information.

Usability Considerations

Determine the Appropriate Medium. For large-scale computer systems, documentation may be delivered in many ways. For example, it may be printed and bound into several volumes, often in three-ring binders. Each binder may contain a specific category of information: user error codes, system messages, and so on. In addition, this information may also be delivered via the web or on a CD. If you can, use the document type that is most familiar to the audience. And if you need to upgrade (for example, if your company determines that the printed format becomes outdated too quickly and the information should be delivered entirely via the web), make sure you provide plenty of transition time for the users. Allow users to have their paper manuals and the new electronic information at the same time until they become familiar with the new medium.

Also, if you intend to use both paper and electronic documentation, plan them at the same time to make sure the terminology and information are consistent.

Understand What Information Your Audience Does and Doesn't Need. In the old days of written manuals, writers tended to include every detail about the product. Often manual writers were engineers who worked closely on the project and were eager to explain all the technical details, the history of the project, and so on. Although this might be interesting to some readers, end users generally don't need this sort of information.

Understand the Physical Location Where People Will Use the Information. If users of the document are working at a computer in an office, for example, you may want to design a manual that stays open easily so people can read and type at the same time. If your audience is network administrators, who are usually able to access the system when they encounter a problem, consider placing the information online.

Write from the User's Point of View. Manuals are for users, and they should be written to reflect user needs. Instead of abstract headings, such as "Installation of the Microprocessor," try writing from the user's point of view. Headings in the form of questions a user might actually ask, such as "How do I install the microprocessor?" can be very helpful. Also, make sure your material reflects what users really *care* about. If a long history of the product is not appropriate for this audience, omit it.

Include Diagrams, Screen Samples, and Illustrations. Because manuals can be long documents, it's helpful to break up the text with visuals (see Figure 13.9). Visuals can also provide users with a clearer idea of what to do or what to look for on the screen.

Adopt a Style That Is Appropriate for Your Audience. Most of the time, a neutral, informative style is most appropriate for a manual. However, for certain subjects, a more informal, energized style may be useful. Consider the following examples from the Conflict Catcher user manual. (Conflict Catcher software helped Macintosh users solve problems with system crashes, freeze-ups, and other technical difficulties with early versions of its operating system.)

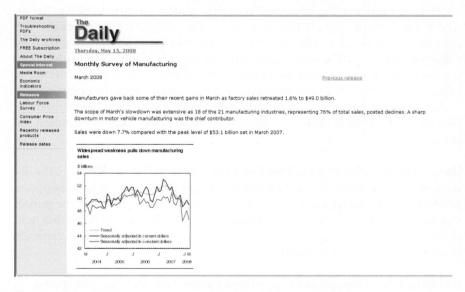

Figure 13.9 **Page from a Statistics Canada Report That Combines Text and Visuals.**
Source: Statistics Canada, www.statcan.ca/Daily/English/080515/d080515a.htm, September 5, 2008.

"Conflict Catcher's ability to *tame these little programs* can have considerable impact on your daily Macintosh life." (p. 3)

"On the other hand, there's *no need for paranoia.* When a System Folder is truly corrupted, the problematic file is frequently the System Suitcase file." (p. 96)

Note the upbeat, almost comic ring to these sentences. "Tame these little programs" and "no need for paranoia" are not standard phrases in technical writing. But in the case of this software, the writer probably knew that users who need Conflict Catcher are already in a bad mood because of computer trouble. The casual tone is designed to calm users down and get them to focus on the material so they can solve the problem.

Checklist for Instructions, Procedures, and Manuals

Content
- Is the material based on a prior task analysis?
- Does the title promise exactly what the instructions deliver?
- Is the background adequate for the intended audience?
- Is all needless information omitted?
- Do notes, cautions, or warnings appear before the step, whenever needed?
- Are visuals adequate for clarifying the steps?
- Has the document been tested for usability by actual audience members?
- Is follow-up/contact information provided for users to obtain assistance?
- Is the user directed to other sources (online help, website, manual) for further information if needed?

Organization
- Does the introduction provide a brief overview of the task?
- Do the instructions follow the exact sequence of steps?
- Is all the information for a particular step close together?
- Are visuals beside or near the step, and set off by white space?

Style
- Do steps generally have short sentences?
- Does each step begin with an action verb?
- Are all steps in the active voice and imperative mood?
- Are the terms used for specific parts/steps consistent throughout?
- Is the style appropriate for the audience?

Page Design
- Do white space and highlights set off discussion from steps?
- Are the steps in a numbered list?
- Are notes, cautions, or warnings set off or highlighted?
- Is the design based on the physical location where people will use the information?
- For a long document, are there enough access points for users to find what they are looking for—including chapter divisions if needed?

Technical Marketing Material

Technical marketing material is designed to persuade an audience to purchase a product or service. Unlike proposals (see Chapter 14), which are also used to sell a product or service, technical marketing materials tend to be less formal and more dynamic, colourful, and varied. A typical proposal is tailored to one client's specific needs and usually follows a standard format; marketing literature, by contrast, seeks to present the product in its best light for a broad array of audiences and needs. And unlike non-technical sales material, technical marketing documents are designed for science and technology products and are often aimed at knowledgeable readers. A team of scientists looking to purchase a new electron microscope wants marketing material that provides specific technical information. Even for a general audience (for example, home computer users), technical marketing material must deal with specialized concepts not ordinarily found in non-technical sales materials.

Technical communicators with a flair for the creative are often hired as technical marketing specialists. Some situations that call for technical marketing material include the following:

- *Cold calls*: Sales representatives sending material to a range of potential new customers;
- *On-site visits*: Sales representatives and technical experts visiting a customer to see if a new product or service might be of interest;
- *Display booths*: Booths at industry trade shows displaying engaging, interesting material that people can take away to read at their leisure;
- *Web information*: Webpages serving as the primary place users go to find information on a technical product or service.

Audience and Purpose Analysis

When creating marketing materials, you need a clear sense of your audience. Who are the readers of these materials: Managers? Technical experts? Purchasing agents? The level of technical language you use will be based on the answer. Also, make sure you know how audiences will use the documents. The main purpose of most marketing materials is to make potential customers aware of your product or service and to sell them your particular company, brand, or model. Marketing materials are essentially persuasive documents.

Types of Technical Marketing Material

Brochures. The term *brochure* covers many types of documents. A typical brochure is a standard-size piece of paper folded in thirds, but a brochure can be designed in many sizes, depending on purpose, audience, and budget. Brochures are used to introduce a product or service, provide pricing information, and explain how customers can contact the company.

Webpages. Many companies are using the web for their marketing materials. The advantage of a webpage (see Figure 13.10) over a printed document is that if you change the price, specifications, version, look and feel, or other features of

Figure 13.10 **Websites are easily updated when a product is changed or a new version is released.**

Source: Used with permission from Hewlett-Packard (Canada) Co.

the product, you can easily make immediate changes to the website. Webpages also allow you to build in interactivity: customers can give you feedback, request additional information, or place orders.

Letters.   Letters can also be used for technical marketing. If a potential customer requests details about a product or service, you may send this information along with a brief cover letter. The letter should not only thank the customer for his or her interest, but also point out the specific features of your product or service that match this customer's needs.

Large Colour Documents. Some companies produce technical marketing material that is far more comprehensive than a typical brochure. If you've ever looked at the glossy booklets for a new car, you've seen how these large colour documents market a product. The high-quality photography, slick colour printing, and glossy feel are designed to evoke the feeling of owning a new car. These booklets also include technical specifications, such as engine horsepower and wheelbase size.

Typical Components of Technical Marketing Material

Name of Product.   Most technical marketing material is designed to explain a product, so the name of this product should be clear and prominent.

Category or Type of Product or Service.   It is important to place your product in relation to others of its class. For example, a brochure for a pacemaker will explain that this product is a medical device and will compare the pacemaker to other similar medical devices.

Features. Technical marketing material should describe the product's main features and explain the distinguishing features of this specific product.

Technical Specifications.   Many types of technical marketing materials provide specifications: product size, weight, electrical requirements, and so on.

Visuals. Visuals, especially diagrams and colour photographs, are extremely effective in marketing materials. On the web, you can use colour easily and efficiently. Four-colour brochures are expensive to print, but colour on the web is simply a matter of using the correct HTML tags.

Frequently Asked Questions (FAQs). Some marketing materials attempt to answer customer questions with a "frequently asked questions" (FAQ) section.

Usability Considerations

Learn as Much as You Can About the Background and Experience of Decision Makers. Although your materials may be read by a range of people, your main goal is to get the attention of those who make the final policy and purchasing decisions. So your brochure, website, or other material should be geared toward their level of expertise and needs. For example, the medical device brochure in Figure 13.11 uses technical language ("flex fatigue") for its audience of medical professionals, whereas the car battery brochure in Figure 13.12 uses simpler language for a more general audience. Also, if you know that the decision makers value a product's effectiveness over its cost, emphasize quality, not price. For example, although cost is always a factor, physicians ultimately want medical devices to work properly.

Use Upbeat, Dynamic Language. Be careful not to overdo it though. Technical people tend to dislike an obvious sales pitch.

Use Visuals and Colour. Colour images can accurately convey the shape and feel of the item; also, colour can add excitement and visual interest to your materials. If you create both print and web material, make sure your colour choices are consistent so that you convey an overall look and feel for your company and product.

Emphasize the Special Appeal of This Product or Service. Briefly explain how this product or service fits the reader's exact needs, and provide solid evidence to support your claim.

 Checklist for Technical Marketing Material

- Is the document based on a detailed audience and purpose analysis?
- Is the material geared toward the needs and level of expertise of the ultimate decision makers?
- Is the format (brochure, webpage, letter, etc.) appropriate?
- Is the name of the product highly visible?
- Is the product clearly situated in relation to others in its class?
- Does the document describe the product's main features as well as unique features?
- Does the document emphasize the special appeal of this product or service?
- Does the document provide the product's technical specifications, as needed?
- Is an FAQ list included, as needed?
- Are visuals used extensively and effectively?
- Is colour used effectively to convey an overall look and feel for the company and the product?
- Is the language dynamic and upbeat—without sounding like a sales pitch?

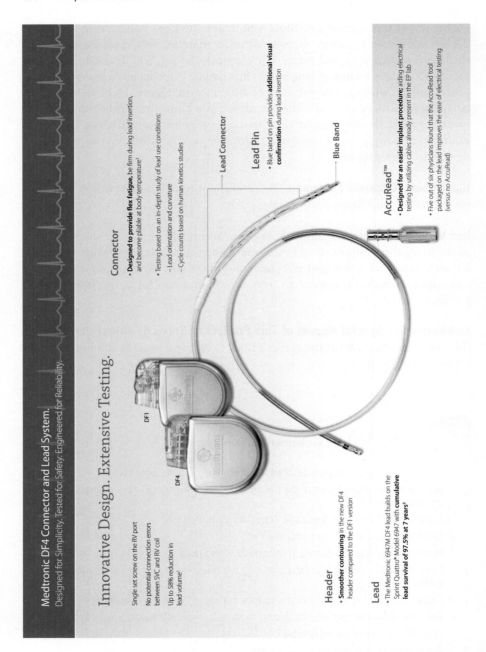

Figure 13.11 A Brochure for Medical Devices. This brochure clearly shows the product and its parts. The bullet points address the audience of medical professionals.
Source: Medtronic, Inc.

Outside panels

Inside panels

Figure 13.12   A Three-Panel, Foldout Brochure for a General Audience. The three-dimensional illustration in outside panel A enables readers to visualize the product immediately. Inside panel B—at the brochure's very centre and highlighted by a yellow screen—convincingly supports panel A's claim by listing the features and specifications that make this battery special. *Source:* Courtesy of Toyota Motor Sales, U.S.A., Inc.

Exercises

1. How do specifications come into play in your workplace or even your home? Find one example of specs used in your home or workplace, and complete a usability analysis. For example, if you recently purchased an item that needed to be assembled, it probably came with a list of parts. How easily were you able to find the parts listed in the specs? What could the writers have done to improve the usability of this document?

2. Choose a pair of manuals for the same product but targeted at two different audiences—for example, a Honda Canada owner's manual and its simplified version. How do the instructions differ? Is the language appropriate for the audiences? How are the visuals different?

3. Choose a set of instructions for a media device, such as an iPod, Blu-ray disc player, BlackBerry, or Nintendo 3DS. Rewrite the instructions for a different audience. What details do you need to add or omit? Then trade your instructions with someone else in your group to test their usability.

4. **FOCUS ON WRITING.** Find two examples of product documentation, one that you consider good and one that you think is bad. These can be from any source. With one or two other students, list the features that make the good one good and the bad one bad. Then draft a memo to the writer of the bad documentation, outlining things he or she should do to improve on the next version.

The Collaboration Window

For this project, work in groups of four. Two group members will serve as marketing managers, with the task of presenting a new product to an audience of potential clients and customers. The other two group members will serve as engineering specialists, with the task of developing the specifications and technical features of the product that marketing is planning to present. Your group has been asked by the CEO to prepare a range of technical marketing materials that can be used by sales reps to sell the new product.

First, determine the product that you are going to develop marketing materials for. Will it be a new piece of software? A new digital media device? A medical tool or device? Once you have decided, the engineering team should develop specifications for the new product while the marketing team decides what features should be highlighted in marketing the new product.

Working as a group, first prepare an audience and purpose analysis for your product. To whom will you primarily be selling it? What are their needs, and how are you going to meet their needs with your new product? How can you persuade them to purchase your product?

Once your audience analysis is complete, decide as a group what media you want to use to reach that audience: Brochures? A website? Live presentations? Posters? Choose the two most effective media for your audience, and focus on them.

Working collaboratively, create draft versions of your marketing materials in the two selected media. For a more intensive project, revise your draft versions and develop finished working models of your technical marketing materials. Prepare a brief presentation to share your sales pitch and marketing materials with the rest of your class.

The Global Window

Assume the following scenario: Members of your environmental consulting firm travel in teams worldwide on short notice to manage various environmental emergencies (toxic spills, chemical fires, and the like). Because of the rapid response required for these assignments and the international array of clients being served, team members have little or no time to research the particular cultural values of each client. Members typically find themselves having to establish immediate rapport and achieve agreement as they collaborate with clients during highly stressful situations.

Too often, however, ignorance of cultural differences leads to misunderstanding and needless delays in critical situations. Clients can lose face when they feel they are being overtly criticized and when their customs or values are ignored. When people feel insulted, or offended by inappropriate behaviour, communication breaks down.

To avoid such problems, your boss has asked you to prepare a set of brief, general instructions titled "How to Avoid Offending International Clients." For immediate access, the instructions should fit on a pocket-sized quick reference card.

Working alone or in groups, do the research and design the reference card.

MyCanadianTechCommLab

Go to MyCanadianTechCommLab at www.mycanadiantechcommlab.com for additional online exercises and problems.

CHAPTER 14

Complex Communication Situations

Chapter Objectives

By the end of this chapter you will be able to:

1. Write definitions and descriptions.

2. Write a proposal.

3. Write a report in a standard format.

Janaka Abeyaratna, Montreal, Quebec

A graduate of Concordia University's Physics program, Janaka Abeyaratna now works as a senior software engineer in Montreal. Having worked in the software industry for over 20 years, he has seen and experienced first-hand the changes that his field of employment has gone through. He notes that one of the biggest obstacles that the software industry still needs to overcome is a lack of understanding of the actual problem or task at hand: too many companies place too much emphasis on the "code first, think later" approach. Janaka thinks that "without good documentation, it is next to impossible to develop good design documentation, forcing the developer to code blindly in the same way a construction worker would try to build a high-rise without a blueprint."

He says that his success relies on "critical teamwork, the importance of understanding the needs of clients, communicating with them, and documenting their needs and providing them with solutions."

Definitions and Descriptions

Definitions explain a term or concept that is specialized or unfamiliar to an audience. In some cases, a term may have more than one meaning, and a clearly written definition tells readers exactly how the term is being used. Such precision is important in technical fields, where terms and phrases usually have specific meanings. Engineers talk about "elasticity" or "ductility"; bankers discuss "amortization" or "fiduciary relationships." For people both inside and outside the fields, these terms must be defined.

Descriptions, like definitions, help define an idea. In addition, descriptions use words and visuals to create a picture of the product or process, such as the structure of a bicycle frame or the process of nuclear fusion.

Definitions and descriptions are interrelated and provide the basis for virtually any type of technical explanation. For example, an audience of electrical engineering students may need a definition of a solenoid, a turbine, or some other electrical component and a description of their parts. Lay audiences often need descriptions and definitions to tell them what a circuit breaker is and how it works in the case of a power surge.

Audience and Purpose Analysis

When writing definitions and descriptions, make sure the language and content match the audience's background and experience. For a group of electrical engineers, your definition or description of a solenoid can be brief and to the point, and you can use highly technical language. For engineering students, your definition would need more detail. For general audiences, your definition would require simplified language without technical jargon. See Figure 14.1 for a definition and description that includes a diagram to help general readers understand the entire process by which chemical contaminants are removed from soil. Figure 14.2 is a brief description of a stethoscope for nursing students.

In determining the purpose of a definition or description, you need to understand why a particular audience needs or wants this information. If you are describing an automobile bumper jack for a general audience (as in Figure 14.3), you may learn that your readers' main purpose is to understand how the jack works so that they can use it to change a car tire. Therefore, the description or definition should be written in clear language and should avoid highly technical terms. It should follow an outline format or other layout that uses headings and white space so that readers can get in and out of the document quickly. And it should include diagrams or drawings to help readers see the whole picture.

Types of Definitions and Descriptions

Brief Definitions and Brief Descriptions. Often you can clarify the meaning of a word by using a more familiar synonym or a clarifying phrase, as in

| The *leaching field* (sieve-like drainage area) requires crushed stone.

Dubbed the "lasagna" process because of its layers, this technology cleans up liquid-borne organic and inorganic contaminants in dense, claylike soils. Initial work is focused on removing chlorinated solvents.

Because clay is not very permeable, it holds ground water and other liquids well. Traditional remediation for this type of site requires that the liquid in the soil (usually ground water) be pumped out. The water brings many of the contaminants with it, then is chemically treated and replaced—a time-consuming and expensive solution.

The lasagna process, on the other hand, allows the soil to be remediated *in situ* by using low-voltage electric current to move contaminated ground water through treatment zones in the soil. Depending on the characteristics of the individual site, the process can be done in either a horizontal or vertical configuration. (See figure below.)

The first step in the lasagna process is to "fracture" the soil, creating a series of zones. In a horizontal configuration, a vertical borehole is drilled and a nozzle inserted; a highly pressurized mixture of water

and sand (or another water/solid mix) is injected into the ground at various depths. The result: a stack of pancake-shaped, permeable zones in the denser, contaminated soil. The top and bottom zones are filled with carbon or graphite so they can conduct electricity. The zones between them are filled with treatment chemicals or microorganisms that will remediate the contaminants.

When electricity is applied to the carbon and graphite zones, they act as electrodes, creating an electric field. Within the field, the materials in the soil migrate toward either the positive or negative electrode. Along with the migrating materials, pollutants are carried into the treatment zones, where they are neutralized or destroyed.

The vertical configuration works in much the same way, differing only in installation. Because the electrodes and treatment zones extend down from the surface, this configuration does not require the sophisticated hydraulic fracturing techniques that are used in the horizontal configuration.

Schematic Diagram of the Lasagna Process

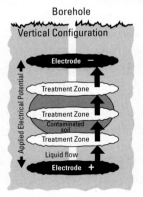
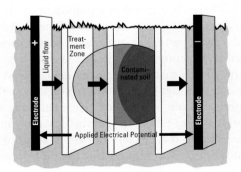

Figure 14.1 **A Definition and Description of the "Lasagna Process" for Filtering Contaminants Out of Soil.**
Source: Adapted from Japikse (1994), p. 27.

A Description of the Standard Stethoscope

The stethoscope is a listening device that amplifies and transmits body sounds to aid in detecting physical abnormalities.

This instrument has evolved from the original wooden, funnel-shaped instrument invented by a French physician, R. T. Lennaec, in 1819. Because of his female patients' modesty, he found it necessary to develop a device, other than his ear, for auscultation (listening to body sounds).

This report explains to the beginning paramedical or nursing student the structure, assembly, and operating principle of the stethoscope.

The standard stethoscope is roughly 24 inches long and weighs about 5 ounces. The instrument consists of a sensitive sound-detecting and amplifying device whose flat surface is pressed against a bodily area. This amplifying device is attached to rubber and metal tubing that transmits the body sound to a listening device inserted in the ear.

The stethoscope's Y-shaped structure contains seven interlocking pieces: (1) diaphragm contact piece, (2) lower tubing, (3) Y-shaped metal piece, (4) upper tubing, (5) U-shaped metal strip, (6) curved metal tubing, and (7) hollow ear plugs. These parts form a continuous unit (Figure 1).

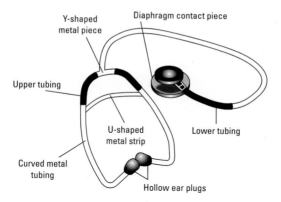

FIGURE 1 Stethoscope with Diaphragm Contact Piece (Front View)

The seven major parts of the stethoscope provide support for the instrument, flexibility of movement for the operator, and ease in use.

In an operating cycle, the diaphragm contact piece, placed against the skin, picks up sound impulses from the body's surface. These impulses cause the plastic diaphragm to vibrate. The amplified vibrations, in turn, are carried through a tube to a dividing point. From here, the amplified sound is carried through two separate but identical series of tubes to hollow ear plugs.

Figure 14.2 **A Short Description of a Standard Stethoscope.**

I. Introduction: General Description

A. Definition, Function, and Background of the Item
B. Purpose (and Audience—for classroom only)
C. Overall Description (with general visuals, if applicable)
D. Principle of Operation (if applicable)
E. List of Major Parts

II. Description and Function of Parts

A. Part One in Your Descriptive Sequence
   1. Definition
   2. Shape, dimensions, material (with specific visuals)
   3. Subparts (if applicable)
   4. Function
   5. Relation to adjoining parts
   6. Mode of attachment (if applicable)
B. Part Two in Your Descriptive Sequence (and so on)

III. Summary and Operating Description

A. Summary (used only in a long, complex description)
B. Interrelation of Parts
C. One Complete Operating Cycle

Figure 14.3 A Longer Description of an Automobile Bumper Jack. This first page provides an outline of the description.

Description of a Standard Bumper Jack

Introduction—General Description

The standard bumper jack is a portable mechanism for raising the front or rear of a car through force applied with a lever. This jack enables even a frail person to lift one corner of a 2-ton automobile.

The jack consists of a molded steel base supporting a free-standing, perpendicular, notched shaft (Figure 1). Attached to the shaft are a leverage mechanism, a bumper catch, and a cylinder for insertion of the jack handle. Except for the main shaft and leverage mechanism, the jack is made to be dismantled. All its parts fit neatly in the car's trunk.

The jack operates on a leverage principle, with the operator's hand traveling 18 inches and the car only $\frac{3}{8}$ of an inch during a normal jacking stroke. Such a device requires many strokes to raise the car off the ground but may prove a lifesaver to a motorist on some deserted road.

Five main parts make up the jack: base, notched shaft, leverage mechanism, bumper catch, and handle.

Description of Parts and Their Function

Base. The rectangular base is a molded steel plate that provides support and a point of insertion for the shaft (Figure 2). The base slopes upward to form a platform containing a 1-inch depression that provides a stabilizing well for the shaft. Stability is increased by a 1-inch cuff around the well. As the base rests on its flat surface, the bottom end of the shaft is inserted into its stabilizing well.

Shaft. The notched shaft is a steel bar (32 inches long) that provides a vertical track for the leverage mechanism. The notches, which hold the mechanism in position on the shaft, face the operator.

The shaft vertically supports the raised automobile, and attached to it is the leverage mechanism, which rests on individual notches.

Leverage Mechanism. The leverage mechanism provides the mechanical advantage needed for the operator to raise the car. It is made to slide up and down the notched shaft. The main body of this pressed-steel mechanism contains two units: one for transferring the leverage and one for holding the bumper catch.

The leverage unit has four major parts: the cylinder, connecting the handle and a pivot point; a lower pawl (a device that fits into the notches to allow forward and prevent backward motion), connected directly to the cylinder; an upper pawl, connected at the pivot point; and an "up-down" lever,

Figure 14.3 (*Continued*)

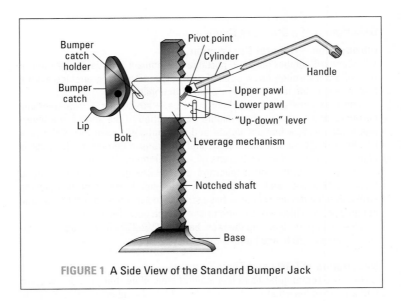

FIGURE 1 A Side View of the Standard Bumper Jack

which applies or releases pressure on the upper pawl by means of a spring (Figure 1). Moving the cylinder up and down with the handle causes the alternate release of the pawls, and thus movement up or down the shaft—depending on the setting of the "up-down" lever. The movement is transferred by the metal body of the unit to the bumper catch holder.

The holder consists of a downsloping groove, partially blocked by a wire spring (Figure 1). The spring is mounted in such a way as to keep the bumper catch in place during operation.

Bumper Catch. The bumper catch is a 9-inch molded plate that attaches the leverage mechanism to the bumper and is bent to fit the shape of the bumper. Its outer $\frac{1}{2}$ inch is bent up to form a lip (Figure 1), which hooks behind the bumper to hold the catch in place. The two sides of the plate are bent back 90 degrees to leave a 2-inch bumper contact surface, and a bolt is riveted between them. This bolt slips into the groove in the leverage mechanism and provides the attachment between the leverage unit and the car.

Jack Handle. The jack handle is a steel bar that serves both as lever and lug bolt (or lugnut) remover. This round bar is 22 inches long, $\frac{5}{8}$ inch in diameter, and is bent 135 degrees roughly 5 inches from its outer end. Its outer

Figure 14.3 (*Continued*)

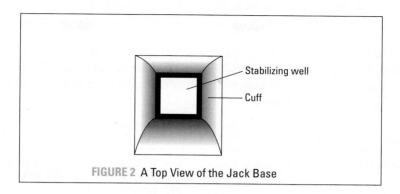

FIGURE 2 A Top View of the Jack Base

end is a socket wrench made to fit the wheel's lug bolts. Its inner end is beveled to form a bladelike point for prying the wheel covers and for insertion into the cylinder on the leverage mechanism.

Conclusion and Operating Description

One quickly assembles the jack by inserting the bottom of the notched shaft into the stabilizing well in the base, the bumper catch into the groove on the leverage mechanism, and the beveled end of the jack handle into the cylinder. The bumper catch is then attached to the bumper, with the lever set in the "up" position.

As the operator exerts an up-down pumping motion on the jack handle, the leverage mechanism gradually climbs the vertical notched shaft until the car's wheel is raised above the ground. When the lever is in the "down" position, the same pumping motion causes the leverage mechanism to descend the shaft.

Figure 14.3 (*Continued*)

In an online document, such as a webpage or online help system, short definitions such as these can easily be linked to the main word or phrase. A user who clicks on "leaching field" would link to a window that contains the definition and other important information.

A slightly longer way to define a phrase is to use the *term-class-features* method. Begin by stating the *term*. Then indicate the broader *class* that this item belongs to, followed by the *features* that distinguish it from other items in that general grouping. Here are some examples:

Term	Class	Features
Carburetor:	A mixing device...	in gasoline engines that blends air and fuel into a vapour for combustion within the cylinders.
Diabetes:	A metabolic disease ...	caused by a disorder of the pituitary gland or pancreas.

Brief definitions are sufficient when the audience does not require a great deal of information. For example, a single-sentence definition of a leaching field might be adequate in a progress report to a client whose house you are building. But a document that requires more detail, such as a public health report on groundwater contamination, would call for an expanded definition.

Expanded Definitions. Expanded definitions are discussion-length definitions, appropriate when audiences require more detail. Depending on audience and purpose, an expanded definition may be a single paragraph or may be several pages long. For example, if a new device, such as a digital dosimeter (used for measuring radiation exposure), is being introduced for the first time to an audience who needs to understand how this instrument works, your definition would require at least several paragraphs. In such cases, your document would evolve from a simple definition to one that both defines and describes the device.

Typical Components of Expanded Definitions and Descriptions

Etymology. Sometimes a word's origin (etymology) can help users understand its meaning. *Biometrics,* for example, is derived from the Greek *bio,* meaning "life," and *metron,* meaning "measure." You can use a dictionary to learn the origins of most words. Explaining the etymology at the beginning of a definition or description helps the reader remember the term.

History and Background. In some cases, the history or background of a term, concept, or procedure can be useful in defining and describing it. For students or researchers who want in-depth information, history and background are appropriate. However, for users trying to perform a task, history and background can be cumbersome and unnecessary. For example, if someone wanted to install a new modem, he or she might be interested in a quick sentence explaining that *modem* stands for "modulator-demodulator" but would not really care about how modems developed.

Operating Principle. If part of the document's purpose is to teach people to use a product correctly, it is usually helpful to explain how it works. For example, a manual for a garden Rototiller is intended to help people use the tiller. Therefore, users should have a sense of how the tiller operates: it uses gasoline, it needs a clean spark plug, and so on. A list of parts is another way of illustrating how a device operates.

Usability Considerations

Use Appropriate Levels of Technicality. The language in a definition or description needs to match the audience's level of experience. An audience of medical technicians will easily understand jargon related to their field, but non-experts will need language they find familiar. For example, the sentence

| A tumour is a neoplasm.

would be sufficient for most medical professionals. But for an audience outside that field, you would need to unpack the term *neoplasm* and use more accessible language, as in

| A tumour is a growth of cells that occurs independently of surrounding tissue and serves no useful function.

Consider Length and Placement. The length of a definition or description should be appropriate for your audience and purpose. For example, if your audience needed to know only the very basics about a term (such as *tumour*), you could write a short sentence. But if your audience needed more information, you would need to amplify your definition with a description (say, of the process by which tumour cells displace healthy tissue).

Placement is also important. Each time an audience encounters an unfamiliar term or concept, it should be defined or described in the same area on the page or screen. In a printed text, you can accomplish this by placing brief definitions in an outside margin. On the screen, you would use a hypertext link. Hypertext and the web are perhaps the best answer yet to making definitions and descriptions accessible, because readers can click on the item, read about it, and return to their original place on the page.

Use Visuals. Visuals can be very important in definitions and descriptions. You can explain as clearly as you like, but, as the saying goes, a picture is worth a thousand words—even more when used with clear, accurate prose. The cutaway diagram (top view) in Figure 14.4 is a description of an electricity meter, designed for a general audience.

Use Clear, Concise Language. Use sentences that are brief and to the point. Provide readers with the most important information quickly. If all your audience needs is a one-sentence definition, don't write a long description, no matter how interesting you think it might be. Follow these tips to help keep your language clear and simple.

- *Decide on the level of detail.* Definitions vary greatly in length and detail, from a few words in parentheses to a complete essay. How much does this audience need in order to follow your explanation or grasp your point?

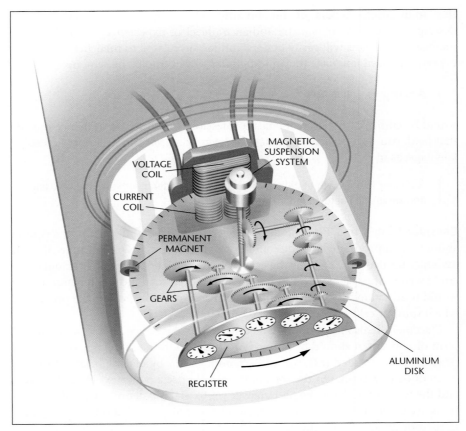

Figure 14.4 Description of an Electricity Meter. This cutaway diagram helps make the written description easier to understand.
Source: Reprinted by permission of George Retseck.

- *Classify the term precisely.* The narrower the classification you provide, the clearer your meaning (see page 312). For example, *stress* is an "applied force"; saying that stress "is what…" or "takes place when…" fails to provide a specific classification. Similarly, *diabetes* is a "metabolic disease," not a "medical term."
- *Differentiate the term accurately.* If the distinguishing features are too broad, they will apply to more than this one item. Defining *brief* as a "legal document used in court" fails to differentiate a brief from all other legal documents (such as wills, affidavits, and so on). Specify what makes this legal document different from all others.
- *Avoid circular definitions.* Do not repeat the word you are defining in the distinguishing features. For example, "Stress is an applied force that places stress on a body" is a circular definition.
- *Use negation to show what a term does not mean.* Telling an audience what a term does not mean helps them frame the meaning. For example, you could point out that *raw statistics* do not qualify as "information," because statistics become information only after they have been evaluated, interpreted, and applied.

Choose Words with Precision. Choose words carefully, and use the same word to refer to the same item. Is a tumour a "growth of cells" or simply "cells"? When describing fibre optic technology, don't suddenly switch and call it "high-speed cable."

In addition, choose descriptive details to suit your purpose and the reader's needs. Select only details that advance your meaning. Use objective details to provide a picture of something exactly as a camera would record it. Use subjective details to convey your impressions—to give readers a new way of seeing or appreciating something, as in a marketing brochure (see Figure 13.12).

Always select details that are concrete and specific enough to convey an unmistakable picture. Most often, description works best at the lowest levels of abstraction and generality.

Vague	Exact
at high speed	100 kilometres per hour
a tiny office	a 2.5- by 3-metre office
the seal	the rubber O-ring

Use sensory details as needed. Allow readers to see, hear, and feel. Let readers touch and taste. Use vivid comparisons to make the picture come to life. Rely on action verbs to convey the energy of movement.

Use Comparisons and Examples. By comparing new information to ideas your audience already understands, you help build a bridge between people's current knowledge and the new ideas. For example, for a group of non-experts, you could explain how earthquakes start in this manner:

> Imagine an enormous block of gelatin with a vertical knife slit through the middle of its lower half. Giant hands are slowly pushing the right side forward and the left side back along the slit, creating a strain that eventually splits the block. (*Earthquake hazard analysis,* 1984, p. 8)

Use an Appropriate Organizational Sequence. For longer descriptions, choose the organizational pattern that is most consistent with your purpose. If you want to describe how something looks or what parts it has, use a *spatial* sequence: describe the items as your audience will see them. If you want to describe how something works, use a *functional* sequence: describe the workings (functions) of the device. And if you want to describe how something is assembled, use a *chronological* sequence (see "Brief Instructions" and "Procedures" in Chapter 13).

In addition, always begin with some type of orienting statement. Descriptions rarely call for a standard topic or thesis statement, because their goal is simply to catalogue the details that readers can visualize. Any description, however, should begin by telling readers what to look for.

Checklist for Definitions and Descriptions

- Does the length of the definition or description suit its audience and purpose?
- Is the expanded definition adequately developed for its audience?
- Are visuals used adequately and appropriately?
- Does the definition appear in the appropriate location?
- Are comparisons and examples used to enhance understanding?
- Are any details missing, needless, or confusing for this audience?
- Does the description follow the clearest possible sequence?
- Will the level of technicality connect with the audience?
- Is the language clear and concise?
- Is the terminology precise and consistent?

Long Reports

When your purpose is to inform an audience, offer a solution to a problem, report progress, or make a detailed recommendation, you may need to write a long report. Long reports are often structured like a small book, with a table of contents, appendixes, and an index. Like short reports (see Chapter 11), long reports present ideas and facts to interested parties, decision makers, and other audiences. Technical professionals rely on reports as a basis for making informed decisions on a range of matters, from the possible side effects of a new pain medication to the environmental risks posed by a certain gasoline additive.

Long reports are called for in situations where an audience needs detailed information, statistics, and background information—the whole story. For example, your team of engineers needs to make far-reaching decisions about the best site for a toxic waste containment field. You have several months to research and make a decision, so you hire a consulting firm to report on all the relevant information. Their resulting product, a long report describing the geological conditions of potential sites, might contain an appendix with detailed comparisons of topsoil, groundwater, and other conditions.

Audience and Purpose Analysis

Do your best to determine who will read the report. For instance, even if the report is addressed to team members, it may be sent on to other managers, the legal department, or sales and marketing. If you can learn about the actual audience members in advance, you can anticipate their various needs as you create the report. Before you start the report, be clear about its true purpose. For example, you may be under the impression that the report is intended simply to inform an audience. But after some initial research, you learn that your manager really wants you to recommend an action, not just state the facts. Recommending is different from informing, so it's important to understand the reason you are writing the report in the first place. For instance, the writers of the report on organized crime in Canada—excerpted in Figures 14.5 to 14.8—focused on their audience: the Canadian public wanted to know how organized crime in Canada affects Canadian citizens, and what the Canadian government is doing to stop it. The document also has a clear purpose: it states in the introduction that the report "will provide Canadians with an up-to-date snapshot of the scope of the problem and actions that governments and law enforcement have taken to address the problem (Figure 14.5)."

Types of Long Reports

Causal Reports. Causal reports are used in situations where you need to explain what caused something to happen. For example, medical researchers may need to explain why so many apparently healthy people have sudden heart attacks. Or you might need to anticipate the possible effects of a particular decision—for example, the effects of a corporate merger on employee morale.

Here are some guidelines for writing strong causal reports:

- *Be sure the cause fits the effect.* Keep in mind that faulty causal reasoning is extremely common, especially when people ignore other possible causes or confuse mere coincidence with causation.
- *Make the links between cause and effect clear.* Identify the immediate cause (the one most closely related to the effect) as well as the distant causes (the

Introduction

Organized crime affects Canadians' basic rights to peace, order and good government. Although the effects of illicit activities are not always obvious, all Canadians, through one form or another, feel them through victimization, higher insurance rates, fewer tax dollars to support social programs, and the eventual undermining of Canadian institutions and consumers. No community is immune from the effects of organized crime.

As stated on the website of the *Nathanson Centre for the Study of Organized Crime and Corruption*, "since organized criminals seek out countries known to have less effective regulatory and enforcement systems, any jurisdiction that does not have adequate defences is at risk and may cause risk to other countries. As perhaps never before, the policies and enforcement capabilities of any one country have direct consequences globally."[1] Governments therefore have a responsibility to work collaboratively, both domestically and internationally, to address this phenomenon.

Federal, Provincial and Territorial (FPT) Governments continue to work together to find solutions to this pervasive problem. This continued commitment to work together, including with the law enforcement community, and associated partners is strong. A key component in these efforts is the National Coordinating Committee on Organized Crime (NCC), an FPT entity.

This report provides a brief overview of the scope of serious and organized crime in Canada, highlights governments' collective response to this problem, discusses where action should focus, and identifies strategies and approaches recommended by the NCC to reduce its harms. It is not intended to describe every action that FPT Governments have taken or are taking to fight organized crime; instead, it provides an update of recent successes and future objectives.

This report complements the annual report of the Criminal Intelligence Service Canada (CISC)[2], which details trends in organized crime activity and identifies a variety of criminal markets and the threats they pose to Canadians. Taken together, these reports will provide Canadians with an up-to-date snapshot of the scope of the problem and actions that governments and law enforcement have taken to address the problem.

---

[1]   Nathanson Centre website, http://www.yorku.ca/nathanson/default.htm

[2]   The Criminal Intelligence Service Canada (CISC) consists of a Central Bureau in Ottawa that liaises with and collects information and intelligence from ten provincial bureaus that serve all of Canada's provinces and territories.

Figure 14.5 **Introduction to the Working Together to Combat Organized Crime Report.**
Source: Public Safety Canada. (2007). Working Together to Combat Organized Crime: A Public Report on Actions under the National Agenda to Combat Organized Crime (2006). Cat. No. PS4-3/2006. Ottawa: Author. © Her Majesty the Queen in Right of Canada 2007. http://epe.lac-bac.gc.ca/100/200/301/public_safety-securite_publique/working_together_combat-e/PS4-3-2006E.pdf.

ones that precede the immediate cause). For example, the immediate cause of a particular airplane crash might be a fuel tank explosion, caused by a short circuit in frayed wiring, caused by faulty design or poor quality control by the manufacturer. Discussing only the immediate cause only scratches the surface of the problem.

- *Clearly distinguish among possible, probable, and definite causes.* Unless the cause is obvious, limit your assertions by using perhaps, probably, maybe, most likely, could, seems to, appears to, or similar qualifiers that prevent you from making an unsupportable claim.

Comparative Reports. Comparative reports rate similar items based on specific criteria. For example, you may need to answer questions such as "Which type of security procedure—firewall or encryption—should we install in our company's computer system?"

Here are some guidelines for writing strong comparative reports:

- *Rest the comparison on a clear and definite basis.* Make comparisons based on costs, uses, benefits and drawbacks, appearance, or results. In evaluating the merits of competing items, identify your specific criteria and rank them in order of importance.
- *Give both items balanced treatment.* Discuss points for each item in identical order.
- *Support and clarify the comparison or contrast through credible examples.* Use research, if necessary, to find examples that readers can visualize.
- *Follow either a block pattern or a point-by-point pattern.* In the block pattern, first one item is discussed fully and then the next. Choose a block pattern when the overall picture is more important than the individual points. In the point-by-point pattern, one point about both items is discussed, then the next point, and so on. Choose a point-by-point pattern when specific points might be hard to remember unless placed side-by-side.

Block pattern	Point-by-point pattern
Item A	First point of **Item A**
First point	First point of **Item B**
Second point	
Third point, etc.	
Item B	Second point of **Item A**
First point	Second point of **Item B**
Second point	
Third point, etc.	

- *Order your points for greatest emphasis.* Try ordering your points from least to most important, dramatic, useful, or reasonable. Emphasize the most striking point by placing it last.
- If you are writing an evaluative comparison, offer your final judgment. Base your judgment squarely on the criteria presented.

Feasibility Reports. Feasibility reports are used when your purpose is to assess the practicality of an idea or plan. For example, if your company needs to know whether increased business will justify the cost of an interactive website, you would need to do some research and describe the results in a feasibility report.

Sometimes these categories overlap. Any single study may in fact require you to take several approaches. The sample report on organized crime discussed here is an example. The report is designed to answer the question, "How has organized crime affected the general public?"

Here are some guidelines for writing strong feasibility reports:

- *Consider the strength of supporting reasons.* Decide carefully which are the best reasons supporting the action or decision being considered, based on solid evidence.
- *Consider the strength of opposing reasons.* Remember that people usually see only what they want to see. Avoid the temptation to overlook or downplay opposing reasons, especially for an action or decision that you have been promoting. Consider alternative points of view and examine all the evidence.
- *Recommend a realistic course of action.* After weighing all the pros and cons, make your recommendation. But be prepared to change your mind if you discover that what seemed like the right course of action turns out to be wrong.

A General Model for Long Reports

After analyzing your audience and purpose, do some basic research. Then sketch a rough outline with headings and subheadings for the report.

Introduction. The introduction engages and orients the audience and provides background as briefly as possible for the given situation. Often writers who are familiar with the product are tempted to write long introductions because they have a lot of background knowledge about the product or issue. But readers don't generally need long history lessons about the topic. In the introduction, identify the topic's origin and significance, define or describe the problem or issue, and explain the report's purpose. Briefly identify your research methods (interviews, literature searches, and so on). List working definitions, but if you have more than two or three, place definitions in a glossary. Finally, briefly state your conclusion. Don't make readers wade through the entire report to find out what you are recommending or advising.

Body. The body describes and explains your findings. Present a clear and detailed picture of the evidence, interpretations, and reasoning on which you will base your conclusion. Divide topics into subtopics, and use informative headings as aids to navigation, as in the body section of the organized crime report excerpted in Figure 14.6. The body of your report will vary greatly, depending on the audience, topic, purpose, and situation.

Conclusion. As you can see in the portion of the organized crime report excerpted in Figure 14.7, the conclusion is important because it answers the questions that originally sparked the analysis. In the conclusion, you summarize, interpret, and recommend. Although you have interpreted evidence at each stage of your analysis, the conclusion presents a broad interpretation and suggests a course of action where appropriate. Your conclusion should provide a clear and consistent overall perspective. Don't introduce new ideas, facts, or statistics in the conclusion.

Front Matter and End Matter in Long Reports

A long document must be easily accessible and must accommodate users with various interests. Preceding the report is *front matter:* the title page, letter of transmittal, table of contents, and abstract or summary of the report's content. Following the report (as needed) is *end matter:* the glossary, appendixes, and list of references cited. End matter can either provide supporting data or help users follow technical sections. Users can refer to any of these supplements or skip them altogether, according to their needs.

Title Page. The title page gives the report title, the names of all authors and their affiliations, or the name of the organization that commissioned the report (see Figure 14.8). The title announces the report's purpose and subject by using descriptive words such as *analysis, proposal, feasibility,* or *progress.*

Letter of Transmittal. Many long reports include a letter of transmittal, addressed to a specific reader. This letter might

- acknowledge individuals and organizations that helped with the report
- refer to sections of special interest
- discuss limitations of the study or any problems in gathering data
- discuss possible follow-up investigations
- offer personal (or off-the-record) observations
- urge the recipient to take immediate action

If a report is being sent to numerous people who are variously qualified and bear various relationships to you, individual letters of transmittal may vary.

Scope of Organized Crime in Canada

The *Criminal Code of Canada* defines a criminal organization as a group, however organized, that:

> *(a)* is composed of three or more persons in or outside Canada; and,

> *(b)* has as one of its main purposes or main activities the facilitation or commission of one or more serious offences that, if committed, would likely result in the direct or indirect receipt of a material benefit, including a financial benefit, by the group or by any of the persons who constitute the group.[3]

In the 1990s, organized crime was characterized primarily, but not exclusively, by outlaw motorcycle gangs (OMGs), the illicit drug trade and associated turf wars. Today, organized crime activities have expanded beyond these "traditional" activities to include migrant smuggling, trafficking in humans and firearms, marihuana grow operations, identity theft, sexual exploitation of children on the Internet, the production and smuggling of counterfeit goods and money, motor vehicle theft, and more.

Until recently, globalization and technological sophistication were considered emerging trends in organized crime - today they are the norm. Due to the advanced capabilities of these groups, they can be found virtually anywhere where there is a profit to be made through criminal ventures. According to the 2006 annual CISC report, there are nearly 800 organized crime groups operating in Canada.[4] Although the majority of these groups are concentrated in urban centers, many are now operating from smaller communities across the country. As such, governments and the law enforcement community must remain diligent and proactive in their efforts to prevent the displacement of organized crime.

Another notable characteristic of today's organized crime groups is the shift from mainly ethnic based groups to multicultural criminal organizations. CISC reports that although ethnic and cultural heritage remains an influencing principle within the organized crime environment, the growing number of multi-ethnic groups is based on criminal capabilities rather than ethnicity.[5] Similarly, the structure of organized crime groups is much more flexible today than in the past. Hierarchical groups continue to exist, most notably through OMGs. Law enforcement, however, is identifying groups that are based on temporary alliances requiring particular skills to complete a specific criminal enterprise. Once the criminal venture is completed, these individuals may or may not continue to work together.[6]

In recent years, organized crime groups have become more complex and sophisticated,

---

[3]   *Criminal Code of Canada*, section 467.1(1).
[4]   *Criminal Intelligence Service Canada, 2006 Annual Report on Organized Crime in Canada.*
[5]   Ibid.
[6]   Ibid.

Figure 14.6 **Body of the Working Together to Combat Organized Crime Report.**
Source: Public Safety Canada. (2007). Working Together to Combat Organized Crime: A Public Report on Actions under the National Agenda to Combat Organized Crime (2006). Cat. No. PS4-3/2006. Ottawa: Author. © Her Majesty the Queen in Right of Canada 2007. http://epe.lac-bac.gc.ca/100/200/301/public_safety-securite_publique/working_together_combat-e/PS4-3-2006E.pdf.

as have new types of crime. These groups are increasingly using new and evolving technology to commit crime and to communicate with other criminal groups. For example, communications devices are frequently used to target sensitive personal and financial information in order to conduct identity theft and mass marketing fraud. Organized crime groups are also expanding into legitimate business activities, as well as branching out into new markets in Canada.

Building a Collective Response: National & Regional Coordination

National Coordinating Committee on Organized Crime

Following a recommendation made at the National Forum on Organized Crime in 1997, the NCC was created. The NCC, a body composed of FPT government officials, prosecutors, and representatives from the law enforcement community was created to identify key issues for action. Within the NCC, there are five Regional Coordinating Committees (RCCs), which ensure that local concerns and perspectives are brought to the table. The NCC has three main responsibilities:

- to identify issues and policy priorities related to the problem of organized crime;
- to advise FPT Deputy Ministers on the development, coordination and implementation of policies, legislation and programs aimed at combating organized crime; and,
- to encourage coordination of anti-organized crime activities among various players at the regional and local level.

National Agenda to Combat Organized Crime

In 2000, FPT Ministers responsible for Justice endorsed the *National Agenda to Combat Organized Crime*. The *National Agenda* recognizes that the fight against organized crime is a national priority that requires all levels of government, the law enforcement community and other partners to work together. The *National Agenda* identifies four main pillars to be addressed:

- national and regional coordination;
- legislative and regulatory tools;
- research and analysis; and,
- communications and public education.

The NCC is responsible for assisting in the development and implementation of the *National Agenda* in order to better combat organized crime.

Figure 14.6 (*Continued*)

2006 Overview

In 2006, the NCC continued to build on the four pillars that form the basis of the *National Agenda*. These pillars assist in meeting the ultimate objectives of:

> 1) preventing and reducing organized crime; and
> 2) preventing and reducing the harms caused by organized crime

Governance

During 2006 there was significant debate surrounding the governance of the NCC and consideration as to how it may be strengthened. The NCC is unique in that it is the only body, among the many bodies in Canada that address organized crime, which brings together both police and policy makers to discuss issues of common interest. Several measures were identified to enhance governance of the NCC:

- The NCC Executive and plenary bodies should be combined into one main body instead of two, which would take responsibility for strategically advising Deputy Ministers on serious and organized crime. It should work to set the National Strategy agenda and analyze action plans and implementation strategies, as well as focus on information-sharing and priority-issues discussions;

- Funding should be provided to the RCCs to support meetings;

- The NCC Secretariat should be strengthened to allow for better communication and information flow between RCCs and the NCC; and,

- In addition to the co-chairmanship by the RCMP and Public Safety Canada, NCC membership should include members of the FPT ADM Committee on Policing Issues, selected representatives from the Canadian Association of Chiefs of Police (CACP), a representative from each of the Department of Foreign Affairs and International Trade (DFAIT), Financial Transactions and Reports Analysis Center of Canada (FINTRAC), Criminal Intelligence Service Canada (CISC), Canada Border Services Agency (CBSA), Public Prosecution Service of Canada, and the Criminal Law Policy Section within the Department of Justice. The total membership would be approximately 25, including Co-Chairs.

These new measures would facilitate national cooperation as closer links are established with local agencies and other FPT bodies that are involved in addressing the complexities of organized crime.

Figure 14.6 (*Continued*)

Public Education

Efforts continued to be directed at enhancing public education through the development of a national communications strategy to educate Canadians about organized crime. Public opinion research shows that the average Canadian believes that organized crime is serious and that it is present in their community, but that it does not affect them personally. The objectives of national communications efforts will include educating Canadians about the reality of organized crime and its reach, scope and effects on daily lives; promoting FPT actions, cooperation, operational efforts and successes; and increasing cohesion with other groups to build a unified approach to public communication.

Furthermore, it was agreed that the work of the NCC and its partnerships across the country should be highlighted as an addendum to CISC's annual report. Towards this end, the NCC Secretariat is exploring the option of streamlining the two publications on organized crime.

Data and Evaluation

In an effort to strengthen the data and evaluation pillar of the *National Agenda*, salient evaluation findings on current anti-organized crime initiatives were brought forward to the NCC. Key findings were presented from recently evaluated initiatives, including the Measures to Combat Organized Crime (MCOC), First Nations Organized Crime (FNOC), Integrated Market Enforcement Teams (IMETs), and Integrated Proceeds of Crime (IPOC). The performance information gathered to date has been limited to federal partners. To move forward, information from provincial/territorial partners will be necessary in order to provide a truly national picture. In recognition of this fact, the NCC Executive has acknowledged the need to enhance information-sharing and adequate resourcing, at both the federal and provincial/territorial levels, in order to strengthen organized crime-related performance measurement and evaluation.

Several key data sources for identifying the extent of organized crime were explored. One such source is the Uniform Crime Reporting Survey (UCR), Version 2.2, which includes new variables on organized crime, including street gangs, hate-motivated crime, cybercrime and geo-coding. One of the two major police records management systems (RMS) was able to implement the new survey for January 2005. The first data from this survey were released on February 6, 2007 for the two police services able to provide an entire year of 2005 data: Ottawa and London. The other major vendor of RMS is expected to incorporate these new fields during 2007. As a result, the majority of police services should be collecting UCR 2.2 data by 2008.

Currently, the Canadian Centre for Justice Statistics has developed a pilot Survey of Fraud Against Businesses and administered it to 600 establishments. The analysis of the pilot data is ongoing and the intention is to conduct a national survey in early 2008. The project is designed to survey small, medium and large business establishments for the

Figure 14.6 (*Continued*)

Conclusion

According to CISC, organized crime in Canada will continue to pose serious economic, health and public safety threats through involvement in the array of criminal activities identified in this report and more. In particular, the illicit drug trade will continue to provide organized crime groups with their largest source of illicit earnings. Although FPT governments have made considerable progress to date in combating serious and organized crime in Canada, there is much that still needs to be done, including developing a strategic approach to illicit drugs and street gangs, implementing a coordinated and effective national fraud strategy, strengthening the witness protection program and facilitating the management of complex cases. No one jurisdiction or country can combat organized crime on its own. Continued national and international cooperation is critical to addressing this issue effectively.

Figure 14.7 **Conclusion of the Working Together to Combat Organized Crime Report.**
Source: Public Safety Canada. (2007). Working Together to Combat Organized Crime: A Public Report on Actions under the National Agenda to Combat Organized Crime (2006). Cat. No. PS4-3/2006. Ottawa: Author. © Her Majesty the Queen in Right of Canada 2007. http://epe.lac-bac.gc.ca/100/200/301/public_safety-securite_publique/working_together_combat-e/PS4-3-2006E.pdf.

Table of Contents. Help readers find the information they're looking for by providing a table of contents. In designing your table, follow these guidelines:

- Number the front-matter (transmittal letter, abstract) pages with lowercase roman numerals. (The title page, though not listed, is counted as page i.) Number glossary, appendix, and endnote pages with Arabic numerals, continuing the page sequence of your report proper, in which page 1 is the first page of the report text.
- Include no headings in the table of contents not listed as headings or subheadings in the report; however, the report may contain subheadings not listed in the table of contents.
- List headings in the table of contents exactly as they are in the report.
- List headings at various levels in varying type styles and indention.
- Use *leader lines* (. . . . .) to connect headings to page numbers. Align rows of dots vertically, each above the other.

Note that word processing software such as Microsoft Word includes automatic features for creating and formatting tables of contents.

List of Tables and Figures. On a separate page following the table of contents or integrated with it, list the tables and figures appearing in the report. You can also use your software's automatic features for creating lists of tables and figures.

Public Safety   Sécurité publique
Canada   Canada

WORKING TOGETHER
TO COMBAT
ORGANIZED CRIME

A Public Report on Actions
under the *National Agenda*
to Combat Organized Crime

2006

Canadä

Figure 14.8 **Cover from the Working Together to Combat Organized Crime Report.**
Note how the graphic chosen for the report puts a positive spin on the subject matter.
Source: Public Safety Canada. (2007). Working Together to Combat Organized Crime: A Public
Report on Actions under the National Agenda to Combat Organized Crime (2006). Cat. No. PS4-
3/2006. Ottawa: Author. © Her Majesty the Queen in Right of Canada 2007. http://epe.lac-bac.gc.
ca/100/200/301/public_safety-securite_publique/working_together_combat-e/PS4-3-2006E.pdf.

❋   Abstract or Executive Summary. Reports are often read by many people: researchers, developers, managers, vice presidents, customers. For readers who are interested only in the big picture, the entire report may not be relevant, so long reports are commonly preceded by an abstract (short) or an executive summary (longer). In this brief description, you explain the issue, describe how you researched it, and state your conclusion. Busy readers can then flip through the document to locate sections of importance to them.

In preparing your abstract, follow these suggestions:

- Make sure the abstract stands alone in terms of meaning.
- Write for a general audience. Readers of the abstract are likely to vary in expertise, perhaps more than those who read the report itself; therefore, translate all technical data.
- Add no new information. Simply summarize the report.
- Present your information in the following sequence:

  1. Identify the issue or need that led to the report.
  2. Offer the major findings from the body of the report.
  3. Include a condensed conclusion and recommendations, if any.

Appendixes. Add one or more appendixes to your report if you have large blocks of material or other documents that are relevant but will bog readers down if placed in the middle of the document itself. For example, if your report on the cost of electricity at your company refers to another report issued by the local utility company, you may wish to include this second report as an appendix.

Other items that belong in an appendix might include complex formulas, interview questions and responses, maps, photographs, sample questionnaires and tabulated responses, texts of laws and regulations, and the like. Do not stuff appendixes with needless information or use them unethically for burying bad or embarrassing news that belongs in the report proper. Title each appendix clearly: "Appendix A: Projected Costs." Mention the appendix early in the introduction, and refer readers to it at appropriate points in the report: "(see Appendix A)."

See, for example, appendixes A and B in this textbook.

Glossary. Use a glossary if your report contains more than two or three technical terms that may not be understood by all audience members. Use standard definitions in your glossary. Refer to company style guides or technical dictionaries. If fewer than five terms need defining, place them in the report introduction as working definitions or use footnote definitions. If you use a separate glossary, announce its location: "(see the glossary at the end of this report)."

List of References. List each of your outside references in alphabetical order or in the same numerical order as they are cited in the report proper.

Not all reports have all of these supplements. For example, the organized crime report omits a list of appendixes, but does make reference to a companion report that readers may benefit from reading. There are also no tables or visuals in the report as there is no statistical information that would be better explained and explored through the use of a visual aid. For examples of many of these supplements in a student-written report, see "Feasibility Analysis of a Career in Technical Marketing," on the website accompanying this text at www.my canadiantechcommlab.com.

Usability Considerations

Clearly Identify the Problem or Goal. To address the true purpose of the situation, you must carefully identify your goal. Begin by defining the main questions involved in the report and then outlining any subordinate questions. For example, your MP might pose this question: "How will organized crime affect the Canadian public?" Answering this question is the main goal of the report; however, this question leads to others, such as "What are the worst types of organized crime?" Create a goal statement, such as "The goal of this report is to examine and evaluate organized crime in Canada."

Provide Enough Information but Not Too Much. Any usable analysis must address the needs, interests, and technical expertise of your audience. A long history of the development of the pacemaker may be interesting to you but inappropriate for your report. As you plan the report, find out how much of the information you've gathered readers need in order to make a decision. Also, make sure your technical terms are not too complex for your audience. If you have a mixed audience, provide a glossary where readers can look up unfamiliar terms. If your report is posted to a website, you can use hyperlinks for glossary terms.

Provide Accurate Information. Make sure your information is as accurate as possible and, to the best of your ability, without bias. Use reputable information sources, particularly for statistical data. Be careful when taking information from the web; websites often sound credible but can be based on biased or inaccurate information (see Chapter 5). Also, make sure you interpret information fairly and provide valid conclusions based on your best research. Assume, for example, that you were writing a report to recommend the best brand of chainsaws for a logging company. In reviewing test reports, you learned that one brand, Bomarc, is easiest to operate, but also has the fewest safety features. Both pieces of information should be included in the report, regardless of your personal preference for this brand.

Use Appropriate Visuals. As discussed in Chapter 8, visual information can make complex statistics and numerical data easy to understand. Graphs are especially useful for analyzing rising or falling trends, levels, and long-term forecasts. Tables and charts are helpful for comparing data. Photographs and diagrams are an excellent way to show a component or special feature. Be sure your visual is placed near the accompanying text, and be careful not to overuse visuals.

Use Informative Headings. Headings and subheadings in your report announce what each section contains. The heading "Data Analysis" does not really say much, whereas the heading "Physiological Effects and Health Risks" offers a clear, informative preview of the content of a section.

Write Clearly and Concisely. Even readers who need every bit of information in your report don't want to be bogged down with cumbersome, long-winded, and hard to read prose. Keep your language crisp and clear. Use active voice whenever possible. Ask a colleague or editor to copy edit your report before it is printed.

Use Action Verbs. Especially when recommending a plan of action, use action verbs such as *examine, evaluate, determine,* or *recommend.* Avoid nominalizations (verbs converted into nouns): for example, don't use *determination* when you mean *determine.*

 Checklist for Long Reports

- Does the report grow from a clear audience and purpose analysis?
- Does the report address a clearly identified problem or goal?
- Are the report's length and information adequate and appropriate for the subject?
- Is the information accurate and unbiased?
- Is there enough information for readers to make an informed decision?
- Are all necessary components (including front and end matter) provided?
- Are visuals used whenever possible to aid communication?
- Are headings informative and adequate?
- Are action verbs used generously?
- Is the level of technicality appropriate for the intended audience?
- Is the language clear and concise?

Proposals

Proposals encourage an audience to take some form of direct action: to authorize a project, purchase a service or product, or otherwise support a specific plan for solving a problem. Although proposals often contain the same basic elements as reports, they have one specific purpose: to propose an action or series of actions. This purpose differs from more generic reports, which can be used for other purposes, as noted earlier. Proposals can be called for in a variety of situations: a request to fund a training program for new employees, a suggestion to change the curriculum in your English or biology department, or a bid to the Department of National Defence on a vehicle contract. Depending on the situation, proposals may be short or long and may be written in the form of a report, a letter, or a memo.

Audience and Purpose Analysis

In science, business, industry, government, and education, proposals are written for any number of audiences: managers, executives, directors, clients, board members, or community leaders. Inside or outside the organization, these people review various proposals and then decide whether the plan is worthwhile, whether the project will materialize, and whether the service or product is useful. At the most general level, the purpose is to persuade your audience. More specifically, proposals often answer questions about the nature of the problem or product, the benefits of your proposed plan, cost, completion dates, schedules, and so on.

Types of Proposals

Proposals may be solicited or unsolicited. Solicited proposals are those that have been requested by a client or customer. For example, if you represent an engineering firm specializing in highway construction, you may receive a request for proposal (RFP) from a local township asking you to bid on a road project. Typically, an RFP is issued to numerous companies, and your proposal will need to stack up against all the others. Unsolicited proposals have not been specifically requested. If you are a new advertising agency in town, you may send out short proposals to local radio stations suggesting that they use your agency for their advertising needs.

Because the audience for a solicited proposal has made the request, you may not need to spend as much time introducing yourself or providing background on the product or service. For an unsolicited proposal (sometimes called a "cold call" in sales), you will need to catch your readers' attention quickly and provide incentives for them to continue reading: perhaps by printing a price comparison of your fees on the first page, for example.

Both solicited and unsolicited proposals can take the following forms.

Planning Proposal. A planning proposal offers solutions to a problem or suggestions for improvement. It might be a request for funding to expand the campus newspaper, an architectural plan for new facilities at a ski resort, or a plan to develop energy alternatives to fossil fuels. Figure 14.9 is a short planning proposal that was solicited and will be used internally within the company. The XYZ Corporation has contracted a team of communication consultants to design in-house writing workshops, and the consultants must convince the client that their methods will succeed. After briefly introducing the problem, the authors develop their proposal under three headings and two subheadings, making the document easy to read and to the point.

Research Proposal. Research (or grant) proposals request approval and funding for research projects. A chemist at a university might address a research proposal to Environmental Canada for funds to identify toxic contaminants in local groundwater. Research proposals are solicited by many agencies, such as the Innovation in Canada portal, and each organization has its own requirements and guidelines for proposal format and content. To be successful, research proposals must follow these guidelines and carefully articulate the goals of the project. Proposal readers are usually other scientists or related professionals, so writers should use language that is appropriate for other experts. Research proposals might also be submitted by students requesting funds for undergraduate research projects. In Figure 14.10, a student writer used the prescribed form for a research proposal related to the goals of the program.

Sales Proposal. Sales proposals offer services or products and may be solicited or unsolicited. If solicited, several firms may be competing for the contract, so your proposal may be ranked by a committee against several others. Sales proposals can be cast as letters if the situation calls for them to be brief. If the situation requires a longer proposal, you follow the guidelines for writing a report: use a title page, make sure you have clear headings, and so on. A successful sales proposal persuades customers that your product or service surpasses those of any competitors. In the sample sales proposal in Figure 14.11, the writer explains why this machinery is best for the job, what qualifications the company can offer, and what costs are involved. What you include in a sales proposal is determined by the guidelines from the client or by a thorough analysis of the kind of information your audience needs.

Typical Components of Proposals

After conducting your audience and purpose analysis, you should perform some basic research. For example, you might look into the very latest technology for solving the problem or doing the project; compare the costs, benefits, and drawbacks of various approaches; contact others in your field for their suggestions; and so on.

Dear Mary:

Thanks for sending the writing samples from your technical support staff. Here is what we're doing to design a realistic approach.

Assessment of Needs
After conferring with technicians in both Jack's and Terry's groups and analyzing their writing samples, we identified this hierarchy of needs:

• improving readability
• achieving precise diction
• summarizing information
• organizing a set of procedures
• formulating various memo reports
• analyzing audiences for upward communication
• writing persuasive bids for transfer or promotion
• writing persuasive suggestions

Proposed Plan
Based on the needs listed above, we have limited our instruction package to eight carefully selected and readily achievable goals.

Course Outline. Our eight, two-hour sessions are structured as follows:

1. achieving sentence clarity
2. achieving sentence conciseness
3. achieving fluency and precise diction
4. writing summaries and abstracts
5. outlining manuals and procedures
6. editing manuals and procedures
7. designing various reports for various purposes
8. analyzing the audience and writing persuasively

Classroom Format. The first three meetings will be lecture-intensive with weekly exercises to be done at home and edited collectively in class. The remaining five weeks will combine lecture and exercises with group editing of work-related documents. We plan to remain flexible so we can respond to needs that arise.

Limitations
Given our limited contact time, we cannot realistically expect to turn out a batch of polished communicators. By the end of the course, however, our students will have begun to appreciate writing as a deliberate process.

If you have any suggestions for refining this plan, please let us know.

Figure 14.9 A Planning Proposal.

To: Dr. John Lannon
From: T. Sorrells Dewoody
Date: 16 March 2012
Subject: *Proposal for Determining the Feasibility of Marketing*
            Dead Western White Pine

Introduction
Over the past four decades, huge losses of western white pine have occurred in the northern Rockies, primarily attributable to white pine blister rust and the attack of the mountain pine beetle. Estimated annual mortality is 318 million board feet. Because of the low natural resistance of white pine to blister rust, this high mortality rate is expected to continue indefinitely.

   If white pine is not harvested while the tree is dying or soon after death, the wood begins to dry and check (warp and crack). The sapwood is discolored by blue stain, a fungus carried by the mountain pine beetle. If the white pine continues to stand after death, heart cracks develop. These factors work together to cause degradation of the lumber and consequent loss in value.

Statement of Problem
White pine mortality reduces the value of white pine stumpage because the commercial lumber market will not accept it. There are two major implications of this problem: First, in the face of rising demand for wood, vast amounts of timber lie unused; second, dead trees are left to accumulate in the woods, where they are rapidly becoming a major fire hazard here in northern British Columbia and elsewhere.

Proposed Solution
One possible solution to the problem of white pine mortality and waste is to search for markets other than the conventional lumber market. The last few years have seen a burst of popularity and growing demand for weathered barn boards and wormy pine for interior paneling. Some firms around the country are marketing defective wood as specialty products. (These firms call the wood from which their products come "distressed," a term I will use hereafter to refer to dead and defective white pine.) Distressed white pine will quite possibly find a place in such a market.

Scope
To assess the feasibility of developing a market for distressed white pine, I plan to pursue six areas of inquiry:

1. What products are presently being produced from dead wood, and what are the approximate costs of production?

Figure 14.10 An Undergraduate Research Proposal.

2. How large is the demand for distressed-wood products?
3. Can distressed white pine meet this demand as well as other species meet it?
4. Does the market contain room for distressed white pine?
5. What are the costs of retrieving and milling distressed white pine?
6. What prices for the products can the market bear?

Methods
My primary data sources will include consultations with Dr. James Hill, Professor of Wood Utilization, and Dr. Sven Bergman, Forest Economist—both members of the College of Forestry, Wildlife, and Range. I will also inspect decks of dead white pine at several locations and visit a processing mill to evaluate it as a possible base of operations. I will round out my primary research with a letter and telephone survey of processors and wholesalers of distressed material.

Secondary sources will include publications on the uses of dead timber and a review of a study by Dr. Hill on the uses of dead white pine.

My Qualifications
I have been following Dr. Hill's study on dead white pine for two years. In June of this year, I will receive my B.S. in forest management. I am familiar with wood milling processes and have firsthand experience at logging. My association with Dr. Hill and Dr. Bergman gives me the opportunity for an in-depth feasibility study.

Conclusion
Clearly, action is needed to reduce the vast accumulations of dead white pine in our forests. The land on which they stand is among the most productive forests in northern British Columbia. By addressing the six areas of inquiry mentioned earlier, I can determine the feasibility of directing capital and labor to the production of distressed white pine products. With your approval, I will begin research at once.

Figure 14.10 (*Continued*)

Subject: *Proposal to Dig a Trench and Move Boulders at Bliss Site*

Dear Mr. Haver:

I've inspected your property and would be happy to undertake the landscaping project necessary for the development of your farm.

The backhoe I use cuts a span 3 feet wide and can dig as deep as 18 feet—more than an adequate depth for the mainline pipe you wish to lay. Because this backhoe is on tracks rather than tires and is hydraulically operated, it is particularly efficient in moving rocks. I have more than twelve years of experience with backhoe work and have completed many jobs similar to this one.

After examining the huge boulders that block access to your property, I am convinced they can be moved only if I dig out underneath and exert upward pressure with the hydraulic ram while you push forward on the boulders with your D-9 Caterpillar. With this method, we can move enough rock to enable you to farm that now inaccessible tract. Because of its power, my larger backhoe will save you both time and money in the long run.

This job should take 12 to 15 hours, unless we encounter subsurface ledge formations. My fee is $200 per hour. The fact that I provide my own dynamiting crew at no extra charge should be an advantage to you because you have so much rock to be moved.

Please phone me anytime for more information. I'm sure we can do the job economically and efficiently.

Figure 14.11 A Sales Proposal.

I. Introduction
  A. Statement of Problem and Objective
  B. Background
  C. Need
  D. Benefits
  E. Qualifications of Personnel
  F. Data Sources
  G. Limitations and Contingencies
  H. Scope

II. Body
  A. Methods
  B. Timetable
  C. Materials and Equipment
  D. Personnel
  E. Available Facilities
  F. Needed Facilities
  G. Cost
  H. Expected Results
  I. Feasibility

III. Conclusion
  A. Summary of Key Points
  B. Request for Action

Figure 14.12 A General Proposal Outline That Can Be Adapted to Various Situations.

Then generate a rough outline with headings and subheadings for the proposal. The outline in Figure 14.12 is general enough to adapt to your specific situation.

As noted, proposals can be short (letter or memo format) or long (report format). For a long proposal, include the components and supplements ordinarily contained in a long report: abstract, introduction, body, conclusion, and appendixes. Include a letter of transmittal, especially if your proposal is unsolicited.

Background. A background section (sometimes used as an introduction) can be brief or long. In Figure 14.9, the writer's opening sentence ("Thanks for sending the writing samples from your technical support staff") provides a quick reminder of the context for the project. This sentence is brief because the writer correctly assumes that the reader is very familiar with the project. For a new audience, this single sentence might need to be expanded into a longer paragraph of background on the project. The background section may contain a statement of the problem or issue. If the topic warrants it, the background section may take up several pages.

Objective. If your audience needs this information spelled out, you may wish to provide a clear statement of the proposal's objectives: "Our objective is to offer a plan to make areas of the library quiet enough for serious study."

Clear Statement of What Is Being Proposed. Whether your proposal is short or long, make it easy for your audience to locate the exact details of what you are proposing. In the research proposal shown in Figure 14.10, the third heading, "Proposed Solution," is the obvious place for readers to turn if they want to see the details of the solution.

Budget and Costs. If your proposal involves financial costs, make sure your cost and budget section is accurate and easy to understand. If you work with an accountant or other financial specialist, ask that person to check your figures. If the proposal is solicited, make sure you follow the client's guidelines for establishing a budget.

Usability Considerations

Understand the Audience's Needs. The proposal audience wants specific suggestions to meet their specific needs. Their biggest question is "What will this plan do for me?" Make your proposal demonstrate a clear understanding of the client's problem and expectations, and then offer an appropriate solution. In the planning proposal in Figure 14.9, the writer begins with a clear assessment of needs and then moves quickly into a proposed plan of action.

Maintain a Clear Focus on Benefits. Show your readers that you understand what they will gain by adopting your plan. The planning proposal in Figure 14.9 includes a numbered list of exactly what tasks will be accomplished after the technical support staff takes the instruction courses.

Use Honest and Supportable Claims. Because they typically involve large sums of money as well as contractual obligations, proposals require a solid ethical and legal foundation. False promises not only damage the writer's or company's reputation but also invite lawsuits. If the solutions you offer have certain limitations, make sure you say so. For example, if you are proposing to install a new network server, make it clear what capabilities this server has, as well as what it cannot do under certain circumstances.

Use Appropriate Visuals. See Chapter 8 for a discussion of visuals.

Write Clearly and Concisely. Make sure your document is easy to read, uses action verbs, and avoids puffed-up language or terms that are too technical for your audience. If necessary for a mixed audience with differing technical levels, include a glossary.

Use Convincing Language. There is no need to be coy when writing a proposal. You are trying to sell yourself or your ideas. So be sure to write a document that will move people to action:

- *Spell out the problem (and its causes) clearly and convincingly.* Give enough detail for your audience to appreciate the problem's importance. Answer the implied question "Why is this such a big deal?"
- *Point out the benefits of solving the problem.* Answer the implied question "Why should we spend time, money, and effort to do this?"
- *Use statistics* ("For the third year in a row, our firm has been ranked as the number-one architecture firm in the Prairie provinces.") and *direct sentences* ("We know you will be satisfied with the results.").
- *Offer a realistic solution.* Stick to claims or assertions you can support. Answer the implied question "How do we know this will work?"
- *Address anticipated objections to your solution.* Consider carefully the audience's skepticism on this issue. Answer the implied question "Why should we accept the things that seem wrong with your plan?"
- *Induce readers to act.* Decide exactly what you want readers to do, and give reasons why they should be the ones to act. Answer the implied question "What action am I supposed to take?"

Checklist for Proposals

- Are all required proposal components included?
- Is the problem clearly identified?
- Is the objective clearly identified?
- Is the proposed plan, service, or product stated clearly and prominently?
- Does the proposal demonstrate a clear understanding of the client's problem and expectations?
- Is the background section appropriate for this audience's needs?
- Does the proposal maintain a clear focus on benefits?
- Is the proposed solution appropriate and realistic?
- Is the cost and budget section accurate and easy to understand?
- Are the claims honest and supportable?
- Are all foreseeable limitations identified?
- Are visuals used effectively?
- Is the language convincing and precise?
- Does the tone encourage acceptance of the proposal?

Exercises

1. **FOCUS ON WRITING.** Choose a situation and an audience, and prepare an expanded technical definition specifically designed for this audience's level of technical understanding. Use the usability considerations on pages 313–316:
   - Decide on the level of detail.
   - Classify the term precisely.
   - Differentiate the term accurately.
   - Avoid circular definitions.
   - Use negation to show what a term does not mean.
   - Expand your definition selectively.

2. **FOCUS ON WRITING.** Choose another situation and audience, and prepare a technical description for this audience's level of technical understanding. Refer to the usability considerations on pages 313–316.

3. **FOCUS ON WRITING.** Choose a specific situation and audience, and prepare a long report that documents a causal, comparative, or feasibility analysis—or some combination of these types. As you prepare your report, refer to the usability considerations on pages 328–329.

4. **FOCUS ON WRITING.** Since technical communication must be as concise and clear as possible, avoid using clichés in your writing. As a class, create a list of clichés and then rewrite the clichés in clear, conventional language. Some examples you can try are *last but not least, you're on the right track, we're in hot water*, or *clear as a* bell.

The Collaboration Window

1. Working in groups of four, develop an unsolicited proposal for solving a problem, improving a situation, or satisfying a need in your school, community, or workplace. Begin by brainstorming as a group to come up with a list of possible issues or problems to address in your proposal. Narrow your list, and work as a group to focus on a specific issue or idea that you think will work well as the topic for a persuasive proposal. Review pages 331–339 for details on the different types of proposals and the components of each.

   Your proposal should address a clearly identified audience of decision makers and stakeholders on the issue you are discussing. Conduct an audience and purpose analysis to define the characteristics of the audience you are trying to persuade.

2. Finding the right words for a description or definition is crucial for helping your reader understand your message. In a group, choose one member to write the names of ordinary items (e.g., ice cream, kiwi, microwave, fax machine) on folded pieces of paper. Each member picks one item and has to describe it to the group using only words (gestures and facial expressions are not allowed) and the other members have to guess what the item is. Use the term-category-features model for stronger definitions.

3. Choose a specific audience and purpose, based on a real-life situation at school or at work, and write out some ideas for how you would determine whether this situation is an appropriate one for a formal report. List all possible readers (audience members) and all possible purposes. List the kinds of questions your report will need to answer, and then list the kinds of research you will need to do in order to write the report. Bring this document to class for discussion.

 ## The Global Window

Compare the style of Canadian proposals (for example, see https://buyandsell.gc. ca/) with proposals created in other countries. Is the format the same? Are there more proposals for certain purposes in Canada than in another country? You can learn about this topic by interviewing an expert in international business (someone you meet on the job, during an internship, or through your advisor). You can also search the web for information on international business communication. Describe your findings in a short memo that you will share with your classmates.

MyCanadianTechCommLab

Go to MyCanadianTechCommLab at www.mycanadiantechcommlab.com for additional online exercises and problems.

Grammar

Punctuation

Punctuation Mark	How It's Used	Examples
Period (.) For more on the period, see sentence fragments and run-on sentences on pages 347–349.	A period is used at the end of a complete idea to signal the end of a sentence.	*Use of white space is an important consideration when designing documents. However, there are no strict rules about how much white space should be on a page.*
Semicolon (;) For more on the semicolon, see sentence fragments and run-on sentences on pages 347–349.	A semicolon is used at the *end* of a complete idea to signal a pause but not the end of the sentence. A semicolon is always followed by another complete idea that is closely related to the one before it.	*Use of white space is an important consideration when designing documents; however, there are no strict rules about how much white space should be on a page.*
	A semicolon can also be used between items in a series when the items themselves contain commas.	*This summer we plan to visit relatives in Fredericton, New Brunswick; Calgary, Alberta; and Vancouver, British Columbia.*
Colon (:) For more on the colon, see lists on page 345.	Like the semicolon, a colon is used at the end of a complete idea to signal a pause. However, a colon doesn't need to be followed by another complete idea. Usually, the information that follows the colon explains or clarifies the information that comes before the colon. Often a colon is used at the end of a *complete sentence* to introduce a list.	*We can't reopen for business this week: The renovation work is not yet complete.* *Before we can reopen for business, we will need to order the following supplies: printer paper, printer cartridges, envelopes, and postage stamps.*
	A colon is not used to introduce a list after *including* or *such as.*	*We will need to order office supplies, including printer paper, printer cartridges, envelopes, and postage stamps.*

(continued)

Punctuation Mark	How It's Used	Examples
Comma (,) For more on the comma, see sentence fragments and run-on sentences on pages 347–349.	Commas are used to set off an appositive—words that identify or explain someone or something that's already been stated.	*Sue Jones, the first person we interviewed, was the most qualified candidate.*
	A comma is used between two complete ideas connected with a coordinating conjunction (and, but, for, or, nor, yet).	*We interviewed Sue Jones first, and she turned out to be the most qualified candidate.*
	A comma is used to separate an incomplete idea from a complete idea when the incomplete idea comes first.	*Because she has the most experience, we all agreed that Sue Jones was the most qualified candidate.*
	When the incomplete idea comes after the complete idea, no comma should be used.	*We all agreed that Sue Jones was the most qualified candidate because she has the most experience.*
Apostrophe (')	Use an apostrophe to form possessives. For singular words, even those that end in *s*, use an apostrophe followed by *s* to form the possessive. For plurals that end in *s*, use only the apostrophe.	*When you design a document, the user's needs should always come first.* *When you design documents, users' needs should always come first.*
	Also use apostrophes to form contractions.	*Can't, shouldn't, wouldn't, won't, etc.*
Quotation Marks (" ")	Use quotation marks around words that are spoken.	*Many survey respondents replied, "That's none of your business!"*
	Use quotation marks around the titles of songs, stories, poems, and parts of longer works, such as chapter titles.	*I found the lyrics to "Over the Rainbow" in Chapter 7, "Hits of the 1930s and 1940s."*
	NOTE: Periods and commas belong inside quotation marks. Colons and semicolons belong outside quotation marks. Question marks belong inside quotation marks if they are part of the material being quoted, otherwise they belong outside.	

(continued)

Punctuation Mark	How It's Used	Examples
Italics/Underlining	Use italics or underlining for titles of books, journals, magazines, films, and newspapers. Also use them for foreign words, technical terms, or words highlighted as words. Use italics sparingly for special emphasis.	*Star Wars* is still my favourite movie. The word _khaki_ was misspelled throughout the catalogue. _Do not_ leave your child unsupervised in the infant swing.
Parentheses ( )	Use parentheses to set off explanatory material that could be deleted without altering the meaning of the sentence.	*In general, the survey indicates that people are satisfied with the current document (see Appendix B for complete survey results).*
Dashes (—)	Use a dash to set off explanatory material that you want to emphasize.	_Storyteller_—a collection of short stories by Leslie Marmon Silko—is an excellent book for use in introductory literature classes.

Lists

Lists of items can be treated in one of two ways: as part of the text (embedded lists) or displayed with one item on each line (vertical lists).

Embedded Lists

On an embedded list, a series of items is integrated into a sentence, as here:

> The file menu allows you to perform the following tasks: create a new file, open an existing file, and save a current file.

Embedded lists can be numbered, as in the next example. To number an embedded list, use parentheses around the numerals and either commas or semicolons between the items.

> If you wish to apply for admission to the program, you must (1) submit official transcripts of all previous academic work, (2) complete a department application form, (3) submit at least three letters of recommendation from former employers or teachers, and (4) submit GRE scores.

Vertical Lists

Embedded lists are appropriate when you only need to list a few short items. Vertical lists, with numerals, letters, or bullets, are more appropriate than embedded lists when you need to list several items. Use numerals or letters if the items in the list belong in a particular order (steps in a procedure, for example) and bullets if the order of items is unimportant. Listing items vertically is also a way to increase the white space on a page and to draw a reader's attention to the content of the list. The following examples show how to introduce and punctuate vertical lists.

You can introduce a vertical list with a sentence that contains "the following" or "as follows." End the introductory sentence with a colon.

> Before the second week of class, students must purchase *the following:*
>
> - Printer card
> - Three-ring notebook
> - Course packet
> - Writing handbook

You can also introduce a vertical list with a sentence that ends with a noun. Again, end the introductory sentence with a colon.

> Before the second week of class, students must purchase *four items:*
>
> 1. Printer card
> 2. Three-ring notebook
> 3. Course packet
> 4. Writing handbook

You can also introduce a vertical list with a sentence that is not grammatically complete without the list items.

> To adjust the volume of sound input devices:
>
> 1. Choose Control Panels from the main menu.
> 2. Open the Sound Control panel.
> 3. Select Volumes from the pop-up menu.
> 4. Drag the sliders up and down to achieve the desired volume.

Do not use a colon to introduce a list with a sentence that ends with a verb, a preposition, or an infinitive. Either remove the colon or revise the sentence.

Incorrect because the introductory sentence ends with a verb.

> Before the second week of class, students *need:*
>
> - A printer card
> - An activated university email account
> - A course packet

Incorrect because the introductory sentence ends with a preposition.

> Before the second week of class, students need *to:*
>
> - Purchase a printer card
> - Activate a university email account
> - Purchase a course packet

Incorrect because the introductory sentence ends with an infinitive.

> Before the second week of class, students need *to buy:*
>
> - A printer card
> - A three-ring notebook
> - A course packet
> - A writing handbook

If another sentence comes after the sentence that introduces a list, use periods after both sentences. **Do not** use a colon to introduce the list.

> The next step is to configure the following fields. Consult Chapter 3 for more information on each field.
>
> - Serial port
> - Baud rate
> - Data bits
> - Stop bits

Note that some of the preceding examples use a period after each list item and some do not. As a rule, use a period after each list item if any of the items contains a complete sentence. Do not use a period if none of the list items contains a complete sentence. Also note that items included in a list should be grammatically parallel and comparable. For more on parallelism, see page 353–354.

Sentence Fragments and Run-On Sentences

Two of the most common writing errors involve punctuating strings of words as sentences when they are in fact not sentences. *Sentence fragments* contain too few grammatical elements, and *run-on sentences* contain too many.

Avoiding Sentence Fragments

A sentence fragment is a grammatically incomplete sentence. A grammatically complete sentence consists of at least one subject–verb combination and expresses a complete thought. It might include more than one subject–verb combination, and it might include other words or phrases as well. All the following examples are grammatically complete sentences because they all contain at least one subject–verb combination and they all express complete thoughts.

> This   book   summarizes   recent   criminal   psychology   research.
>   Subject   Verb
>
> The   smudge   tool   creates   soft   effects.
>   Subject   Verb
>
> The   table   of   contents   is   still   incomplete.
>   Subject   Verb

A sentence fragment might contain a subject–verb combination but fail to express a complete idea. The following example is a fragment. Even though it contains a subject–verb combination, it doesn't express a complete thought.

> Although   the   report   was   not   yet   complete.
>   Subject   Verb

This wording leaves a reader waiting for something to complete the thought. To make the sentence grammatically complete, add another subject–verb combination that completes the thought.

> Although   the   report   was   not   yet   complete,   I   began   editing.
>   Subject   Verb   Subject   Verb

Watch out for *although* and other words like it, including *because, if, while, since, when*, and *unless*. These are called subordinating conjunctions: When any of these words is combined with a subject–verb combination, it produces a subordinate clause (a clause that expresses an incomplete idea). This incomplete idea can be turned into a complete sentence only if another subject–verb combination that does express a complete idea is added on.

There are various other kinds of sentence fragments as well. For example, this next group of words is a fragment because it contains no verb.

> DesignPro, a brand-new desktop publishing program.

It can be turned into a complete sentence in a couple of ways.

> DesignPro, a brand-new desktop publishing program, will be available soon.
>
> DesignPro is a brand-new desktop publishing program.

Watch out for sentences that seem to contain a subject–verb combination but actually do not. Verb forms that end in *-ing*, such as *being* in the next phrase, are not complete verbs.

> Dale being a document design expert.

This fragment can be turned into a complete sentence by substituting the verb *is* for *being*.

> Dale is a document design expert.

Avoiding Run-On Sentences

Whereas a sentence fragment is a grammatically incomplete sentence, a run-on sentence suffers from the opposite problem: It contains too many grammatically complete sentences joined together as one. For example, the following run-on sentence contains two subject–verb combinations, each of which expresses a complete thought:

> For emergencies, we dial 911 for other questions, we dial 411.
> Subject Verb   Subject Verb

This sentence can be repaired in various ways. One possibility is to divide it into two sentences.

> For emergencies, we dial 911. For other questions, we dial 411.

Another possibility is to use a semicolon to join the two parts of the sentence. This option indicates a break that is not quite as strong as the period and therefore signals to the reader that the two items are closely related.

> For emergencies, we dial 911; for other questions, we dial 411.

Another possibility is to add a coordinating conjunction (*and, but, for, or, nor, yet*).

> For emergencies, we dial 911, but for other questions, we dial 411.

One **unacceptable** repair would be to add a comma. Doing so would produce a comma splice, which is another kind of run-on sentence.

> For emergencies, we dial 911, for other questions, we dial 411.

Another **unacceptable** repair would be to add a transitional word such as *however, consequently,* or *therefore.* These words alone or with a comma are not appropriate for joining two complete sentences.

> For emergencies, we dial 911, however, for other questions, we dial 411.

Instead, words such as *however, consequently,* and *therefore* (conjunctive adverbs) must be used with a semicolon or period.

> For emergencies, we dial 911; however, for other questions, we dial 411.
>
> For emergencies, we dial 911. However, for other questions, we dial 411.

Usage (Commonly Misused Words)

Be aware of the following pairs of words, which are commonly confused with each other in speech and in writing.

Word Pair	Examples
Affect means "to influence."	Sleep deprivation negatively *affects* driving ability.
Effect used as a noun means a "result."	Sleep deprivation has a negative *effect* on driving ability.
Effect used as a verb means "to cause" or "to bring about."	Management believes that the new policy will *effect* an increase in productivity.
Among is used with three or more people or items.	We can now divide the work *among* the three of us.
Between is used with two people or items.	We used to have to divide all of our work *between* the two of us.
Continually means "repeatedly."	Most young children need to be *continually* reminded to brush their teeth after meals.
Continuously means "nonstop."	The whole time I was driving, it rained *continuously*.
Disinterested means "neutral" or "objective."	Scientists are expected to be *disinterested* in their subject matter.
Uninterested means "bored" or "unconcerned."	Most of the students were *uninterested* in memorizing the grammar rules they were supposed to know for the quiz.
Farther refers to physical distances that can be measured.	I now live *farther* from the grocery store than I used to.
Further refers to abstract distances that can't be measured.	If you have any *further* questions, you'll need to speak with a supervisor.
Fewer refers to quantities that can be counted.	Most students like to take *fewer* credit hours in the spring quarter than they do in the winter quarter.
Less refers to quantities that cannot be counted.	The teacher was *less* concerned than usual about attendance this week.
Infer means "to guess" or "to speculate."	Several people who heard the victim's story were able to *infer* who committed the crime.
Imply means "to insinuate."	Her remarks *implied* that I was at fault.
Lay means "to put down" or "to set down." It requires a direct object.	Please *lay* all your books on the floor during the exam.
Lie means "to recline." It does not require a direct object. (Note that the past tense of *lie* is *lay*.)	Dentists usually advise their patients to *lie* down for several hours after any kind of dental work that requires anesthesia.

(continued)

Word Pair	Examples
Like should be followed by a noun, not by a subject–verb combination.	You look *like* a million bucks.
As if should be followed by a subject–verb combination.	You look *as if* you could use a couple more hours of sleep.
Percent should be used with a specific number to represent a figure.	Only two *percent* of survey respondents approve of the current system.
Percentage should be used to refer to an unspecified amount.	Only a small *percentage* of survey respondents approve of the current system.
Principle means "a fundamental rule or guideline."	Sometimes employees must choose whether to act in accordance with their own personal *principles* or those of the corporation.
Principal, when used as a noun, means "the chief person."	The school *principal* had to call several parents to let them know about the incident.
Principal, when used as an adjective, means "chief."	Her *principal* goal in seeking a new job is to earn more money.

Subject–Verb and Pronoun–Antecedent Agreement

Grammatical agreement involves number (singular or plural), person (first, second, or third), case (nominative or objective), and gender (male, female, or neither).

Subject–Verb Agreement

- Make the verb agree with its subject, not with a word that comes between.

  > The *tulips* in the pot on the balcony *need* watering.

  > The *teacher,* as well as his assistant, *was* reprimanded for his behaviour.

- Treat compound subjects connected by *and* as plural.

  > *Terry and Julie enjoy* collaborating on writing projects.

- With compound subjects connected by *or* or *nor,* make the verb agree with the part of the subject nearer to the verb.

> If my parents or *sister calls,* tell her I will be right back.
>
> Neither the professor nor *the students were* able to figure out what was going on.

- Treat most indefinite pronouns (*anybody, each, everybody,* etc.) as singular.

  > Almost *everybody* who registered for the class *was* there on the first day.

- Treat collective nouns as singular unless the meaning is clearly plural.

  > The *group respects* its leader.
  >
  > The *team were* debating among *themselves.*

- Make the verb agree with its subject even when the subject follows the verb.

  > At the back of the room *were a stereo* and *a small chair.*

Pronoun–Antecedent Agreement

Make pronouns and the words they refer to agree with each other.

> *Everyone* should proceed at *his or her* own pace.
>
> The *committee* finally decided to proceed with *its* building plan.
>
> The *committee* put *their* signatures on the final draft of the report.

Faulty Modification

Faulty modification occurs either when a phrase has no word to modify or when the position of a phrase within a sentence makes it difficult to determine which word the phrase is supposed to modify. For example, the following sentence makes no sense because the phrase "taking a shower" has no word to modify: This phrase is a *dangling modifier.*

> Taking a shower, the baby crawled out of his crib.

Revised as follows, the meaning of the sentence is clear:

> While I was taking a shower, the baby crawled out of his crib.

Here are some additional examples of sentences containing dangling modifiers.

> Faulty   *While dialing the phone,* the cat ran out the open door.
>
> Revised   As Joe dialed the phone, the cat ran out the open door.

Faulty	*After completing the student financial aid application form,* the Financial Aid Office will forward it to the appropriate provincial agency.
Revised	After you complete the student financial aid application form, the Financial Aid Office will forward it to the appropriate provincial agency.

The next sentence is unclear because the phrase "that was really boring" is supposed to modify "a weekend." But because of the position of this phrase in the sentence, a reader would mistakenly think it was the cabin, rather than the weekend, that was boring. This phrase is a *misplaced modifier*.

| We spent a weekend at the cabin that was really boring.

Revised as follows, the meaning of the sentence is much clearer.

| We spent a really boring weekend at the cabin.

Here are some additional examples of sentences containing misplaced modifiers.

Faulty	Joe typed another memo on our computer *that was useless.*
Revised	Joe typed another useless memo on our computer.

Faulty	He read a report on the use of non-chemical pesticides *in our conference room.*
Revised	In our conference room, he read a report on the use of non-chemical pesticides.

Faulty	She volunteered to deliver the radioactive shipment *immediately.*
Revised	She immediately volunteered to deliver the radioactive shipment.

Parallel Structure

Parallel structure is a fancy way of saying that similar items should be expressed in similar grammatical form. For example, the following sentence is not parallel:

| She enjoys many outdoor activities, including running, kayaking, and the design of new wilderness trails.

This sentence is essentially a list of items. The first two items, *running* and *kayaking,* are expressed as gerunds with *-ing* endings. The third item, *the design of* *new wilderness trails,* is not a gerund; it is a nominalization. To make this sentence parallel, you would revise as follows:

> She enjoys many outdoor activities, including *running, kayaking,* and *designing new wilderness trails.*

Items on bulleted and numbered lists must also be parallel. (For more on bulleted and numbered lists, see pages 345–347.) For example, on the list included in the following paragraph, the first two items are parallel, but the third is not.

> As the enclosed résumé illustrates, I have held several jobs relevant to the security management position your company is currently attempting to fill:
>
> * Park ranger for the city of Banff
> * Security guard at the West Edmonton Mall
> * I also worked as a part-time bouncer at Charlie's Tavern, a local bar

To make the third item parallel with the first two, revise it as follows:

> * Bouncer at Charlie's Tavern, a local bar

Other places to look for series of items that should be parallel include outlines, procedures, and sequences of subheadings within the same document.

Transitions Within and Between Paragraphs

You can choose from three techniques to achieve smooth transitions within and between paragraphs.

1. Use transitional expressions. These are words such as *again, furthermore, in addition, meanwhile, however, also, although, for example, specifically, in particular, as a result, in other words, certainly, accordingly, because,* and *therefore.* Such words serve as bridges between ideas.

2. Repeat key words, phrases, and concepts. Begin a sentence or paragraph by referring to something that was mentioned in the previous sentence or paragraph. The following paragraphs provide examples.

Original paragraph

> Breast cancer is a leading cause of death for women over 50. All women should learn to do monthly breast self-examinations. Doctors can easily teach women how to do these examinations, and public health organizations publish pamphlets to teach women how to do them. Many women think breast cancer will never happen to them, so they don't do self-examinations.

Revised paragraph

> Breast cancer is a leading cause of death for women over 50. *Because breast cancer is so common and so deadly,* all women should learn to do monthly breast self-examinations. *Women* can easily *learn* to do these *examinations* from doctors or from pamphlets published by public health organizations. However, *even though breast self-examinations are easy to learn,* many women don't do them because they think breast cancer will never happen to them.

The italicized words in the revised paragraph indicate places where key information from one sentence is repeated in the sentence that follows. (Also note that the transitional word *however* is inserted at the beginning of the last sentence.)

3. Use forecasting statements to tell the reader where you are going next. The following are examples of forecasting statements:

> The next step is to examine Johnson's points further. (The writer would then proceed to examine Johnson's points.)
>
> Of course we can also explore other avenues. (The writer would then proceed to explore these avenues.)
>
> There are at least two reasons why pay equity legislation in Canada will never close the gap between men's and women's salaries. (The writer would then proceed to list and explain these reasons.)

Use these methods as revision guidelines, but remember that they will not solve every organizational problem that occurs in real-life writing situations. If you encounter a situation where you think you need a better transition but none of these methods seems appropriate, it may be that you need to delete or move some information. Sometimes writers include information that is irrelevant to their topic, and sometimes information in one paragraph would tie in more easily with a different paragraph. In these situations, better transitions are not possible without doing some major revision first.

Mechanics

The mechanical aspects of writing a document include abbreviation, hyphenation, capitalization, use of numbers, and spelling. (Keep in mind that not all of these are actual rules; some may depend on style guides used in your field or your company.)

Abbreviations

The following should *always* be abbreviated:

- Titles such as *Ms., Mr., Dr.,* and *Jr.* when they are used before or after a proper name
- Time designations that are specific (400 BCE, 5:15 a.m.)

The following should *never* be abbreviated:

- Military, religious, or political titles (*Reverend, Prime Minister*)
- Time designations that are used without actual times (Sarah arrived early in the morning—not "early in the a.m.")

Avoid abbreviations whose meanings might not be clear to all readers. Units of measurement can be abbreviated if they appear frequently in your report. However, a unit of measurement should be spelled out the first time it is used. Avoid abbreviations in visual aids unless saving space is absolutely necessary.

Hyphenation

Hyphens divide words at line breaks and join two or more words used as a single adjective if they precede the noun (but not if they follow it):

> Com-puter (at a line break)
>
> The rough-hewn wood
>
> An all-too-human error
>
> The wood was rough hewn
>
> The error was all too human

Other commonly hyphenated words include the following:

- Most words that begin with the prefix *self-* (*self-reliance, self-discipline*—see your dictionary for any exceptions)
- Many words that begin with the prefix *non-* (*non-technical, non-expert, non-profit, non-scientist*—see your dictionary for any exceptions)
- Combinations that might be ambiguous (*re-creation* versus *recreation*)
- Words that begin with *ex* when *ex* means "past" (*ex-faculty member* but *excommunicate*)
- All fractions, along with ratios, that are used as adjectives and that precede the noun, and compound numbers from twenty-one through ninety-nine (*a two-thirds majority, thirty-eight windows*)

Capitalization

Capitalize the first words of all sentences as well as titles of people, books, and chapters; languages; days of the week; months; holidays; names of organizations or groups; races and nationalities; historical events; important documents; and names of structures or vehicles. In titles of books, films, and the like, capitalize the first and last words and all others except articles, short prepositions, and coordinating conjunctions (*and, but, for, or, nor, yet*).

Do not capitalize the seasons (spring, winter) or general groups (the younger generation, the leisure class).

Capitalize adjectives derived from proper nouns (*Chaucerian English*).

Capitalize words such as street, road, corporation, university, and college only when they accompany a proper noun (Yonge Street, Power Corporation, Saint Mary's University).

Capitalize *north, south, east,* and *west* when they denote specific regions (*the South, the Northwest*) but not when they are simply directions (*turn east at the light*).

Use of Numbers

Numbers expressed in one or two words can be written out or written as numerals. Use numerals to express larger numbers, decimals, fractions, precise technical figures, or any other exact measurements.

543	2 800 357 (For documents for a U.S. audience, use commas: 2,800,357.)
3.25	15 pounds of pressure
50 kilowatts	4000 rpm

Use numerals for dates, census figures, addresses, page numbers, exact units of measurement, percentages, times with a.m. or p.m. designations, and monetary and distance figures.

page 14	1:15 p.m.
18.4 kilograms	9 metres
12 litres	$15

Do not begin a sentence with a numeral. If the figure needs more than two words, revise your word order.

> Six hundred students applied for the 102 available jobs.
>
> The 102 available jobs attracted 650 applicants.

Do not use numerals to express approximate figures, time not designated as a.m. or p.m., or streets named by numbers less than 100.

> About seven hundred and fifty
>
> Four fifteen
>
> 108 East Forty-Second Street

In contracts and other documents in which precision is vital, a number can be stated both in numerals and in words:

> The tenant agrees to pay a rental fee of three hundred seventy-five dollars ($375.00) monthly.

Spelling

Always use the spell-check function in your word-processing software. However, don't rely on it exclusively. Take the time to use your dictionary for all writing assignments. And if you are a poor speller, ask someone else to proofread every document before you present it to your primary audience.

Documentation

Quoting the Words of Others

You must place quotation marks around all exact wording you borrow, whether the words were written, spoken (as in an interview or presentation), or posted electronically. Even a single borrowed sentence or phrase, or a single word used in a special way, needs quotation marks, with the exact source properly cited. These sources include people with whom you collaborate.

If your notes don't identify quoted material accurately, you might forget to credit the source. Even when this omission is unintentional, you face the charge of *plagiarism* (misrepresenting someone else's words or ideas as your own). Possible consequences of plagiarism include expulsion from school, loss of a job, and lawsuits.

Research writing is a process of independent thinking in which you work with the ideas of others in order to reach your own conclusions; unless the author's exact wording is essential, try to paraphrase instead of quoting borrowed material.

Paraphrasing the Words of Others

Paraphrasing means more than changing or shuffling a few words; it means restating the original idea in your own words—sometimes in a clearer, more direct, and emphatic way—and giving full credit to the source.

To borrow or adapt someone else's ideas or reasoning without properly documenting the source is plagiarism. To offer as a paraphrase an original passage that is only slightly altered—even when you document the source—is also plagiarism. Equally unethical is offering a paraphrase, although documented, that distorts the original meaning.

What You Should Document

Document any insight, assertion, fact, finding, interpretation, judgment, or other "appropriated material that readers might otherwise mistake for your own" (Gibaldi & Achtert, 1988, p. 155)—whether the material appears in published form or not. Specifically, you must document

- any source from which you use exact wording
- any source from which you adapt material in your own words
- any visual illustration: charts, graphs, drawings, or the like (see Chapter 8 for documenting visuals)

In some instances, you might have reason to preserve the anonymity of unpublished sources ("A number of employees expressed frustration with... ")— for example, to allow people to respond candidly without fear of reprisal (as with employee criticism of the company) or to protect their privacy (as with certain material from email inquiries or electronic newsgroups). You must still document the fact that you are not the originator of this material by providing a general acknowledgment in the text ("Interviews with Polex employees, May 2011") but not in your list of references.

You don't need to document anything that is considered *common knowledge:* material that appears repeatedly in general sources. In medicine, for instance, it has become common knowledge that foods containing animal fat contribute to higher blood cholesterol levels. So in a report on fatty diets and heart disease, you would probably not need to document that well-known fact. But you would document information about how the fat–cholesterol connection was discovered, what subsequent studies have found (say, the role of saturated versus unsaturated fats), and any information for which some other person or group could claim specific credit. If the borrowed material can be found in only one specific source, not in multiple sources, document it. When in doubt, document the source.

Documenting Sources

Cite borrowed material twice: at the exact place you use that material and at the end of your document. Documentation practices vary widely, but all systems work almost identically. A brief reference in the text names the source and refers readers to the complete citation, which allows readers to retrieve the source.

Many disciplines, institutions, and organizations publish their own style guides or documentation manuals. Here are a few:

> Geographical Research and Writing
>
> Style Manual for Engineering Authors and Editors
>
> IBM Style Manual

Four common documentation styles are those of the Modern Language Association (MLA), used mostly in the humanities; the American Psychological Association (APA), used mostly in the social sciences; the Council of Science Editors (CSE), used mostly in the physical and applied sciences; and the Institute of Electrical and Electronic Engineers (IEEE), used by electrical and electronic engineers. Consult the most recent edition of the *MLA Handbook for Writers of Research Papers,* the *Publication Manual of the American Psychological Association,* the CSE manual, *Scientific Style and Format,* or the *IEEE Editorial Style Manual* (http://www.ieee.org/documents/stylemanual.pdf) for guidance on documenting sources according to these systems. For information on a documentation style designed specifically for electronic and internet sources, see *The Columbia Guide to Online Style* (2006) by Janice R. Walker and Todd Taylor.

Using MLA Documentation Style

In MLA style, in-text parenthetical references briefly identify each source. Full documentation then appears in a Works Cited section at the end of the document. The parenthetical reference usually includes the author's surname and the exact page number where the borrowed material can be found:

```
One notable study indicates an elevated risk of leukemia for

children exposed to certain types of electromagnetic fields

(Bowman et al. 59).
```

Readers seeking the complete citation for Bowman et al. can refer easily to the Works Cited section, listed alphabetically by author:

```
Bowman, J. D., D. C. Thomas, S. J. London, J. M. Peters.

    "Hypothesis: The Risk of Childhood Leukemia Is Related to

    Combinations of Power-Frequency and Static Magnetic Fields."

    Bioelectromagnetics 16.1 (1995): 48–59. Print.
```

This complete citation includes page numbers for the entire article as well as the medium of publication: Print, Web, CD-ROM, Film, DVD, Personal interview, etc.

MLA Parenthetical References

For clear and informative parenthetical references, observe these rules:

- If your discussion names the author, do not repeat the name in your parenthetical reference; simply give the page number:

```
Bowman et al. explain how their recent study indicates an ele-
vated risk of leukemia for children exposed to certain types of
electromagnetic fields (59).
```

- If you cite two or more works in a single parenthetical reference, separate the citations with semicolons:

```
(Jones 32; Leduc 41; Gomez 293-94)
```

- If you cite two or more authors with the same surnames, include the first initial in your parenthetical reference to each author:

```
(R. Jones 32)

(S. Jones 14-15)
```

- If you cite two or more works by the same author, include the first significant word from each work's title, or a shortened version of the title:

```
(Lamont, Biophysics 100-01)

(Lamont, Diagnostic 81)
```

- If the work is by an institutional or corporate author or if it is unsigned (that is, the author is unknown), use only the first few words of the institutional name or the work's title in your parenthetical reference:

```
(American Medical Assn. 2)

("Distribution Systems" 18)
```

To avoid distracting the reader, keep each parenthetical reference brief. The easiest way to keep parenthetical references brief is to name the source in your discussion and place only the page number in parentheses.

For a paraphrase, place the parenthetical reference *before* the closing punctuation mark. For a quotation that runs into the text, place the reference *between* the final quotation mark and the closing punctuation mark. For a quotation set off (indented) from the text, place the reference one space *after* the closing punctuation mark.

MLA Works Cited Entries

The Works Cited list includes each source that you have paraphrased or quoted in your document. In preparing the list, type the first line of each entry flush with the left margin. Indent the second and subsequent lines five spaces. Double-space within and between each entry. Use one character space after any period, comma, or colon.

Following are examples of complete citations as they would appear in the Works Cited section of your document. Shown after each citation is the corresponding parenthetical reference as it would appear in the text. A handy, quick,

---

INDEX TO SAMPLE MLA WORKS CITED ENTRIES

Books

1. Book, single author, 364
2. Book, two or three authors, 364
3. Book, four or more authors, 364
4. Book, anonymous author, 364
5. Multiple books, same author, 364
6. Book, one or more editors, 364
7. Book, indirect source, 365
8. Anthology selection or book chapter, 365

Periodicals

9. Article, magazine, 366
10. Article, journal with new pagination for each issue, 366
11. Article, journal with continuous pagination, 366
12. Article, newspaper, 366

Other Sources

13. Encyclopedia, dictionary, or other alphabetical reference, 367
14. Report, 367
15. Conference presentation, 367

16. Interview, personally conducted, 368
17. Interview, published, 368
18. Letter, unpublished, 368
19. Questionnaire, 368
20. Brochure or pamphlet, 368
21. Lecture, 368
22. Government document, 369
23. Document with corporate authorship, 369
24. Map or other visual, 369
25. Unpublished dissertation, report, or miscellaneous items, 369

Electronic Sources

26. Online database, 370
27. Computer software, 370
28. CD-ROM, 371
29. Listserv, 371
30. Usenet, 371
31. Email, 372
32. Website, 372
33. Article in an online periodical, 372
34. Real-time communication, 372

online reference for MLA style can be found at the Purdue Online Writing Lab: http://owl.english.purdue.edu/owl/resource/747/01/.

MLA Works Cited Entries for Books. Any citation for a book should contain the following information: author, title, editor or translator, edition, volume number, and facts about publication (city, publisher, date).

1. Book, Single Author—MLA

> Kerzin-Fontana, Jane B. *Technology Management: A Handbook*. 3rd ed.
>
>   Delmar: American Management Assn., 2005. Print.
>
> Parenthetical reference: (Kerzin-Fontana 3–4)

If several cities of publication are listed on the title page, give only the first. For unfamiliar cities, include the two-letter postal abbreviation for the province. For well-known cities (e.g., New York, Toronto), omit the province or state. For unfamiliar cities in other countries, include an abbreviation of the country name.

2. Book, Two or Three Authors—MLA

> Aronson, Linda, Roger Katz, and Candide Moustafa. *Toxic Waste*
>
>   *Disposal Methods*. New Haven: Yale UP, 2004. Print.
>
> Parenthetical reference: (Aronson, Katz, and Moustafa 121–23)

Shorten publisher's names—"Simon" for Simon & Schuster, "Ottawa UP" for Ottawa University Press, etc. For page numbers with more than two digits, give only the final two digits for the second number.

3. Book, Four or More Authors—MLA

> Santos, Ruth J., et al. *Environmental Crises in Developing*
>
>   *Countries*. New York: Harper, 1998. Print.
>
> Parenthetical reference: (Santos et al. 9)

Et al. is the abbreviated form of the Latin *et alia,* meaning "and others."

4. Book, Anonymous Author—MLA

> *Structured Programming*. Boston: Meredith, 2005. Print.
>
> Parenthetical reference: (*Structured* 67)

5. Multiple Books, Same Author—MLA

> Chang, John W. *Biophysics*. Boston: Little, 1999. Print.

———. *Diagnostic Techniques*. New York: Radon, 1994. Print.

Parenthetical reference: (Chang, *Biophysics* 123–26); (Chang, *Diagnostic* 87)

When citing more than one work by the same author, do not repeat the author's name; type three hyphens followed by a period. List the works alphabetically by title.

6. Book, One or More Editors—MLA

Morris, A. J., and Louise B. Pardin-Walker, eds. *Handbook of New Information Technology*. New York: Harper, 1996. Print.

Parenthetical reference: (Morris and Pardin-Walker 34)

For more than three editors, name only the first, followed by *et al.*

7. Book, Indirect Source—MLA

Kline, Thomas. *Automated Systems*. Boston: Rhodes, 1992. Print.

Stubbs, John. *White-Collar Productivity*. Miami: Harris, 1999. Print.

Parenthetical reference: (qtd. in Stubbs 116)

When your source has quoted or cited another source, list each source in its appropriate alphabetical place on your Works Cited page. Use the name of the original source (here, Kline) in your text and precede your parenthetical reference with "qtd. in," or "cited in" for a paraphrase.

8. Anthology Selection or Book Chapter—MLA

Bowman, Joel P. "Electronic Conferencing." *Communication and Technology: Today and Tomorrow*. Ed. Al Williams. Denton: Assn. for Business Communication, 1994. 123–42. Print.

Parenthetical reference: (Bowman 129)

The page numbers in the complete citation are for the selection cited from the anthology.

MLA Works Cited Entries for Periodicals. A citation for an article should give this information (as available): author, article title, periodical title, volume or number (or both), date (day, month, year), and page numbers for the entire article—not just the pages cited. List the information in this order, as in the following examples.

9. Article, Magazine—MLA

```
DesMarteau, Kathleen. "Study Links Sewing Machine Use to
      Alzheimer's Disease." Bobbin Oct. 1994: 36–38. Print.
```

```
Parenthetical reference: (DesMarteau 36)
```

No punctuation separates the magazine title and date. Nor is the abbreviation *p.* or *pp.* used to designate page numbers.

If no author is given, list all other information, beginning with the title:

```
"Distribution Systems for the New Decade." Power Technology 18
      Oct. 2000: 18+. Print.
```

```
Parenthetical reference: ("Distribution Systems" 18)
```

This article begins on page 18 and continues on page 21. When an article does not appear on consecutive pages, give only the number of the first page, followed immediately by a plus sign. Use a three-letter abbreviation for any month spelled with five or more letters.

10. Article, Journal with New Pagination for Each Issue—MLA

```
Thackman-White, Joan R. "Computer-Assisted Research." American
      Library Journal 51.1 (2005): 3–9. Print.
```

```
Parenthetical reference: (Thackman-White 4–5)
```

Because each issue in a given year will have page numbers beginning with 1, readers need the issue number. The 51 denotes the volume number; 1 denotes the issue number. Omit *The, A,* or *An* if it is the first word in a journal or magazine title.

11. Article, Journal with Continuous Pagination—MLA

```
Barnstead, Marion H. "The Writing Crisis." Journal of Writing
      Theory 12 (2004): 415–33. Print.
```

```
Parenthetical reference: (Barnstead 415–16)
```

When page numbers continue from one issue to the next for the full year, readers won't need the issue number because no other issue in that year repeats these same page numbers. (Include the issue number, however, if you think it will help readers retrieve the article.) The 12 denotes the volume number.

12. Article, Newspaper—MLA

```
Baranski, Vida H. "Errors in Technology Assessment." Globe and
      Mail 15 Jan. 2005, sec. 2: 3. Print.
```

```
Parenthetical reference: (Baranski 3)
```

When a daily newspaper has more than one edition, cite the edition after the date. Omit any introductory article in the newspaper's name (not *The Globe and Mail*). If no author is given, list all other information. If the newspaper's name does not include the city of publication, insert it, using *square* brackets: *StarPhoenix* [Saskatoon, SK]. Exceptions would be the national dailies *The Globe and Mail* and *The National Post*.

MLA Works Cited Entries for Other Sources. Miscellaneous sources range from unsigned encyclopedia entries to conference presentations to government publications. A full citation should give this information (as available): author, title, city, publisher, date, and page numbers.

13. Encyclopedia, Dictionary, or Other Alphabetical Reference—MLA

```
"Communication." The Business Reference Book. 1998 ed. Print.

Parenthetical reference: ("Communication")
```

Begin a signed entry with the author's name. For any work arranged alphabetically, omit page numbers in the citation and the parenthetical reference. For a well-known reference book, include only an edition (if stated) and a date. For other reference books, give the full publication information.

14. Report—MLA

```
Electrical Power Research Institute (EPRI). Epidemiologic Studies
    of Electric Utility Employees. (Report No. RP2964.5). Palo
    Alto: EPRI, Nov. 1994. Print.

Parenthetical reference: (Electrical Power Research Institute
    [EPRI] 27)
```

If no author is given, begin with the organization that sponsored the report.

For any report or other document with group authorship, include the group's abbreviated name in your first parenthetical reference, and then use only that abbreviation in any subsequent reference: (EPRI 27).

15. Conference Presentation—MLA

```
Smith, Abelard A. "Radon Concentrations in Molded Concrete."
    First British Symposium in Environmental Engineering.
    London, 11–13 Oct. 1998. Ed. Anne Hodkins. London:
    Harrison, 1999. 106–21. Print.

Parenthetical reference: (Smith 109)
```

This citation is for a presentation that has been included in the published proceedings of a conference. For an unpublished presentation, include the presenter's name, the title of the presentation, and the conference title, location, and date, but do not underline or italicize the conference information.

16. Interview, Personally Conducted—MLA

```
Nasser, Gamel. Chief Engineer for Northern Electric. Personal
        interview. North Bay, ON. 2 Apr. 2006.
Parenthetical reference: (Nasser)
```

17. Interview, Published—MLA

```
Lescault, James. "The Future of Graphics." Executive Views of
        Automation. Ed. Karen Prell. Miami: Haber, 2000. 216–31.
        Print.

Parenthetical reference: (Lescault 218)
```

The interviewee's name is placed in the entry's author slot.

18. Letter, Unpublished—MLA

```
Rogers, Leonard. Letter to the author. 15 May 2006.

Parenthetical reference: (Rogers)
```

19. Questionnaire—MLA

```
Taylor, Lynne. Questionnaire sent to 612 Toronto business
        executives. 14 Feb. 2000.

Parenthetical reference: (Taylor)
```

20. Brochure or Pamphlet—MLA

```
Investment Strategies for the 21st Century. Vancouver: BC
        Economics Assn., 1999. Print.

Parenthetical reference: (Investment)
```

If the work is signed, begin with its author.

21. Lecture—MLA

```
Dumont, R. A. "Managing Natural Gas." Lecture. U of Alberta, Cal-
        gary. 15 Jan. 2006.

Parenthetical reference: (Dumont)
```

If the lecture title is not known, write simply *Address, Lecture,* or *Reading.* Include the sponsor and the location if available.

22. Government Document—MLA

British Columbia Ministry of Transportation. *Resource Summary*.

Vancouver: BC Min. of Transportation, 2007. Print.

Parenthetical reference: (British Columbia Ministry of

Transportation 49)

If the author is unknown (as here), list the information in this order: name of the government, name of the issuing agency, document title, place, publisher, and date.

23. Document with Corporate Authorship—MLA

Hermitage Foundation. *Global Warming Scenarios for the Year 2030*.

Montreal: Natl. Res. Council, 2000. Print.

Parenthetical reference: (Hermitage Foundation 123)

24. Map or Other Visual—MLA

Deaths Caused by Breast Cancer, by County. Map. *Scientific*

American Oct. 1995: 32D.

Parenthetical reference: (Deaths Caused)

If the creator of the visual is listed, give that name first. Identify the type of visual (*Map, Graph, Table, Diagram*) immediately following the title.

25. Unpublished Dissertation, Report, or Miscellaneous Items—MLA

Author (if known). "Title." Sponsoring organization or

publisher, date. Page numbers. Print.

For any work that has group authorship (corporation, committee, task force), cite the name of the group or agency in place of the author's name.

MLA Works Cited Entries for Electronic Sources. Citation for an electronic source with a printed equivalent should begin with that publication information (see relevant sections above). But whether or not a printed equivalent exists, any citation should enable readers to retrieve the material electronically. However, MLA style no longer requires the use of URLs (electronic addresses) since they may change (unlike Digital Object Identifiers or DOIs; see the APA section below) and most documents can be found by search engine or database. For those that cannot be easily found, including the URL is still recommended.

The Modern Language Association recommends the following general conventions.

Publication Dates: For sources taken from the internet, include the date the source was posted to the internet or last updated or revised as well as the date you accessed the source.

Uniform Resource Locators (URLs): Where you are using URLs, include the full and accurate address (including the access mode identifier—*http, ftp, gopher,* or *telnet*). Enclose URLs in angle brackets (< >). When a URL continues from one line to the next, break it only after a slash. Do not add a hyphen.

Page Numbering: Include page or paragraph numbers when given by the source.

Medium of Publication: Include the word "Web" for online sources just before the date of access, which should be the last item unless you are also including the URL.

26. Online Database—MLA

```
Sahl, J. D. "Power Lines, Viruses, and Childhood Leukemia."
        Cancer Causes Control 6.1 (Jan. 1995): 83. MEDLINE DIALOG.
        Web. 7 Nov. 1995.

Parenthetical reference: (Sahl 83)
```

For entries with a printed equivalent, begin with publication information, then the database title (underlined or italicized). The access date is important because frequent updating of databases can produce different versions of the material.

For entries with no printed equivalent, give the title and date of the work in quotation marks, followed by the electronic source information:

```
Argent, Roger R. "An Analysis of International Exchange Rates for
        2004." Accu-Data. Dow Jones News Retrieval. Web. 10 Jan.
        2005.

Parenthetical reference: (Argent 4)
```

If the author is not known, begin with the work's title.

27. Computer Software—MLA

```
Virtual Collaboration. New York: Harper, 1994. Diskette.

Parenthetical reference: (Virtual)
```

Begin with the author's name, if known.

28. CD-ROM—MLA

> Cavanaugh, Herbert A. "EMF Study: Good News and Bad News."
>
>   *Electrical World* Feb. 1995: 8. *ABI/INFORM*. ProQuest. Sept.
>
>   1995. CD-ROM.

> Parenthetical reference: (Cavanaugh 8)

If the material is also available in print, begin with the information about the printed source, followed by the electronic source information: name of the database (underlined), vendor name, electronic publication date, and CD-ROM designation. If the material has no printed equivalent, list its author (if known) and title (in quotation marks), followed by the electronic source information.

If you are citing an abstract of the complete work, insert *Abstract,* followed by a period, immediately after the work's page numbers.

For CD-ROM reference works and other material not routinely updated, give the title of the work, followed by the CD-ROM designation, place, electronic publisher, and date:

> *Time Almanac.* Washington: Compact, 1994. CD-ROM.

> Parenthetical reference: (*Time Almanac* 74)

Begin with the author's or editor's name, if known.

29. Listserv—MLA

> Korsten, A. "Major Update of the WWWVL Migration and Ethnic Rela-
>
>   tions." 7 Apr. 1998. ERCOMER News. Web. 8 Apr. 1998.

> Parenthetical reference: (Korsten)

Begin with the author's name (if known), followed by the title of the work (in quotation marks), publication date, name of discussion group, *Web* designation, and date of access. The parenthetical reference includes no page number because none is given in an online posting.

30. Usenet, Discussion Group, or Blog—MLA

> Dorsey, Michael. "Environmentalism or Racism." 25 Mar. 1998. Web.
>
>   1 Apr. 1998.

> Parenthetical reference: (Dorsey)

31. Email—MLA

```
Wallin, John Luther. "Frog Reveries." Message to the author. 12

    Oct. 2006. E-mail.

Parenthetical reference: (Wallin)
```

Cite personal email as you would printed correspondence. If the document has a subject line or title, enclose it in quotation marks.

For publicly posted email (say, a newsgroup or discussion list), include the address and date of access.

32. Website—MLA

```
Dumont, R. A. "An Online Course in Technical Writing." 10 Jul.

    2005. U of Toronto Online. Web. 18 May 2006 <http://www.

    utoronto.ca/english.html>.

Parenthetical reference: (Dumont 7–9)
```

Begin with the author's name (if known), followed by the title of the work (in quotation marks), posting date, name of website, date of access, and web address (in angle brackets). Note that a web address that continues from one line to the next is broken only after a slash. No hyphen is added.

33. Article in an Online Periodical—MLA

```
Jones, Francine L. "The Effects of NAFTA on Labor Union Member-

    ship." Cambridge Business Review 2.3 (1999): 47–64. Web. 4

    Apr. 2000.

Parenthetical reference: (Jones 48–49)
```

Information about the printed version is followed by the date of access to the website and the electronic address.

34. Real-Time Communication—MLA

Synchronous communication occurs in a "real time" forum and includes MUDs (multiuser dungeons), MOOs (MUD object-oriented software), IRC (internet relay chat), and FTPs (file transfer protocols). The message typed in by the sender appears instantly on the screen of the recipient, as in a personal interview.

```
Mendez, Michael R. Online debate. "Solar Power versus Fossil Fuel
     Power." 3 Apr. 1998. College TownMOO. Web. 3 Apr. 1998.

Parenthetical reference: (Mendez)
```

Begin with the name of the communicator, and indicate the type of communication (personal interview, online debate, and so on), topic title, posting date, name of forum, medium of publication (Web), and access date.

MLA Works Cited Page

Place your Works Cited section on a separate page at the end of the document. Arrange entries alphabetically by author's surname. When the author is unknown, list the title alphabetically according to its first word (ignoring introductory articles). For a title that begins with a numeral, alphabetize the entry as if the numeral were spelled out.

Using APA Documentation Style

One popular alternative to MLA style is set out in the *Publication Manual of the American Psychological Association*. APA style is useful when writers wish to emphasize the publication dates of their references. A parenthetical reference in the text briefly identifies the source, date, and page numbers:

```
In a recent study, mice continuously exposed to an electromag-
netic field tended to die earlier than mice in the control group
(de Jager & de Bruyn, 1994, p. 224).
```

The full citation then appears in the alphabetical listing of references, at the report's end:

```
de Jager, L., & de Bruyn, L. (1994). Long-term effects of a
     50-Hz electric field on the life expectancy of mice. Review of
     Environmental Health, 10, 221–224.
```

Because it emphasizes the date, APA style (or some similar author-date style) is preferred in the sciences and social sciences, where information quickly becomes outdated.

APA Parenthetical References

APA's parenthetical references differ from MLA's as follows: The APA citation includes the publication date, a comma separates each item in the reference, and *p.* or *pp.* precedes the page number. When a subsequent reference to a work follows closely after the initial reference, the date need not be included. Here are specific guidelines:

- If your discussion names the author, do not repeat the name in your parenthetical reference; simply give the date and page number:

```
Researchers de Jager and de Bruyn explain that experimental mice
exposed to an electromagnetic field tended to die earlier than
mice in the control group (1994, p. 224).
```

When two authors of a work are named in the text, their names are connected by *and,* but in a parenthetical reference, their names are connected by an ampersand (&).

- If you cite two or more works in a single reference, list the authors in alphabetical order and separate the citations with semicolons:

```
(Gomez, 1992; Jones, 2001; Leduc, 1996)
```

- If you cite a work with three to six authors, try to name them in your text to avoid an excessively long parenthetical reference.

```
Franks, Oblesky, Ryan, Jablar, and Perkins (1993) studied the
role of electromagnetic fields in tumor formation.
```

In any subsequent references to this work, name only the first author, followed by *et al.* (Latin abbreviation for "and others").

- If you cite two or more works by the same author published in the same year, assign a letter to each work, alphabetized by title:

```
(Lamont, 1990a, p. 135)
```

```
(Lamont, 1990b, pp. 67–68)
```

Other examples of parenthetical references appear with their corresponding entries in the following discussion of the list of references.

APA References Entries

The APA References list includes each source that you have cited in your document. In preparing the list, type the first line of each entry flush with the left margin. Indent the second and subsequent lines five spaces. Skip one character space after a period, comma, or colon. Double-space within and between entries.

Following are examples of complete citations as they would appear in the References section of your document. Shown immediately below each entry is its corresponding parenthetical reference as it would appear in the text. Note the capitalization, abbreviation, spacing, and punctuation in the sample entries.

INDEX TO SAMPLE APA WORKS CITED ENTRIES

Books

1. Book, single author, 376
2. Book, two authors, 376
3. Book, three to seven authors, 376
4. Book, more than seven authors, 376
5. Book, anonymous author, 377
6. Multiple books, same author, 377
7. Book, one to five editors, 377
8. Book, indirect source, 377
9. Anthology selection or book chapter, 377

Periodicals

10. Article, magazine, 378
11. Article, journal with new pagination for each issue, 378
12. Article, journal with continuous pagination, 378
13. Article, newspaper, 379

Other Sources

14. Encyclopedia, dictionary, or other alphabetical reference, 379
15. Report, 379

16. Conference presentation, 380
17. Interview, personally conducted, 380
18. Interview, published, 380
19. Personal correspondence or interview, 380
20. Brochure or pamphlet, 381
21. Lecture, 381
22. Government document, 381
23. Miscellaneous items, 381

Electronic Sources

24. Online database abstract, 382
25. Online database article, 382
26. Computer software or software manual, 382
27. CD-ROM abstract, 383
28. CD-ROM or internet reference work, 383
29. Personal email, 383
30. Website, 383
31. Newsgroup, discussion list, or online forum, 383
32. Electronic version of print book, 384
33. Electronic only-book, 384

A handy, quick, online reference for APA style can be found at the Purdue Online Writing Lab: http://owl.english.purdue.edu/owl/section/2/10/.

APA References Entries for Books. Any citation for a book should contain all applicable information in the following order: author, date, title, editor or translator, edition, volume number, and facts about publication (city and publisher).

1. Book, Single Author—APA

```
Kerzin-Fontana, J. B. (2005). Technology management: A handbook
        (3rd ed.). Delmar, NY: American Management Association.

Parenthetical reference: (Kerzin-Fontana, 2005, pp. 3–4)
```

Use only initials for an author's first and middle name. Capitalize only the first words of a book's title and subtitle and any proper nouns and adjectives. Identify an edition other than the first in parentheses between the title and the period.

2. Book, Two Authors—APA

```
Davidson, C. N, & Goldberg, D. T. (2009). The future of learning
        institutions in a digital age (The John D and Catherine T.
        MacArthur Foundation Reports on Digital Media and Learn-
        ing). Cambridge, MA: The MIT Press.

Parenthetical reference: (Davidson & Goldberg, 2009, pp. 5–6)
```

3. Book, Three to Seven Authors—APA

```
Aronson, L., Katz, R., & Moustafa, C. (2004). Toxic waste
        disposal methods. New Haven, CT: Yale University Press.

Parenthetical reference: (Aronson, Katz, & Moustafa, 2004)
```

Use an ampersand (&) before the name of the final author listed in an entry. As an alternative parenthetical reference, name the authors in your text and include the date (and page numbers, if appropriate) in parentheses.

4. Book, More than Seven Authors—APA

```
Fogle, S. T., et al. (1998). Hyperspace technology. Boston:
        Little, Brown.

Parenthetical reference: (Fogle et al., 1998, p. 34)
```

Et al. is the Latin abbreviation for *et alia,* meaning "and others."

5. Book, Anonymous Author—APA

```
Structured programming. (2005). Boston: Meredith Press.

Parenthetical reference: (Structured Programming, 2005, p. 67)
```

In your list of references, place an anonymous work alphabetically by the first word in its title, ignoring *The, A,* or *An.* In your parenthetical reference, capitalize all key words in a book or article title.

6. Multiple Books, Same Author—APA

```
Chang, J. W. (1997a). Biophysics. Boston: Little, Brown.

Chang, J. W. (1997b). MindQuest. Chicago: Pressler.

Parenthetical reference: (Chang, 1997a, 1997b)
```

Two or more works by the same author not published in the same year are distinguished by their dates alone, without the added letter. They are listed chronologically, earliest to latest.

7. Book, One to Five Editors—APA

```
Morris, A. J., & Pardin-Walker, L. B. (Eds.). (2003). Handbook of
    new information technology. New York: HarperCollins.

Parenthetical reference: (Morris & Pardin-Walker, 2003, p. 79)
```

For more than five editors, name only the first, followed by *et al.*

8. Book, Indirect Source—APA

```
Stubbs, J. (1998). White-collar productivity. Miami: Harris.

Parenthetical reference: (as cited in Stubbs, 1998, p. 47)
```

When your source has cited another source, list only this second source in the References section, but name the original source in the text: "Kline's study (as cited in Stubbs, 1998, p. 47) supports this conclusion."

9. Anthology Selection or Book Chapter—APA

```
Bowman, J. (1994). Electronic conferencing. In A. Williams (Ed.),
    Communication and technology: Today and tomorrow (pp. 123–
    142). Denton, TX: Association for Business Communication.

Parenthetical reference: (Bowman, 1994, p. 126)
```

The page numbers in the complete reference are for the selection cited from the anthology.

APA References Entries for Periodicals. A citation for an article should give this information (as available), in order: author, publication date, article title (without quotation marks), volume or issue number (or both), and page numbers for the entire article, not just the pages cited.

10. Article, Magazine—APA

```
DesMarteau, K. (1994, October). Study links sewing machine use to
     Alzheimer's disease. Bobbin, 36, 36-38.

Parenthetical reference: (DesMarteau, 1994, p. 36)
```

If no author is given, provide all other information. Capitalize the first word in an article's title and subtitle, and any proper nouns and adjectives. Capitalize all key words in a periodical title. Italicize the periodical title, comma, and volume number.

11. Article, Journal with New Pagination for Each Issue—APA

```
Thackman-White, J. R. (2005). Computer-assisted research.
     American Library Journal, 51(1), pp. 3-9.

Parenthetical reference: (Thackman-White, 2005, pp. 4-5)
```

Because each issue in a given year has page numbers that begin at 1, readers need the issue number (in this instance, 1). The 51 denotes the volume number, which is italicized.

12. Article, Journal with Continuous Pagination—APA

```
Barnstead, M. H. (2004). The writing crisis. Journal of Writing
     Theory, 12, 415-433.

Parenthetical reference: (Barnstead, 2004, pp. 415-416)
```

The 12 denotes the volume number. When page numbers continue from issue to issue for the full year, readers won't need the issue number, because no other issue in that year repeats the same page numbers.

13. Article, Newspaper—APA

Baranski, V. H. (2005, January 15). Errors in technology
assessment. *The Globe and Mail*, p. 83.

Parenthetical reference: (Baranski, 2005, p. 83)

In addition to the year of publication, include the month and day. If the newspaper's name begins with *The*, include it in your citation. Include *p.* or *pp.* before page numbers. For an article on non-consecutive pages, list each page, separated by a comma.

APA References Entries for Other Sources. Miscellaneous sources range from unsigned encyclopedia entries to conference presentations to government documents. A full citation should give this information (as available): author, publication date, work title (and report or series number), page numbers (if applicable), city, and publisher.

14. Encyclopedia, Dictionary, or Other Alphabetical Reference—APA

James, R. K. (Ed.). (2001). *The business reference book.* Boston:
Business Resources Press.

Parenthetical reference: (James, 2001, p. 255)

For an entry that is signed, use the author's name and place the editor's name after the title.

15. Report—APA

Electrical Power Research Institute. (1994). *Epidemiologic
studies of electric utility employees* (Rep. No. RP2964.5).
Palo Alto, CA: Author.

Parenthetical reference: (Electrical Power Research Institute,
[EPRI], 1994, p. 12)

If authors are named, list them first, followed by the publication date. When citing a group author, include the group's abbreviated name in your first parenthetical reference, and use only that abbreviation in any subsequent reference. When the agency or organization is also the publisher, list *Author* in the publisher's slot.

16. Conference Presentation—APA

```
Smith, A. A. (1999). Radon concentrations in molded concrete. In
    A. Hodkins (Ed.), First British Symposium on Environmental
    Engineering (pp. 106–121). London: Harrison Press.
```

Parenthetical reference: (Smith, 1999, p. 109)

In parentheses is the date of publication. The name of the symposium is a proper name and so is capitalized.

For an unpublished presentation, include the presenter's name, year and month, title of the presentation, title of the symposium (italicized), and all available information about the conference or meeting: "Symposium conducted at..."

17. Interview, Personally Conducted—APA

```
Parenthetical reference: (G. Nasser, personal interview, April 2,
    2002)
```

This material is considered a non-recoverable source and so is cited in the text only, as a parenthetical reference. If you name the respondent in the text, do not repeat the name in the citation.

18. Interview, Published—APA

```
Jable, C. K. (2000). The future of graphics [interview with James
    Lescault]. In K. Prell (Ed.), Executive views of automation
    (pp. 216–231). Miami: Haber Press, 2001.
```

Parenthetical reference: (Jable, 2000, pp. 218–223)

Begin with the name of the interviewer, followed by the interview date and title (if available), the designation (in *square* brackets), and the publication information, including the date.

19. Personal Correspondence or Interview—APA

```
Parenthetical reference: (L. Rogers, personal communication, May
    15, 2001)
```

This material is considered non-recoverable and so is cited in the text only, as a parenthetical reference. If you name the person in the text, do not repeat the name in the citation.

20. Brochure or Pamphlet—APA

This material follows the citation format for a book entry (see page 376). After the title of the work, include the designation *Brochure* or *Pamphlet* in square brackets.

21. Lecture—APA

Dumont, R. A. (2001, January 15). *Managing natural gas*. Lecture presented at the University of Alberta, Calgary.

Parenthetical reference: (Dumont, 2001)

If you name the lecturer in the text, do not repeat the name in the citation.

22. Government Document—APA

British Columbia Ministry of Transportation. (2007). *Standards for bridge maintenance*. Burnaby: Author.

Parenthetical reference: (British Columbia Ministry of Transportation, 1997, p. 49)

If the author is unknown, present the information in this order: name of the issuing agency, publication date, document title, place, and publisher. When the issuing agency is both author and publisher, list *Author* in the publisher slot.

For any governmental document, identify the level of government (federal, provincial, or municipal) before the date.

Ontario Provincial Government. (2001). *Funding for the academies*. Ottawa: Canada Printing Office.

Parenthetical reference: (Ontario Provincial Government, 2001, p. 41)

23. Miscellaneous Items (unpublished manuscripts, dissertations, and so on)—APA

Author (if known). (Date of publication). Title of work. Sponsoring organization or publisher.

For any work that has group authorship (corporation, committee, and so on), cite the name of the group or agency in place of the author's name.

APA References Entries for Electronic Sources. Any citation for electronic media should allow readers to identify the original source (printed or electronic) and provide an electronic path for retrieving the material.

Begin with the publication information for the printed equivalent. Then, in square brackets, name the electronic source ([CD-ROM], [Computer software]), the protocol—the set of standards that ensures compatibility among the different products designed to work together on a particular network (Bitnet, Dialog, FTP, Telnet), and any other items that define a clear path (service provider, database title, access code, retrieval number, site address).

A Digital Object Identifier (DOI) is the new standard for identifying an online document. While URLs may change, DOIs do not. For example, D. Brownlie's annotated bibliography "Toward effective poster presentations" can be found at either www. ingentaconnect.com/content/mcb/007/2007/00000041/F0020011/ art00001 or doi:10.1108/03090560710821161. Typing or pasting either of these into the address bar of your browser will take you to the document. Use the DOI whenever it is available.

24. Online Database Abstract—APA

Sahl, J. D. (1995). Power lines, viruses, and childhood leukemia. *Cancer Causes Control, 6*(1), 83. Abstract retrieved November 7, 2001, from the MEDLINE database.

Parenthetical reference: (Sahl, 1995)

Note that the entry ends with a period. Entries that close with a URL (see examples 30 and 31) or DOI have no period at the end.

25. Online Database Article—APA

Alley, R. A. (2003, January). Ergonomic influences on worker satisfaction. *Industrial Psychology, 5*(11), 93–107. Retrieved February 10, 2004, from the PsycARTICLES database.

Parenthetical reference: (Alley, 1995)

26. Computer Software or Software Manual—APA

Virtual collaboration [Computer software]. (1994). New York: HarperCollins.

Parenthetical reference: (Virtual, 1994)

For citing a manual, replace the *Computer software* designation in square brackets with *Software manual.*

27. CD-ROM Abstract—APA

Cavanaugh, H. (1995). An EMF study: Good news and bad news [CD-
ROM]. *Electrical World, 209*(2), 8. Abstract retrieved April
7, 2002, from ProQuest File: ABI/INFORM.

Parenthetical reference: (Cavanaugh, 1995)

The "8" in the entry denotes the page number of this one-page article.

28. CD-ROM or Internet Reference Work—APA

Grossman, P., et al. (Eds.). (1997). *Time almanac* [Electronic
version]. Washington: Compact, 1997.

Parenthetical reference: (Grossman et al., 1997, p. 20)

If the work on CD-ROM or on the web has a printed equivalent, APA prefers that it be cited in its printed form. If you consulted the work online, write *Electronic version* in square brackets after the title.

29. Personal Email—APA

Parenthetical reference: Fred Flynn (personal communication, May
10, 2006) provided these statistics.

Instead of being included in the list of references, personal email is cited directly in the text.

30. Website—APA

Dumont, R. A. (2005, July 10). An online course in composition.
Retrieved May 18, 2006, from http://www.utoronto.ca/
english.html

Parenthetical reference: (Dumont, 2005)

If the web address continues from one line to the next, divide it only after a slash and do not add a hyphen or any other punctuation.

31. Newsgroup, Discussion List, or Online Forum—APA

Labarge, V. S. (2001, October 20). A cure for computer viruses
[Msg. 2237]. Message posted to http://forums.ntnews.com/
webin/webz198@.dsg9567

Parenthetical reference: (Labarge, 2001)

32. Electronic version of print book—APA

Andrew, C., Gattinger, M., Jeannotte, M. S., Straw, W. (2005). *Accounting for Culture: Thinking Through Cultural Citizenship*. Ottawa: University of Ottawa Press. Retrieved from http://www.ruor.uottawa.ca/en/handle/10393/19613

33. Electronic only-book—APA

Ceccarelli, M. (2011). *Technology developments: the role of mechanism and machine science and IFToMM*. Retrieved from http://www.springerlink.com/content/978-94-007-1300-0

APA References List

APA's References section is an alphabetical listing (by author) equivalent to MLA's Works Cited section. Like Works Cited, the reference list includes only works actually cited in the text. Unlike MLA style, APA style calls for only recoverable sources to appear in the reference list. Therefore, personal interviews, email messages, and other unpublished materials are cited in the text only.

Using CSE and Other Numbered Documentation Styles

In a numbered documentation system, each work is assigned a number sequentially the first time it is cited. This same number is then used for any subsequent reference to that work. Numbered documentation is often used in the physical sciences (astronomy, chemistry, geology, physics) and in the applied sciences (mathematics, medicine, engineering, and computer science).

Particular disciplines have their own preferred documentation styles, described in manuals such as these:

- American Chemical Society, *The ACS Style Guide for Authors and Editors*
- American Institute for Physics, *AIP Style Guide*
- American Medical Association, *Manual of Style*

One widely consulted guide for numerical documentation is *Scientific Style and Format: The CSE Manual for Authors, Editors, and Publishers,* from the Council of Science Editors. (In addition to its citation-sequence system for documentation, the CSE offers a name-year system that basically duplicates the APA system described on pages 373–384.)

CSE Numbered Citations

In the numbered version of CSE style, a citation in the text appears as a super-script number immediately following the source to which it refers:

> A recent study[1] indicates an elevated leukemia risk among children exposed to certain types of electromagnetic fields. Related studies[2-3] tend to confirm the EMF–cancer hypothesis.

When referring to two or more sources in a single note, separate the numbers by a hyphen if they are in sequence and by commas but no space if they are out of sequence: [2,6,9].

The full citation for each source then appears in the numeric listing of references at the end of the document.

References

1. Baron, KL, et al. The electromagnetic spectrum. New York: Pearson; 2005. 476 p.

2. Klingman, JM. Nematode infestation in boreal environments. J Entymol 2003; 54:475–8.

CSE References Entries

CSE's References section lists each source in the order in which it was first cited. In preparing the list, which should be double-spaced, begin each entry on a new line. Type the number flush with the left margin, followed by a period and a space. Align subsequent lines directly under the first word of line 1.

Following are examples of complete citations as they would appear in the References section for your document.

INDEX TO SAMPLE CSE ENTRIES

Books

1. Book, single author, 386
2. Book, multiple authors, 386
3. Book, anonymous author, 386
4. Book, one or more editors, 386
5. Anthology selection or book chapter, 386

Periodicals

6. Article, magazine, 386
7. Article, journal with new pagination for each issue, 387
8. Article, journal with continuous pagination, 387
9. Article, newspaper, 387
10. Article, online source, 387

CSE References Entries for Books. Any citation for a book should contain all available information in the following order: number assigned to the entry, author or editor, title (and edition), facts about publication (place, publisher, date), and number of pages. Note the capitalization, abbreviation, spacing, and punctuation in the sample entries.

1. Book, Single Author—CSE

1. Kerzin-Fontana JB. Technology management: a handbook. 3rd ed. Delmar, NY; American Management Assoc; 2005. 356 p.

2. Book, Multiple Authors—CSE

2. Aronson L, Katz R, Moustafa C. Toxic waste disposal methods. New Haven: Yale Univ Pr; 2004. 316 p.

3. Book, Anonymous Author—CSE

3. [Anonymous]. Structured programming. Boston: Meredith Pr; 2005. 267 p.

4. Book, One or More Editors—CSE

4. Morris AJ, Pardin-Walker LB, editors. Handbook of new information technology. New York: Harper; 2003. 345 p.

5. Anthology Selection or Book Chapter—CSE

5. Bowman JP. Electronic conferencing. In: Williams A, editor: Communication and technology: today and tomorrow. Denton, TX: Assoc for Business Communication; 1994. p 123–42.

CSE References Entries for Periodicals. Any citation for an article should contain all available information in the following order: number assigned to the entry, author, article title, periodical title, date (year, month), volume and issue number, and inclusive page numbers for the article. Note the capitalization, abbreviation, spacing, and punctuation in the sample entries.

6. Article, Magazine—CSE

6. DesMarteau K. Study links sewing machine use to Alzheimer's disease. Bobbin 1994 Oct:36–8.

7. Article, Journal with New Pagination Each Issue—CSE

```
7. Thackman-White JR. Computer-assisted research. Am Library J
      2005;51(1):3–9.
```

8. Article, Journal with Continuous Pagination—CSE

```
8. Barnstead MH. The writing crisis. J Writing Theory
      2004;12:415–33.
```

9. Article, Newspaper—CSE

```
9. Baranski VH. Errors in technology assessment. Boston Times
      2005 Jan 15;Sect B:3.
```

10. Article, Online Source—CSE

```
10. Alley RA. Ergonomic influences on worker satisfaction. Indus-
      trial Psychology [article online]. 2003 Jan;5(11). Avail-
      able from: ftp.pub/journals/industrialpychology/2003 via
      the INTERNET. Accessed 2004 Feb 10.
```

Citation for an article published online follows a similar format, with these differences: write *article online* in square brackets between the article title and publication date; after "Available from," give the DOI or URL followed by a period and your access information.

For more guidelines and examples, consult the *CSE Manual* or go to www. wisc.edu/writing/Handbook/DocCSE.html and www.lib.ohio-state.edu/guides/cbegd. html.

IEEE Style

The IEEE (Institute of Electrical and Electronics Engineers) documentation style is most commonly used by electrical and electronics engineers, as well as by those who work in the computer science realm. The IEEE reference list is arranged by the order of the citations in the document (not alphabetical order).

1. Book, Single Author—IEEE

```
[1] J. B. Kerzin-Fontana, Technology Management: A Handbook, 3rd
      ed., Delmar: American Management Assn., 2005.
```

INDEX TO SAMPLE IEEE ENTRIES

Books

1. Book, single author, 387
2. Book, two or three authors, 388
3. Book, four or more authors, 389
4. Book, anonymous author, 389
5. Multiple books, same author, 389
6. Book, one or more editors, 389
7. Book, indirect source, 389
8. Anthology selection or book chapters, 389

Periodicals

9. Article, magazine, 389
10. Article, journal with new pagination for each issue, 390
11. Article, journal with continuous pagination, 390
12. Article, newspaper, 390

Other Sources

13. Encyclopedia, dictionary, or other alphabetical reference, 390
14. Report, 390
15. Conference presentation, published, 390

16. Conference presentation, unpublished, 390
17. Interview, personally conducted, 391
18. Interview, published, 391
19. Letter, unpublished, 391
20. Questionnaire, 391
21. Brochure or pamphlet, 391
22. Lecture, 391
23. Government document, 392
24. Document with corporate authorship, 392
25. Map or other visual, 392
26. Unpublished dissertation, report, or miscellaneous items, 392

Electronic Sources

27. Online database, 392
28. Computer software, 392
29. CD-ROM, 393
30. Listserv, 393
31. Usenet, 393
32. Email, 393
33. Website, 393
34. Real-time communication, 393

2. Book, Two or Three Authors—IEEE

[2] L. Aronson, R. Katz, and C. Moustafa, *Toxic Waste Disposal Methods*, New Haven: Yale UP, 2004.

3. Book, Four or More Authors—IEEE

[3] R. J. Santos, *et al.*, *Environmental Crises in Developing Countries*, New York: Harper, 1998.

4. Book, Anonymous Author—IEEE

[4] *Structured Programming*, Boston: Meredith, 2005.

5. Multiple Books, Same Author—IEEE

[5] J. W. Chang, *Diagnostic Techniques*, New York: Radon, 1994.

[6] ___, *Biophysics*, Boston: Little, 1999.

List sources by the same author by their reference number rather than alphabetically.

6. Book, One or More Editors—IEEE

[7] A. J. Morris and L. B. Pardin-Walker, Eds., *Handbook of New Information Technology*, New York: Harper, 1996.

7. Book, Indirect Source—IEEE

[8] T. Kline, *Automated Systems*, Boston: Rhodes, 1992.

[9] J. Stubbs, *White-Collar Productivity*, Miami: Harris, 1999.

List both your source (Stubbs) and the original source (Kline) in the reference list.

8. Anthology Selection or Book Chapter—IEEE

[10] J. P. Bowman, "Electronic conferencing," in *Communication and Technology: Today and Tomorrow*, A. Williams, Ed., Denton: Assn. for Business Communication, 1994, pp. 123–142.

9. Article, Magazine—IEEE

[11] K. DesMarteau, "Study links sewing machine use to Alzheimer's disease," *Bobbin*, pp. 36–38, Oct. 1994.

[12] "Distribution systems for the new decade," *Power Technology*, p. 18+, Oct. 2000.

10. Article, Journal with New Pagination for Each Issue—IEEE

[13] J. R. Thackman-White, "Computer-assisted research," *American Library Journal*, vol. 51, no. 1, pp. 3–9, 2005.

11. Article, Journal with Continuous Pagination—IEEE

[14] M. H. Barnstead, "The writing crisis," *Journal of Writing Theory*, vol. 12, pp. 415–433, 2004.

12. Article, Newspaper—IEEE

[15] V. H. Baranski, "Errors in technology assessment," *Globe and Mail* (Jan. 15, 2005), sec. 2:3.

13. Encyclopedia, Dictionary, or Other Alphabetical Reference—IEEE

[16] "Communication," *The Business Reference Book*, 1998 ed.

14. Report—IEEE

[17] Electrical Power Research Institute (EPRI), "Epidemiologic studies of electric utility employees," EPRI, Palo Alto, CA, Rep. RP2964.5, 1994.

15. Conference Presentation, Published—IEEE

[18] A. A. Smith, "Radon concentrations in molded concrete," in *First British Symposium in Environmental Engineering*, 1998, pp. 106–121.

16. Conference Presentation, Unpublished—IEEE

[19] A. A. Smith, "Radon concentrations in molded concrete," presented at the First British Symposium in Environmental Engineering, London, England, 1998.

17. Interview, Personally Conducted—IEEE

[20] G. Nasser (private communication), 2006.

Unpublished interviews that will not be published or are not available in an archive or a library do not need to be cited with a reference number. If you do not cite the interview with a reference number, you must mention the interviewee's name in the document itself.

For example:

> In a personal interview, Gamel Nasser discussed Northern Electric's business plan.

18. Interview, Published—IEEE

[21] J. Lescault, "The future of graphics," in *Executive Views of Automation*, K. Prell, Ed., Miami: Haber, 2000, pp. 216-231.

19. Letter, Unpublished—IEEE

[22] L. Rogers (private communication), 2006.

Unpublished letters that will not be published or are not available in an archive or a library do not need to be cited with a reference number. If you do not cite the letter with a reference number, you must mention the name of the letter's author in the document itself.

For example:

> In a letter to the author, Leonard Rogers analyzes the impact of viruses on computer research.

20. Questionnaire—IEEE

[23] L. Taylor, Questionnaire, Feb. 14, 2000.

21. Brochure or Pamphlet—IEEE

[24] BC Economics Assn., *Investment Strategies for the 21st Century*, Vancouver: BC Economics Assn., 1999.

22. Lecture—IEEE

[25] R. A. Dumont. Class Lecture, Topic: "Managing Natural Gas." University of Alberta, Calgary, Jan. 15, 2006.

23. Government Document—IEEE

[26] British Columbia. Ministry of Transportation. *Standards for Bridge Maintenance*, Burnaby: BC Min. of Transportation, 1997.

[27] Canada. Parliament. House of Commons. 33rd Parliament, 1st Session, No. 134. *Order Papers and Notices*, Ottawa: Queen's Printer.

[28] United States. Congressional Record. March 10, 1999, pp. 2178–2192.

24. Document with Corporate Authorship—IEEE

[29] Hermitage Foundation, *Global Warming Scenarios for the Year 2030*, Washington: Natl. Res. Council, 2000.

25. Map or Other Visual—IEEE

[30] Deaths Caused by Breast Cancer, by County. [Map]. *Scientific American*, p. 32D, Oct. 1995.

26. Unpublished Dissertation, Report, or Miscellaneous Items—IEEE

[31] A. A. Author, "Title of item," doctoral dissertation, Department, University, City, Province or Country, Year.

27. Online Database—IEEE

[32] J. D. Sahl, "Power lines, viruses, and childhood leukemia," *Cancer Causes Control*, vol. 6, no. 1, p. 83, Jan. 1995. [Online]. MEDLINE, Available: http://www.ncbi.nlm.nih.gov/pubmed/7718739. [Accessed Sep. 18, 2008].

[33] R. R. Argent, "An analysis of international exchange rates for 2004," *Accu-Data*. [Online]. Dow Jones News Retrieval, Available: electronic address. [Accessed Jan. 10, 2005].

28. Computer Software—IEEE

[34] *Virtual Collaboration*. [Diskette]. New York: Harper, 1994.

29. CD-ROM—IEEE

[35] H. A. Cavanaugh, "EMF study: good news and bad news,"
     Electrical World, p. 8, Feb. 1995. [CD-ROM]. ProQuest,
     Available: electronic address. [Accessed Sep. 1995].

[36] *Time Almanac.* [CD-ROM]. Washington: Compact, 1994.

30. Listserv—IEEE

[37] A. Dimitrov, "Minority issues in Latvia, No. 49," *ERCOMER
     News,* May 2, 2002. [Online]. Available: http://www.
     minelres.lv/minelres/archive/05022002-20:49:44-27893.
     htmlelectronic address. [Accessed April 8, 1998].

31. Usenet—IEEE

[38] M. Dorsey, "Environmentalism or racism," March 25, 1998.
     [Online]. Available: <news:alt.org.sierra-club>

32. Email—IEEE

[39] J. L. Wallin. "RE: Frog Reveries." Personal email (Oct. 12,
     2006).

33. Website—IEEE

[40] R. A. Dumont, "An online course in technical writing," Uni-
     versity of Toronto, Dec. 10, 2004. [Online]. Available:
     http://www.utoronto.ca/writing.html.

[41] F. L. Jones, "The effects of NAFTA on labor union member-
     ship," *Cambridge Business Review,* vol. 2, no. 3, pp. 47–64,
     1999. [Online]. Available: electronic address. [Accessed
     April 4, 2000].

34. Real-Time Communication—IEEE

[42] M. R. Mendez, "Solar power versus fossil fuel power,"
     College TownMOO, April 3, 1998. [Online debate]. Available:
     electronic address. [Accessed April 3, 1998].

References

Abran, A., Khelifi, A., Suryn, W., & Seffah, A. (2003). Usability Meanings and Interpretations in ISO Standards. *Software Quality Journal, 11*(4), 325–338. doi: 10.1023/A:1025869312943

Batten, K. (2008, May). A spray for the BlackBerry? *SuperLiving Magazine.* Retrieved from www.superliving.com.au/StoryView.asp?StoryID=242345

Bernstein, M. P., et al. (1999, July). Life's far-flung raw materials. *Scientific American,* 42–49.

Bizzell, P. (1992). *Academic discourse and critical consciousness.* Pittsburgh: University of Pittsburgh Press.

Bjork, E., & Ottoson, S. (2007). Aspects of consideration in product development research. *Journal of Engineering Design, 18*(3), 195–207.

Black & Decker (U.S.) Inc. (1993). Instruction Manual.

Blum, D. (1997). Investigative science journalism. In D. Blum & M. Knudson (Eds.), *Field guide for science writers* (pp. 86–93). New York: Oxford.

Brownell, J., & Fitzgerald, M. (1992). Teaching ethics in business communication: The effective/ethical balancing scale. *Bulletin of the Association for Business Communication, 55*(3), 15–18.

Brumberger, E. (2004, February). The rhetoric of typography: Effects on reading time, reading comprehension, and perception of ethos. *Technical Communication,* 15.

Bryan, J. (1992). Down the slippery slope: Ethics and the technical writer as marketer. *Technical Communication Quarterly, 1*(1), 73–88.

Buchhulz, G. A. (2009). The 10 Commandments of Contentology. *Contentology.* Retrieved from http://contentology.com/docs/10.Commandments.of.Contentology. pdf, 1.

Canada News Wire. (2008, March 4). Law Society welcomes Supreme Court of Canada landmark copyright decision, 1. *CBCA Current Events database.* (Document ID: 570912431).

Carlson, S. (1999, July). Detecting earth's electricity. *Scientific American,* 94–95

Centers for Disease Control and Prevention (2004). Molds in the Environment. Retrieved from www.cdc.gov/MOLD/pdfs/pib.pdf

Child, M. L. (2007). Professors Split on Wiki Debate. *The Harvard Crimson.* Retrieved from http://www.thecrimson.com/article/2007/2/26/professors-split-on-wiki-debate-despite/ © 2011 The Harvard Crimson, Inc. All rights reserved. Reprinted with permission.

Christians, C. G., Tackler, M., Rotzoll, K. B., Brittain-McKee, K., & Woods, R. H., Jr. (2005). Introduction. In C. G. Christians, M. Tackler, K. B. Rotzoll, K. Brittain-McKee, & R. H. Woods Jr. (Eds.), *Media ethics: Cases and moral reasoning* (7th ed., pp. 22–24). Boston: Allyn & Bacon.

Columbia Accident Investigation Board. (2003, August). *Report Volume I.* Washington, DC: Author.

Conference Board of Canada. (2000). *Employability Skills 2000+.* Ottawa: Author.

Cooper, C. (2008, February 15). Color my world: Hereditary color vision deficiency can't be cured but can be managed. *Knight Ridder Tribune Business New,* 1. ABI/INFORM Dateline database. (Document ID: 1216685731).

Curtis and Giamanco (2010). Sales Meets Social Media PART TWO. *The New Handshake: Sales Meets Social Media.* Santa Barbara, CA: Greenwood Publishing Group: 122.

Cywinski, M. (2008). Email preferred method of communication for execs. *CanadaOne.* http://www.canadaone.com/ezine/briefs.html?StoryID=08Jan04_1 Reprinted by permission of CanadaOne.

Davidoff, J. (1991). *Cognition through color.* Cambridge, MA: MIT Press.

Detz, J. (2007). 12 Steps to improve your next presentation. In Learning how to communicate. *Vital Speeches of the Day, 73*(12), 540–542. Retrieved from ProQuest.

Digital Copyright Canada. (2008, September). Retrieved from www.digital-copyright.ca/copyright_jargon.shtml

Dragga, S. (1996). Is this ethical? A survey of opinion on principles and practices of document design. *Technical Communication, 43*(3), 255–265.

Dumas, J. S., & Redish, J. C. (1994). *A practical guide to usability testing* (2nd ed.). Norwood, NJ: Ablex.

Earthquake hazard analysis for nuclear power plants. (1984, June). *Energy and Technology Review*, 8.

Fink, C. (1988). *Media ethics*. Boston: Allyn & Bacon.

Garfield, E. (1973). What scientific journals can tell us about scientific journals. *IEEE Transactions on Professional Communication, 16*, 200–202.

Gervais, D. J. (2005). The purpose of copyright law in Canada. *University of Ottawa Law & Technology Journal 2*(2), 315–356.

Gibaldi, J., & Achtert, W.S. (1988). *MLA handbook for writers of research papers*. (3rd ed.) New York: Modern Language Association of America.

Gould, S. J. (1978): Were dinosaurs dumb? *Natural History, 87*(5), 9–16.

Gross, W., & Kisluk, M. (2005, September). Privacy versus patriots. *CA Magazine*. Retrieved from www.camagazine.com/2/7/8/0/9/index1.shtml.

Haefner, R (2010, June 6). More Employers Screening Candidates via Social Networking Sites. *Career Builder*. Retrieved from http://www.careerbuilder.com/Article/CB-1337-Interview-Tips-More-Employers-Screening-Candidates-via-Social-Networking-Sites/

Hall, C. (2010, April 21). Why Foursquare Drives Business: What You Need to Know. *Social Media Examiner*. Retrieved from http://www.socialmediaexaminer.com/why-foursquare-drives-business-what-you-need-to-know

Hargis, G., Hernandez, A., Hughes, P., & Ramaker, J. (1997). *Developing quality technical information: A handbook for writers and editors*. Upper Saddle River, NJ: Prentice Hall.

Hoft, N. L. (1995). *International technical communication: How to export information about high technology*. New York: Wiley.

Hogg, C. (2011, January 19). Study: Smartphones and tablets to outsell computers in 2011. *Digital Journal*. Retrieved from http://digitaljournal.com/article/302719

Horton, S. & Lynch, P.J. (1990). *Web Style Guide*. New Haven: Yale Univeristy Press.

Hughes, M. (1999). Rigor in usability testing. *Technical Communication, 46*(4), 488–495.

Janis, I. L. (1972). *Victims of groupthink: A psychological study of foreign policy decisions and fiascos*. Boston: Houghton-Mifflin.

Japikse, C. (1994). Lasagna in the making. *EPA Journal, 20*(3), 27.

Johannesen, R. L. (1983). *Ethics in human communication* (2nd ed.). Prospect Heights, IL: Waveland Press.

Johnson, R. R. (1997). *User-centered technology: A rhetorical theory for computers and other mundane artifacts.* Albany: State University of New York Press.

Johnson, R. R., Salvo, M. J., & Zoetewey, M. W. (2007). User-centered technology in participatory culture: Two decades "beyond a narrow usability testing." *Professional Communication, 50*(4), 320–332.

Kohl, J. R. (1999). Improving translatability and readability with syntactic cues. *Technical Communication, 46*(2), 149–166.

Kostelnick, C., & Roberts, D. D. (1998). *Designing visible language: Strategies for professional communicators.* Boston: Allyn & Bacon.

Kress, G. (2003). *Literacy in the new media age.* New York: Routledge.

Krizen, A. C., Merrier, P., Logan, J., & Williams, K. (2008). Print and Electronic Messages. In *Business Communication* (7th ed.) Mason OH: Thomson South-Western: 132.

Larson, C. U. (1995). *Persuasion: Perception and responsibility* (7th ed.). Belmont, CA: Wadsworth.

Lavin, M. R. (1992). *Business information: How to find it, how to use it* (2nd ed.). Phoenix: Oryx Press.

Levy, E., Zacks, J., Tversky, B., & Schiano, D. (1996). Gratuitous graphics? Putting preferences in perspective. Paper prepared for the Conference on Human Factors in Computing Systems, April 13–18, 1996, Vancouver, BC. Retrieved from www.sigchi.org/chi96/proceedings/papers/Levy/lev_txt.htm

Lynch, P. J., & Horton, S. (2001). *Web style guide: Basic design principles for creating web sites* (2nd ed.). New Haven, CT: Yale University Press.

Microsoft. (2011). Show Me! What Brain Research Says About Visuals in Power-Point. Retrieved from http://office.microsoft.com/en-us/powerpoint-help/show-me-what-brain-research-says-about-visuals-in-powerpoint-HA010277194.aspx

Munter, M., & Paradi, D. (2006). *Guide to PowerPoint.* Upper Saddle River, NJ: Prentice Hall.

NPD Group. (2011, May 12). Tablet sales poised to surpass eReader: Competing large-screen mobile devices maintain equal market share. Press Release. Retrieved from http://www.npd.com/press/releases/press_110512.html

Norton, D. W. (2000, February/March). Technical communication as business strategy: How changes in discursive patterns affect the value of technical communication in cross-functional team settings. *Technical Communication, 89.*

Parfeni, L. (2011, January 24). Twitter to Make $150 Million in 2011, Triple Its 2010 Revenue. Softpedia. Retrieved from http://news.softpedia.com/news/Twitter-to-Make-150-Million-in-2011-Triple-Its-2010-Revenue-180129.shtml

Patry, W. F. (1985). *The fair use privilege in copyright law.* Washington, DC: Bureau of National Affairs.

Petroski, H. (1996). *Invention by design.* Cambridge, MA: Harvard University Press.

Physicians' Desk Reference (60th ed.) (2006). Montvale, NJ: Thomson.

Plain English Network. (2008, September). Testing your documents. Retrieved from www.plainlanguage.gov/howto/guidelines/FederalPLGuidelines/control.cfm

Public Safety Canada. (2007). Working Together to Combat Organized Crime: A Public Report on Actions under the *National Agenda to Combat Organized Crime* (2006). Cat. No. PS4-3/2006. Ottawa: Author. Retrieved from http://epe.lac-bac.gc.ca/100/200/301/public_safety-securite_publique/working_together_combat-e/PS4-3-2006E.pdf

Radford, G. P., & Goldstein, S. Z. (2002). The role of research methods in corporate communication. *Corporate Communications, 7*(4), 252–256.

Rivera, C. T. (2001). Putting your best presentation forward. *Office Solutions, 18*(7), 34–35. Research Library database. (Document ID: 245455271).

Rominger, C. L. (2010). Website Content Tips: 6 Ways to Grab Readers' Attention. Business Group LLC. Retrieved from http://www.b2bcommunications.com/b2b-resources/b2b-marketing-articles/web-content-tips/

Rosenau, L. (2000, March). Working knowledge: Electricity meters. *Scientific American, 108.*

Rosenfeld, L., & Morville, P. (1998). *Information architecture for the World Wide Web.* Cambridge, MA: O'Reilly.

Rubin, J. (1994). *Handbook of usability testing: How to plan, design, and conduct effective tests.* New York: Wiley.

Ruggiero, V. R. (1998). *The art of thinking: A guide to critical and creative thought* (5th ed.). New York: Longman.

Ryan-Flynn, M. S. (2009). Technical writers. In *The top 100: The fastest-growing careers in the 21st century.* New York: Ferguson, 364.

Seven Things You Should Know About . . . Wikipedia. (2007, June). *Educause Learning Initiative.* Retrieved from http://net.educause.edu/ir/library/pdf/ELI7026.pdf, 2.

Shackelford, R., & Griffis, K. (2007). Teach your students the power of PowerPoint. *Tech Directions, 66*(6), 19–21. ABI/INFORM Global database. (Document ID: 1215410211).

Sinh, C. (2009). *The Facebook Era: Tapping Online Social Networks to Build Better Products.* Upper Saddle River, NJ: Prentice Hall, 3.

Smith, Mike. 20 Do's and Don'ts of Effective Typography. Web Design Ledger. 19 Nov 2009. Retrieved from http://webdesignledger.com/tips/20-dos-and-donts-of-effective-web-typography

Society for Technical Communication. (2011). www.stc.org/education/academic-database

Sophos. (2010). Social Networking. *Sophos Security Threat Report: 2010.* 3. Retrieved from http://www.sophos.com/sophos/docs/eng/papers/sophos-security-threat-report-jan-2010-wpna.pdf

Statistics Canada. (2010a). E-Commerce: Shopping on the Internet. Statistics Canada 27-Sep-2010. Retrieved from http://www.statcan.gc.ca/daily-quotidien/100927/dq100927a-eng.htm

Statistics Canada. (2010b). The output of educational institutions and the impact of learning. Education Indicators in Canada: An International Perspective 2010. Retrieved from http://www.statcan.gc.ca/pub/81-604-x/2010001/ch/cha-eng.htm

Statistics Canada (2009). Internet Use by Individuals, by Type of Activity. Retrieved from http://www40.statcan.gc.ca/l01/cst01/comm29a-eng.htm

Stoddart, J. 2007. *Annual Report to Parliament 2007. Report on the* Personal Information Protection and Electronic Documents Act. Retrieved from www.privcom.gc.ca/information/ar/200708/2007_pipeda_e.asp

Strong, W. S. (1993). *The copyright book: A practical guide.* Cambridge, MA: MIT Press.

Thomas, K. (2011, March 11). Are fraud concerns keeping Canadians wary of shopping online? *Techvibes.* Retrieved from http://www.techvibes.com/blog/are-fraud-concerns-keeping-canadians-wary-of-shopping-online-2011-03-01

Tractinsky, N., & Meyer, J. (1999, September). Chartjunk or goldgraph? Effects of presentation objectives and content desirability on information presentation. *MIS Quarterly, 23*(3), 397–420.

Tufte, E. R. (1990). *Envisioning information.* Cheshire, CT: Graphics Press.

Unger, S. H. (1982). *Controlling technology: Ethics and the responsible engineer.* New York: Holt, Rinehart and Winston.

VanderMey, R., Meyer, V., Van Rys, J., & Sebrenek, P. (2009). Writing and Designing for the Web. In *The College Writer Brief: A Guide to Thinking, Writing, and Researching.* Boston: Houghton Mifflin Company: 404.

Varchaver, N. (2003, February 17). The perils of e-mail. *Fortune,* 96–102.

Walker, J. R., & Ruszkiewicz, J. (2000). *Writing@online.edu., 1st Ed.,* © 2000. Reprinted and Electronically reproduced by permission of Pearson Education, Inc., Upper Saddle River, New Jersey.

Wickens, C. D. (1992). *Engineering psychology and human performance* (2nd ed.). New York: HarperCollins.

Wilford, J. N. (1999, April 6). When no one read, who started to write? *New York Times,* pp. D1, D2.

Yoos, G. (1979). A revision of the concept of ethical appeal. *Philosophy and Rhetoric, 12*(4), 41–58.

Zambelli, G. R. Sr. (1999, July). Aerial fireworks. *Scientific American,* 108

Index

A

abbreviations, 114–115, 356
abstract, 33, 95–96, 328
access points, 291
Access to Information Act, 83, 96
accessibility
   checklist, 17
   as key principle, 5
   as societal dimensions, 16
   of visual communication,
     151–152
   of websites, 108
accuracy
   defined, 5
   as ethical issue, 191
   in long reports, 329
   of online source, 91
   in visual communication, 175
*ACS Style Guide for Authors and
   Editors, The*, 384
action plans, 255
action verbs, 284, 330
active voice, 63–64, 280, 289
addressing of letters, 232–233, 236
adequate content of paragraph, 53
Adobe products, 144, 171
adverbs, 60, 349
affect/ effect, 350
AIP Style Guide, 384
all caps, 221

almanacs, 94
Amazon.ca, 208, 210
American Psychological Association
   (APA). *see* APA documentation
   style
among/ between, 350
APA documentation style, 360,
   373–384
   index to sample entries, 375
   introduced, 373
   parenthetical references, 374
   reference entries, 375–384
   references list, 384
apostrophe, 344
appeal, 299
appearance of website, 108
appendixes, 328
Apple, 115
appositives, 344
area graph, 155
art, copyright-free, 205
as if/ like, 350
assembly instructions, 282
asynchronicity, 111
attachments, 111, 220
attention line, 235
audience
   see also audience and purpose
     analysis
   adapting to, 269

analyzing,   26–29

attention, keeping,   259

as a community,   22

defined,   22

diverse,   104–105

focus on,   6

impatient readers,   104

inducing to act,   339

level of knowledge,   24–26, 31, 33, 45

mixed,   32

needs of,   24, 50–51, 104–105, 338

nonlinear readers,   104

not passive,   33

primary,   29

and purpose,   24–26

secondary,   29

technical expertise,   289, 313

types of,   34–35

viewing of page,   126–128

and visuals,   152–153

audience analysis worksheet,   30–31

audience and purpose analysis

audience analysis,   26–29

audience analysis worksheet, 30–31

audience and purpose interview, 30–31

brief instructions,   280–282

checklist,   35–36

colour, for visual communication, 172

context analysis,   30

definitions and descriptions,   305

discourse communities,   22

email,   218

importance of,   40

letters,   228–229

long reports,   317

manuals,   290–291, 293

memos,   224–225

needs of audience,   24

non-passive audience,   33

presentations,   254–255, 267

procedures,   285

proposals,   331

purpose,   24–26

purpose analysis,   29

résumés,   238

short reports,   246

specifications,   274–279

technical marketing material, 296

tools for enhancing,   32

typical audiences and purposes, 34–35

using information from,   32–33

and visual effectiveness,   126

authoritative decision-making style, 15

B

background

definitions and descriptions, 312–313

of proposal,   337

background of decision makers,   299

band graph,   155

bar graphs,   155–160

basic audience analysis,   26–29

benefits, focus on,   338, 339

between/ among,   350

bias, personal,   97

biased language,   70

bibliographic databases, 92

Bibliographic Retrieval Services
    (BRS), 92–93

bibliographies, 93

bibliography programs, 89

block pattern, 319

blogs
    as communication type, 9
    for research, 85
    for teamwork, 15
    as workplace tool, 116

body
    of email message, 220
    of letter, 233
    long reports, 321
    of memo, 227
    of presentations, 256–257
    of short reports, 249

body language, 260

boldface, 138

book indexes, 94–95

bookmarks, 89

books, documentation of
    APA style, 376–378
    CSE style, 386
    IEEE style, 388
    MLA style, 364–365

Boolean operators, 90

bottom-up medium, 87

brief definitions, 305–312

brief descriptions, 305–312

brief instructions, 280–284
    assembly instructions, 282
    audience and purpose analysis,
        280–282
    checklist for, 295–296
    components of, 282–283

quick reference brochures or cards,
    282
    types of, 282
    usability considerations, 283–284
    wordless instructions, 282

brief reports. *see* short reports

brochures
    example of, 23
    grid structure, 130
    quick reference, 281, 282
    technical, 22, 23, 297, 300, 301

browsers, 108

budget and costs, 338

bulleted lists, 132, 249, 345–347,
    354

bulletin boards, 85

C

call for proposals (CFPs), 8

Canadian Blood Services, 181

Canadian Centre for Occupational
    Health and Safety (CCOHS),
    284

*Canadian Charter of Rights and
    Freedom*, 206

Canadian Copyright Act, 201

Canadian Copyright Licensing
    Agency, 206

Canadian Intellectual Property
    Office, 206

Canadian Internet Policy and Public
    Interest Clinic (CIPPIC), 206

Canadian Red Cross Society (CRCS),
    181–186

Canadian Standards Association
    Model Code for the Protection
    of Personal Information, 206

capitalization, 357

career objectives, 241

C.A.R.S. checklist, 90–91

Cascading Style Sheets (CSS),
    146–147

categorical imperative, 182

category of product, 298

causal reports, 317

cause and effect
    claims, 97
    paragraphs, 55
    reports, 317

cautions, 288

CD-ROMs. *see* compact discs

chapters, 293

charts, 160–163
    flowcharts, 163
    Gantt, 162–163
    organization, 163
    pie, 160–161
    software, 163
    tree, 163

chronological order, 51, 52–54

chronological sequence, 316

chunking, 74, 104

circular definitions, 315

citation. *see* documentation of
        sources

citation indexes, 95

clarity, 5, 7

classification of term, 315

classification paragraphs, 55–56

clauses, 58–61

clichés, 68–69

clip art, 201, 214

close of letter, 233–235

closed-ended questions, 82

coherence, 52

cold calls, 296

colon, 343, 346

colour
    as cultural consideration, 176
    technical marketing material,
        299
    for visual communication,
        172–174, 264

Columbia Guide to Online Style
    (2006) (Walker and Taylor),
    361

Columbia space shuttle, 262–263

combined organization, 242

comma, 344

comma splices, 62

common knowledge, 360

communication
    defined, 4
    digital. *see* digital communication
    non-verbal communication. *see*
        non-verbal communication
    presentation skills. *see*
        presentations
    product-oriented. *see* product-
        oriented communication
    situations, 216
    technical. *see* technical
        communication
    written. *see* written
        communication

community
    discourse, 22
    and technical communication,
        22

community discussion groups, 85

compact discs
    and copyright, 205–206
    document layout, 144
    online documentation, 109
    as a research tool, 92

company ownership, 202

comparative reports,   319

compare and contrast,   319

compare and contrast paragraphs,
55

comparisons,   315–316

complete sentences,   62

completeness,   5

complex communication
definitions and descriptions,
305–316
long reports,   316–330
proposals,   331–339

complex sentences,   58

complex to simple order,   51

complimentary close,   233–235

component parts,   277

compound sentences,   57–58

compound-complex sentences,
58–61

computer analysis,   98

computer projection software,   261

computer screens,   128

computer-supported co-operative
work (CSCW) software,   13

concluding sentence,   52, 53

conclusion
long reports,   321
to presentations,   257, 259, 267

concreteness,   5

Conference Board of Canada's
Employability Skills 2000+,
11, 50

conference calls,   15

confidence,   269

Conflict Catcher,   294–295

conjunctions
coordinating,   344, 349, 357
subordinating,   348

conjunctive adverbs,   349

consequences,   183

consultative decision-making style,
15

contact information,   241

context
analyzing,   30
audience analysis worksheet,
30–31
checklist,   36

context-sensitive information,   32,
45, 110, 290

continually/ continuously,   350

contractions,   344

control group,   44

convincing language,   339

coordinating conjunction,   344,
349, 357

copyright
CD-ROMs,   205–206
checklist,   212
company ownership,   202
copyright-free art,   205
electronic technologies,   203–206
email,   205
establishing,   199
as ethical issue,   184
fair-use doctrine,   201
intellectual property,   198–199
internet,   204
multimedia,   205–206
need to understand,   197
overview of,   197–202
and patent law,   198
and photocopiers,   203
and plagiarism,   198
restrictions on use of material,
199–201
rights of copyright holder,   199
and scanners,   204
source documentation,   203

trademark law,   199

visual communication and,   175

copyright-free art,   205

corporate style guides,   32

costs,   338

Council of Science Editors (CSE). *see* CSE documentation style

course of action,   320

cover letter,   229

credibility

of online source,   91

in presentations,   260, 266

critical thinking,   80

CSE documentation style,   384–387

index to sample entries,   385

introduced,   384

numbered citations,   385

reference entries,   385–387

references,   385

CSE references entries

for books,   386

index to,   385

for periodicals,   386–387

cultural considerations,   173, 175–176, 187

cut and paste,   89

cutaway diagrams,   167

D

danger, warning of,   288

dangling modifiers,   67, 352–353

dashes,   345

Data Privacy Act (EU),   211

databases

library databases,   87

online retrieval services,   92–93

date, format of,   232

decision-making styles,   15

deductive reasoning,   267

definition paragraphs,   56

definitions and descriptions,   305–316

audience and purpose analysis,   305

brief,   305–312

checklist,   315–316

circular definitions,   315

comparisons and examples,   315–316

defined,   305

etymology,   312

expanded definitions,   312–313

history and background,   312

interrelatedness of,   305

language,   314

length and placement,   313

operating principle,   313

organizational sequence,   315–316

technicality, level of,   313

types of,   305–312

usability considerations,   313–315

visuals,   313

word choice,   315

Deloitte Canada,   116

description, in specifications,   277

description paragraphs,   56

descriptions,   305

see also definitions and descriptions

design

see also digital design; document layout

usability and,   42–45

detail, level of,   314

Developing a Departmental Style Guide (Weber),   146

deviation bar graph,   160

diagrams,   165–167, 283, 294

DIALOG,   90, 92–93

dictionaries,   94

differentiation of term,   315

Digg,   118

digital communication

   see also internet

   blogs,   116

   checklist,   121

   described,   103

   designing information. *see* digital
     design

   email. *see* email

   instant messaging (IM),   116–117

   presentation software,   120

   smartphones,   115, 116

   social media. *see* social media

   tablet PC,   115–116

   telecommuting,   120

   virtual teams,   120

digital design,   103–111, 142–144

   see also document layout

   appearance,   108

   audience needs,   104–105

   described,   103

   design issues,   105–108

   electronic documents,   142–144

   hypertext markup language
     (HTML),   105

   interface design,   110–111

   line length,   108

   online documentation,   110

   organization,   105–107

   technical issues,   108–109

   typography,   107

   writing issues,   103–105

Digital Object Identifier (DOI),   382

digital research. *see* internet research

digital technology

   see also digital communication

   for teamwork,   13–15

direct organization,   236

direct sentences,   339

directories,   94

discipline-specific websites,   90

discourse communities,   22

disinterested/ uninterested,   350

display booths,   296

distribution and enclosure notations,
    227, 235

diverse audience,   104–105

division paragraphs,   57

document genre,   33

document layout

   checklist,   147

   chunk information,   74

   compact discs (CDs),   144

   electronic documents,   142–144

   electronic pages,   128

   electronic searching,   140

   formatting,   128–136

   grid structure,   130

   headings,   74–75, 133–135, 142

   importance of,   126

   indexes,   139–140

   lists,   132

   margins,   75, 131

   online help,   143–144

   other media,   144

   overview,   72

   page design,   72

   paragraphs,   131

   PDF files,   144

   readers' view of page,   126–128

   running heads and feet,   140

   search options,   139–140

   for short reports,   249

   style sheets and guides,   145–146

style tools, 146–147
table of contents, 139–140
typography, 136–137, 142
and usability, 72–74
visual effectiveness, 126–128
webpages, 142
white space, 72, 130–131, 343
documentation
    see also manuals
    audience and purpose analysis,
        290–291
    context-sensitive, 45
    described, 290
    online, 109–110
    and privacy, 212
documentation of sources
    APA style, 373–384
    CSE style, 384–387
    IEEE style, 387–393
    importance of, 203
    methodology, 360–361
    MLA style, 361–373
    what to document, 359–360
download files, 89, 90

E

editing
    active voice, 63–64
    biased language, 70
    clichés, 68–69
    complete sentences, 62
    grammar and spelling checkers,
        70
    for grammar and style, 61–71
    idiomatic expressions, 71
    international issues, 70–71
    jargon, 68
    modifiers, 67–68
    nominalizations, 64–65

nouns, unpacking, 65
parallel structure, 68
point of view of user, 70
pronoun references, 66
punctuation, 61–62
run-on sentences, 62–63
for translation, 70–71
word choice, 65
wordy phrases, 66
editor, 10
education
    importance of, 11
    online, 120
    in résumés, 241
effect/ affect, 350
electronic note cards, 89
electronic pages
    documentation. *see* electronic
        sources, documentation of
    layout and design, 128
    research. *see* internet research
    surveys, 82
    webpages. see webpages
electronic paper trail, 111
electronic résumés, 243
electronic searching, 140
electronic sources, documentation of
    APA style, 381–384
    IEEE style, 388
    MLA style, 369–373
electronic surveys, 82
electronic technologies. *see* digital
        communication; technology
electronic text, 128
email, 111–114, 218–221
    asynchronicity, 111
    attachments, 111, 220
    audience and purpose analysis,
        218

checklist,   221–224

as communication type,   9

components of,   219–220

and copyright,   205

electronic paper trail,   111

emoticons,   114–115, 220, 221

ethical and legal issues,   114, 189

features of,   111

flaming,   113, 221

forwarding,   111

hierarchy,   113

issues in use of,   112–113

lists,   86

netiquette,   113, 220

oral or written,   112

speed and reach,   112

style,   220

for teamwork,   13

types of,   218–219

usability considerations,   220–221

usable message,   114

usefulness of,   218

workplace,   220, 222, 223

email lists,   86

embedded lists,   344

emoticons,   114–115, 220, 221

emotion,   267

employability skills,   11

enclosure notations,   227, 235

encyclopedias,   93

end matter,   321

End of Ignorance: Multiplying Our Human Potential, The (Mighton),   273

engineers, as audience,   34

ENVIROLINE,   93

errors,   75

ethical issues,   179–192

  categorical imperative,   182

checklist,   191–193

choices,   182–183

communication types affected by,   188–191

consequences,   183

copyright,   184

cultural considerations,   187

in email,   114, 189

ethical relativism,   182

exaggeration,   187

examples of,   180–182

and graphics,   188

groupthink,   186

guidelines,   192

ideals,   183

in instructions,   190

introduced,   17, 180

legal issues versus,   183–185

in memos,   189

obligations,   182–183

oral presentations,   190–191

persuasive presentations,   266

plagiarism,   184–185

privacy,   185

proposals,   190

reasonable criteria,   182

in reports,   190

responding to,   191

and social pressure,   185–186

suppressing knowledge,   187

tainted blood scandal,   181

utilitarianism,   182

in visual communication,   174–175

Walkerton tragedy,   180–181

webpages,   188

workplace pressures,   186

ethical relativism,   182

etymology,   312

European Union,   206, 211
evaluation
    of evidence,   97
    of information,   96–98
    interpret findings,   97
    of source. *see* source evaluation
    weaknesses, check for,   97
evidence,   97
exaggeration,   187
examples,   315–316
examples in document,   32–33
executive summary,   328
exemplification paragraphs,   55
expanded definitions,   312–313
expanded descriptions,   312–313
experiments,   84
exploded diagrams,   166

F

Facebook,   117, 119–120, 242
facial expression,   268
facts,   266
factual databases,   92
fairness,   175
fair-use doctrine,   201
FAQs,   298
farther/ further,   350
faulty modification,   352–353
feasibility reports,   320
features of product,   298
feedback
    in digital design,   105
    mechanisms for,   46
fewer/ less,   350
flaming,   113, 221
flowcharts,   163
focus groups,   32, 44
follow-up information,   283

fonts. *see* typography
formality,   221
format
    see also document layout
    decision on,   32
    layered,   290
    standard,   279
format errors,   75
Foursquare,   118
fragments,   62, 347–348
frequently asked questions (FAQs),
        298
front matter,   321
full-text databases,   92
functional organization,   242
functional sequence,   316
functional specs,   277
further/ farther,   350
fused sentence,   62

G

Gantt chart,   163
gender
    of audience,   31–32
    bias in language,   70
    in email,   113
general to specific order,   51
global privacy issues,   210–211
glossary,   328
goal,   329
Google Scholar,   91
Gould, Stephen J.,   58–59
Government of Canada Publications,
        96
*Government of Canada Publications
        and Reports,*   96
government publications,   96

government research sites,   85

government standards,   277

grammar

see also punctuation; sentences

adverbs,   60, 349

appositives,   344

common errors,   75

conjunctions,   344, 348, 349, 357

editing for,   61–71

idiomatic expressions,   71

in memos,   227

modifiers,   67–68, 352–353

nominalizations,   64–65

parallel structure,   60, 68, 135,
    353–354

possessives,   344

pronoun–antecedent agreement,
    352

subject–verb agreement,
    351–352

transitions,   54–59, 354–355

usage, word,   350

verbs,   64, 315, 330, 348

grammar checkers,   70

graphics. *see* visual communication

graphics software,   171

graphs,   155–160

area,   155

band,   155

bar,   155–160

ethical issues,   188

line,   155

grid structure,   130

groupthink,   186

Guide to PowerPoint (Paradi),   264

guides to literature,   94

H

handbooks,   94

handouts,   263

headers, email,   219

headings

in letters,   232

levels of,   133–134

in long reports,   330

in memos,   225

online help screen,   144

parallel structure,   135

questions in,   74–75, 135

in short reports,   249, 250

size,   134

and usability,   74–75

using,   133–136

visual consistency,   135

webpage design,   142

Health Canada,   85, 277

help, online,   109, 143–144

Hewlett-Packard,   13

hierarchy

in email,   113

visual,   127–128

history,   312

history of technical communication,
    4

honesty,   338

host server,   219

hypertext format,   104

hypertext links,   220, 313

hypertext markup language (HTML),
    105, 144, 277

hyphenation,   355

I

IBM list of quality characteristics, 5
icons, 167–168
ideals, 183
idiomatic expressions, 71
IEEE documentation style, 361
    index to sample entries, 388
    introduced, 387
    sample entries, 387–393
IEEE Editorial Style Manual, 361
illustrations, 165–168, 294
impatient readers, 104
imperative voice, 284
imply/ infer, 350
independent clauses, 58–61
indexes
    generating, 139–140
    for research, 94–95
indirect organization, 236
inductive reasoning, 267
industry standards, 277
infer/ imply, 350
infinitive, 347
information
    accessibility of, 5
    accurate, 329
    and audience, 33
    bottom-up medium, 87
    chunking, 74, 104
    context-sensitive, 290
    evaluating and interpreting,
        96–98
    managing, 89–90
    relevance of, 6–7
    sufficient, 329
    summarizing, 98
    top-down, 88
    usability of, 5–6

information developer, 10
information plan, 42, 43
information retrieval services, 90,
    92–93
informative presentations, 255
initials, 227
inquiry letter, 231
inside address, 232–233
instant messaging (IM), 15,
    116–117
Institute of Electrical and Electronics
    Engineers (IEEE), 274, 275,
    277
    see also IEEE documentation style
instructional developer, 10
instructions
    see also brief instructions
    assembly, 282
    as communication type, 7–8
    ethical issues, 190
    long, 286
    step-by-step, 282
    wordless, 282
intellectual property, 198–199
interests, personal, 241
interface design, 110–111
internal coherence, 53
international issues, 32, 70–71
International Organization for
    Standardization (ISO), 40,
    167–168, 176
internet
    see also internet research; social
        media; webpages
    browsers, 108
    bulletin boards, 85
    and copyright, 204–205
    ethical issues, 188
    hypertext format, 104

hypertext markup language
(HTML),   105
online documentation,   109–110
and privacy,   208
résumé services,   242
search engines,   140
shopping online,   208–210
specifications,   277
internet research,   84–93
bibliography programs,   89
blogs,   85
bookmarking system,   89
Boolean operators,   90
bulletin boards,   85
C.A.R.S. checklist,   90–91
community discussion groups,
85
described,   84
email lists,   86
evaluation of sources,   87–89
Google Scholar,   91
government sites,   85
information management,   89–90
information retrieval services,   90
keywords,   90
library catalogues,   93
library databases,   87
online magazines,   84
online news sites,   84
online retrieval services,   92–93
online videos,   87
other websites,   87
RSS feeds,   89
wikis,   85–86
interviews
audience and purpose analysis,
30–32
for research,   80–81
intranet,   10

introduction
to long reports,   320–321
to presentations,   256, 259, 267
in specifications,   277
italics,   137–138, 345

J

jargon,   68
justified text,   131

K

Kant, Immanuel,   182
keywords,   90
knowledge, suppressing,   187
Koebel brothers,   180–181
Krever commission,   181

L

language
see also voice
and audience knowledge,   32–33
biased,   70
body language. *see* non-verbal
communication
clear and concise,   314
clichés,   68–69
convincing,   339
and discourse communities,   22
dynamic,   299
idiomatic expressions,   71
international issues,   70–71
jargon,   68
in letters,   237
puffed-up,   237
technicality, appropriate level of,
313

word choice,   33, 65

large colour documents,   298

Law Society of Upper Canada,   203

lawyers, as audience,   34, 35

lay/ lie,   350

layered format,   290

layout of room,   269

leader lines,   326

legal issues

   copyright,   184

   email,   114

   versus ethical issues,   183–185

   patent law,   198

   plagiarism,   184–185

   privacy,   185, 206–208

   trademark law,   199

length

   audience and,   32–33

   of definition and description,
     313

   of email message,   220

   of memo,   227

less/ fewer,   350

letters,   225–238

   addressing,   232–233, 236

   attention line,   235

   audience and purpose analysis,
     228

   checklist,   238

   complimentary close,   233–235

   components of,   232–235

   cover letter,   229

   inquiry letter,   231

   language,   237

   main point,   237

   necessary information,   237

   as technical marketing material,
     298

   transmittal,   229, 321

   types of,   229–231

   usability considerations,   236–237

   use of,   225–228

   word-processing templates,   231

levels of headings,   133–134

library catalogues,   93

library databases,   87

lie/ lay,   350

like/ as if,   350

limitations of findings,   97

line graph,   150, 154, 155, 157

line length,   108

LinkedIn,   242

linking words,   59

list of references,   328–329

lists

   bulleted,   132, 249, 345–347, 354

   embedded,   345

   numbered,   132, 249, 345–346,
     354

   in paragraphs,   132

   parallel structure in,   347, 354

   of tables and figures,   326

   vertical,   345–347

literature guides,   94

long instructions,   286, 287

   see also procedures

long reports,   316–330

   audience and purpose analysis,
     317

   causal reports,   317

   checklist for,   330

   comparative reports,   319

   feasibility reports,   320

   front matter and end matter,
     321–329

   general model for,   320–321

types of, 317–320
usability considerations, 329–330
use of, 316–317

M

magazines, online, 84
main point, 237, 259
managers, as audience, 34, 290
Manual of Style (AMA), 384
manuals, 290–296
    audience and purpose analysis,
        290–291, 293
    checklist, 295–296
    as communication type, 7–8
    components of, 291–293
    described, 290
    medium, 293
    types of, 291
    usability considerations, 293–295
maps, 168, 170
margins, 75, 108, 131
marketing material. *see* technical
        marketing material
marketing surveys, 32
materials, 277
mechanical errors, 75
mechanics
    abbreviations, 356
    capitalization, 357
    hyphenation, 356
    mechanics, 355–358
    numbers, use of, 357–358
    spelling, 358
medical imaging, 171
medium, 293, 370–373
MEDLINE, 93
meeting minutes, 225, 246

meetings, 264–266
memorandum, 225
memorization, 269
memos, 224–225
    audience and purpose analysis,
        224
    brief report, 225
    checklist, 250–251
    as communication type, 9, 224
    components of, 225–227
    ethical issues, 189
    meeting minutes, 225
    transmittal, 225
    types of, 225
    usability considerations, 225–227
message ID number, 219
Mighton, John, 273
Mills, John Stuart, 182
minutes of meetings, 225, 246
misplaced modifiers, 67–68, 353
mixed audiences, 32
MLA documentation style, 361–373
    index to sample entries, 364
    introduced, 361
    parenthetical references, 361–362
    works cited entries, 363–373
    works cited page, 373
*MLA Handbook for Writers of
        Research Papers*, 361
Modern Language Association
        (MLA). *see* MLA
        documentation style
modifiers
    ambiguous, 67–68
    dangling, 67, 352–353
    faulty modification, 352–353
    misplaced, 67–68, 353
multiline graph, 155, 157

multimedia,   205–206
multiple-band graph,   155, 158
multiple-bar graph,   158, 159

N

NASA,   171, 262–263
National Resources Canada,   153
negation,   315
nervousness,   259, 269
netiquette,   113, 220
network administrators,   290–291
news sites, online,   84
newsletters,   130
nominalizations,   64–65
nonlinear readers,   104
non-verbal communication,   268
    body language,   260
    facial expression,   268
    posture,   268
    tone of voice,   268
Norton, David W.,   6
nouns
    nominalizations,   64–65
    unpacking,   65
NPD Group,   116
numbered citations. *see* CSE
    documentation style
numbered lists,   132, 249, 345–346,
    354
numbers,   357–358

O

objections,   339
objective of proposal,   337
obligations,   182–183
observation,   83–84

Office of the Privacy Commissioner,
    206
Online Computer Library Center
    (OCLC),   92
online documentation,   109–110
online documentation specialist,   10
online education,   120
online help,   109, 143–144
online magazines,   83–84
online news sites,   83–84
online résumé services,   242
online retrieval services,   92–93
online shopping,   208–210
online videos,   87
on-site visits,   296
open-ended questions,   82
operating principle,   313
opposing reasons,   320
oral presentations. *see* presentations
organization
    for accessible communication,   5
    block pattern,   319
    combined,   242
    of definitions and descriptions,
        315–316
    direct,   236
    functional,   242
    indirect,   236
    of letters,   236
    of meetings,   265
    methods of,   51
    name, on memo,   225
    point-by-point pattern,   319
    of presentations,   258
    procedures,   289
    of résumés,   241–242
    reverse chronological,   242
    of website,   105–107
organization charts,   163

organizational records,   83
organizational sequence,   316
organizational style guides,   146
orphans,   132
outline
   creation of,   51
   for meetings,   265
   of presentation,   257
   proposals,   332
   sentence outline,   51, 52
   topic outline,   51, 52
overhead transparencies,   263
overview
   creation of,   72
   example of book overview,   73
   of instruction task,   282
   in manuals,   291
   in procedures,   286

P

page design,   72, 126
       see also document layout
paper trail,   111
Paradi, Dave,   264
paragraphs
   adequate content,   53
   cause and effect,   55
   chronological order,   52–54
   classification,   55–56
   coherence with transition devices,
      54–59
   compare and contrast,   55
   definition,   56
   description,   56
   division,   57
   exemplification,   55
   internal coherence,   53
   lists,   132

orphans and widows,   132
   parts of,   52
   process,   56
   structure of,   52–53
   tailoring to purpose,   131
   topic sentence,   52–53
   types of,   52–57
   unity,   53
   writing clear,   52–57
parallel structure,   353–354
   editing for,   68
   in headings,   135
   in lists,   347, 354
   in sentences,   60, 353–354
paraphrasing,   359
parentheses,   345
parenthetical references
   APA style,   374
   MLA style,   361–362
parts of an object,   51
passive voice,   63–64
patent indexes,   95
patent law,   198
Patriot Act (U.S.),   207–208
PayPal,   209
PDF files,   144
percent/ percentage,   350
period,   343
periodical indexes,   95
periodicals, documentation of
   APA style,   378–379
   CSE style,   386–387
   IEEE style,   388
   MLA style,   365–367
personal data,   241
*Personal Information Protection and
      Electronic Documents Act
      (PIPEDA)*,   206–207, 211
personal interests,   241

personal observation,   83–84

persuasive presentations,   255,
      266–267

  emotion,   267

  ethics,   266

  reason,   267

phone surveys,   82

photocopiers,   203

photographs,   168

photography software,   171

physical location

  for manuals, usability of,   293

  for procedures, usability of,   289

pictograms,   163, 164

pie chart,   160–161

PIPEDA,   206–207, 211

placement,   313

plagiarism,   184–185, 198, 359

planning

  see also research

  audience and purpose analysis,
      40

  information plan,   42

  meetings,   265

  for next version,   46

  presentations,   258

  task analysis,   40–41

  and usability,   40–42

planning proposal,   332, 333

podcasts,   9

point of view,   70, 294

point-by-point pattern,   319

positive sentences,   59

possessives,   344

post-secondary education,   11

posture,   268

presentation software,   120, 171,
      261–263

presentation types,   255–256

  action plans,   255

  informative presentations,   255

  persuasive presentations,   255,
      266–267

  sales presentations,   255–256

  training sessions,   255

presentations

  adapt to audience,   269

  audience and purpose analysis,
      254–255, 267

  audience attention,   259

  checklist,   270

  as communication type,   10

  components of,   256–257

  difficult questions,   260

  effective,   254

  ethical issues,   190–191

  group work,   258

  look and style,   260

  meetings,   264–266

  memorization and practise,   269

  nervousness,   259

  non-verbal communication,   268

  outline for,   257

  planning for,   258

  sequence,   258–259

  skills for effective,   258–260

  time constraints,   257

  types of. *see* presentation types

  usability considerations,   269

  visuals,   261–264

pressure, and ethics,   185–186

primary audience,   29

primary purpose,   24–26, 29

primary research,   80–84

  interviews,   80–81

  personal observation and
      experiments,   83–84

public and organizational records,
83
surveys and questionnaires,
81–83
principle/ principal, 350
print files, 89
privacy, 185
checklist, 212–213
in cyberspace, 208
and documentation, 212
global issues, 210–211
legislation governing, 206–208
need to understand, 197
online privacy statements, 210
overview of, 206
shopping online, 208–210
in the United States, 206,
207–208
and videotapes, 212
privacy statements, 210
problem identification, 329, 339
procedure number, 288–289
procedures, 284–289
audience and purpose analysis,
285
checklist, 295–296
as communication type, 7–8
components of, 286–289
long instructions, 286, 287
standard operating procedures
(SOPs), 285, 286
types of, 285–286
usability considerations, 289
use of, 284–285
warnings and cautions, 288
process paragraphs, 56
product-oriented communication
brief instructions, 280–284

documentation and manuals,
290–296
procedures, 284–289
specifications, 274–280
technical marketing material,
296–299
progress reports, 246, 247
project management, 13–15
project management software, 13,
172
pronoun–antecedent agreement,
351
pronouns
ambiguous, 60, 66
and antecedents, 351
correct use of, 59–60
proofreading, 75–76, 112, 115
proper nouns, 237
proposals, 331–339
audience and purpose analysis,
331, 338
checklist, 339
as communication type, 8–9
components of, 332–338
ethical issues, 190
planning proposal, 332, 333
research proposal, 332, 334–335
sales proposal, 332, 336
solicited versus unsolicited, 331
types of, 331–332
usability considerations, 338–339
use of, 331
ProQuest, 92
protocol analysis, 44
provincial abbreviations, 232
public, as audience, 35
public domain, 198, 201
public records, 83

Publication Manual of the American Psychological Association,   360, 372

punctuation,   343–345
  apostrophe,   344
  appositives,   344
  colon,   343, 346
  comma,   344
  dashes,   345
  errors,   75
  italics,   345
  of list,   132
  parentheses,   345
  period,   343
  proper,   61–62
  quotation marks,   344, 359
  semicolon,   343
  underlining,   345
purpose
  see also audience and purpose analysis
  addressing, in short reports,   250
  analyzing,   29
  audience analysis worksheet,   30–31
  defining,   24–26
  primary,   24–26, 29
  secondary,   24–26, 29

Q

qualitative testing,   44
quantitative testing,   44
questionnaires,   81–83
questions
  closed-ended,   82
  difficult,   260
  frequently asked questions (FAQs),   298
  in headings,   74–75, 135
  for interviews,   81
  open-ended,   82
  in surveys,   81–82
quick reference cards,   8, 282
quick reference guides,   45
quotation marks,   344, 359
quotations,   359–360

R

random sample,   82
readability,   137–138
readers. *see* audience
Really Simple Syndication (RSS),   9
reason,   267
reasonable criteria,   182
reasonableness, of online source,   91
recommendations,   246
redundancies,   59
reference cards, quick,   8, 282
reference information, for contact,   293
reference to other documents,   279
references, in résumés,   241
references entries, APA style
  for books,   376–378
  for electronic sources,   381–384
  index to sample entries,   375
  for other sources,   379–381
  for periodicals,   378–379
references entries, CSE style
  for books,   386
  for periodicals,   386–387
references list,   328–329, 375, 384
relativism,   182
relevance,   6–7, 151–152
reports
  causal,   317

as communication type,   8

comparative,   319

ethical issues,   190

feasibility,   320

long. *see* long reports

short. *see* short reports

request for proposals (RFPs),   8–9

research

   see also internet research

   abstracts,   95–96

   almanacs,   94

   bibliographies,   93

   checklist,   98–99

   compact discs (CD-ROMs),   92

   databases,   87, 92–93

   dictionaries,   94

   directories,   94

   encyclopedias,   93

   evidence, evaluation of,   97

   experiments,   84

   government publications,   96

   handbooks,   94

   hard-copy,   93–96

   indexes,   94–95

   interpret findings,   97

   interviews,   80–81

   library catalogues,   93

   limitations of findings,   97

   literature guides,   94

   organizational records,   83

   personal observation,   83–84

   primary,   80–84

   public records,   83

   questionnaires,   81–83

   for short reports,   249

   source evaluation,   87–89, 90–91,
      96–97

   statistical fallacies,   97

   summarizing information,   98

   surveys,   81–83

   thinking critically about,   80

   for usability,   42

   weaknesses, check for,   97

   workplace research,   84

Research in Motion (RIM),   115, 116

Research Libraries Information
     Network (RLIN),   92

research proposal,   333, 335–336

research writing,   359

résumés,   238–242

   attractiveness of,   238

   audience and purpose analysis,
     238

   career objectives,   241

   checklist,   242

   components of,   241

   electronic,   243

   new types of,   243

   online services,   242

   organization of,   241–242

   personal information,   241

   references,   241

   scannable,   243

   templates,   243

retrieval aids,   279

return address,   232

return path,   219

reverse chronological organization,
     242

revising,   44

revision dates,   288–289

RLIN,   92

room layout,   269

RSS feeds,   89, 116

running heads and feet,   140

run-on sentences,   62–63, 347, 349

S

safety instructions,   25

sales presentations,   255–256

sales proposal,   332, 336

sales representatives, as audience,
      35, 290

salutation,   233

sample,   81

samples

   audience analysis worksheet,
         30–31

   book overview,   73

   brochure, technical,   22

   cover letter,   230

   information plan,   43

   memo,   226

   presentation outline,   257

   project planning form,   16

   résumés,   239, 240

   safety instructions,   25

   specifications,   275, 276, 277–279

   task analysis worksheet,   41

   typefaces,   137

   webpage,   105

   wordless instructions,   283

sans-serif fonts,   136–137

scannable résumés,   243

scanners,   204

*Scientific Style and Format: The CSE
      Manual for Authors, Editors, and
      Publishers*,   361, 384

scientists, as audience,   34

script fonts,   136–137

search engines,   90, 140

search options

   effective,   139–140

   electronic searching,   140

   indexes,   139–140

   running heads and feet,   140

   table of contents,   139–140

secondary audience,   29

secondary purpose,   24–26, 29

semicolon,   342

sentence fragments,   62, 347–348

sentence outline,   51, 52

sentences

   clear,   59–61

   comma splices,   62

   complete,   62

   complex,   58

   compound,   57–58

   compound-complex,   58–61

   concluding,   52, 53

   direct,   339

   errors,   75

   fragments,   62, 347–348

   fused,   62

   parallel structure,   60

   patterns,   60–61

   positive,   59

   run-on,   62–63, 347, 349

   short,   105

   simple,   57–60

   supporting,   52

   topic,   52–53

September 11, 2001,   207

serif fonts,   136

shopping online,   208–210

short reports,   243–251

   audience and purpose analysis,
         246

   checklist,   250–251

   components of,   249

   meeting minutes,   225, 246

   memo format,   225

   progress reports,   246, 247

   purpose of,   243

recommendations,   246
types of,   246
usability considerations,   249–250
signature
electronic,   115
of letter,   233–235
SilverPlatter,   92
simple bar graph,   158
simple instructions,   279, 284
simple line graph,   155, 157
simple sentences,   57–60
simple to complex order,   51
simple words,   65
skills, employability,   11
smartphones,   115, 116
social media,   117–119
caution when using,   119
Digg,   118
Facebook,   117, 119–120
Foursquare,   118
for professional networking,   242
Tumblr,   118
Twitter,   117–118
social pressure,   185–186
societal dimensions of technical
communications,   16–17
Society for Technical
Communication (STC),   11,
199
software
bibliography programs,   89
charts,   163
computer projection software,
261
documentation,   45
failures,   269
functional specs,   277
graphics software,   171
photography software,   171

presentation software,   120, 171,
261–263
project management,   13, 172
spreadsheet software,   171–172
virtual teams,   13–14
for visuals,   171–172
word-processing programs,   172
software charts,   163
software interfaces,   110–111
solicited proposals,   331
solution, realistic,   339
source, documentation of. *see*
documentation of sources
source evaluation
C.A.R.S. method,   90–91
hard-copy,   96–97
internet,   87–89, 90–91
spam,   119
spatial sequence,   316
specific to general order,   51
specifications,   274–280
audience and purpose analysis,
274–279
checklist,   280
components of,   277–279
functional specs,   277
government standards,   277
industry standards,   277
internet specs,   277
in technical marketing material,
298
types of,   277
usability considerations,   279–280
use of,   274
spelling
in emails,   221
in letters,   237
mechanics of,   357
in memos,   227

presentation slides,   269

proper nouns,   237

spelling checkers,   70

spreadsheet software,   171–172

standard file formats,   108

standard format,   279

standard operating procedures
     (SOPs),   8, 285, 286

see also procedures

statistical fallacies,   97

statistics,   339

Statistics Canada,   11, 84, 85, 96,
     158, 208

step-by-step instructions,   282, 288

Stoddart, Jennifer,   207

streaming video,   87

structure

of paragraphs,   52–53

parallel. *see* parallel structure

style

in manuals,   294–295

in memos,   227

in presentations,   260

in workplace email,   220

style guides

corporate,   32

for document layout,   146

for documentation,   360–361

style sheets,   145–146

style tools,   146–147

subject line

of letter,   235

of memo,   227

subject–verb agreement,   351–352

subordinate clauses,   58–61

subordinating conjunctions,   348

support for online source,   91

supporting reasons,   320

supporting sentences,   52

suppressing knowledge,   187

Supreme Court of Canada,   203

surveys

marketing,   32

for research,   81–83

symbols,   167–168

T

table of contents,   139–140, 326

tables,   153–155

tablet PC,   115–116

tainted blood scandal,   181

target population,   81

task analysis,   40–41

task definition,   283

Taylor, Todd,   361

teamwork

described,   13

and groupthink,   186

managing,   13, 14–15

and presentations,   258

tools,   13–14

virtual teams,   1–13

technical communication

see also digital communication

accessibility,   5

characteristics of,   5–7

checklist,   17

defined,   5

employability skills,   11

ethical dimensions of,   17

history of,   4

project management,   13–15

relevance,   6–7

research for. *see* research

societal dimensions of,   16–17

teamwork,   13–15

types of,   7–10

usability,   5–6
uses of,   4
virtual teams,   13–15
in the workplace,   10–12
technical communicators,   10
technical expertise,   289
technical issues,   108–109
technical marketing material,
   296–299
   audience and purpose analysis,
      296
   brochures,   297, 300, 301
   checklist,   299
   components of,   298
   large colour documents,   298
   letters,   298
   types of,   297–298
   usability considerations,   299
   use of,   296
   webpages,   297–298
technical report indexes,   95
technical sales presentations,   256
technical terms,   279
technical understanding,   31, 313
technical writer,   10
technicians, as audience,   34–35
technology
   see also digital communication;
      internet; software
   communicating about,   4
   and copyright,   203–206
   ethical issues,   180
   exaggeration,   187
   failures,   269
   photocopiers,   203
   in presentations,   254, 261–263
   scanners,   204
telecommuting,   120
templates

for résumés,   243
   word-processing,   231
term-class-features method,   312
terms, consistent,   279, 284
testing
   of instructions,   284
   of procedures,   289
   of product,   42–44
   qualitative,   44
   quantitative,   44
text, electronic,   128
thinking critically,   80
time constraints,   257
time of receipt,   219
title page,   321
titles,   282, 286
tone of voice,   268
top-down information,   88
topic outline,   51, 52
topic sentence,   52–53
track changes,   15
trademark law,   199
training sessions,   10, 255
transitional devices,   54–59, 354–355
translation,   70–71
transmittal letter,   229, 321
transmittal memos,   225
tree chart,   163
troubleshooting guides,   45
trustworthiness,   266
truth versus facts,   266
Tumblr,   118
Twitter,   117–118
typography
   checklist,   147
   effective use of,   136–137
   font selection,   136–137
   fonts, combining,   137–138
   fonts for readability,   137–138

in headings, 135
online help, 143–144
webpage design, 107, 142

U

underlining, 345
uniform resource locators (URLs),
  370
uninterested/ disinterested, 350
United States, and privacy, 206,
  207–208
unity of paragraph, 53
unsolicited proposals, 331
usability, 225–227
  audience and purpose analysis,
    40
  in brief instructions, 283–284
  checklist, 46
  context-sensitive documentation,
    45
  defined, 40
  definitions and descriptions,
    313–315
  document layout and, 72–74
  in email messages, 114–221
  importance of, 5
  information plan, development of,
    42
  in letters, 236–237
  in long reports, 329–330
  for manuals, 293–295
  planning next version or release,
    46
  in planning stages, 40–42
  in presentations, 269
  in procedures, 289
  after release of information,
    45–46

research of topic, 42
revising for, 44
in short reports, 249–250
in specifications, 279–280
task analysis, 40–41
and technical marketing material,
  299
testing early versions, 42–44
user feedback, 46
and visual communication,
  151–152
in websites, 109
in writing and design stages,
  42–45
usage errors, 75, 349
user experience engineer, 10
user feedback, 46
user guides, 45
user point of view, 70, 294
user preference documents, 32
utilitarianism, 182

V

verbs
  action, 315, 330
  -ing ending, 348
  nominalizations, 64–65
  subject–verb agreement,
    351–352
vertical lists, 345–347
video logs, 9
videos, 87, 264
videotapes, 212
virtual teams, 13–14, 120
visual aids, 261–264
  computer projection software,
    261
  handouts, 263

overhead transparencies,   263
preparing,   264
presentation software,   261–263
videos,   264
whiteboards,   264
visual communication
see also visual aids; visuals
accessibility,   151–152
checklist,   176
colour,   172, 264
cultural considerations,   173,
   175–176
effectiveness of,   5
and ethics,   174–175
importance of,   151–152
medical imaging,   171
relevance,   151–152
software images,   171
usability,   151–152
visual noise,   137, 172, 174
visualization,   171
web-based images,   171
visual consistency,   135
visual effectiveness,   5, 126–128
visual hierarchy,   127–128
visual noise,   137, 172, 174
visualization,   171
visuals
and audience,   152–153
charts. *see* charts
colour,   172, 264
cut-away diagrams,   167
definitions and descriptions,   313
diagrams,   165–167
exploded diagrams,   166
graphs. *see* graphs
illustrations,   165, 195
long reports,   330

manuals,   294
maps,   168, 170
medical images,   171
photographs,   168
pictograms,   163, 164
in presentations,   261–264
in short reports,   249
software images,   171
symbols and icons,   167–168
tables,   153–155
technical marketing material,
   298, 299
use of,   152
web-based images,   171
wordless instruction,   168
vlogs,   9
voice
active,   63–64, 280, 289
imperative,   284
passive,   63–64
tone of,   268
voting decision-making style,   15

W

Walker, Janice R.,   360
Walkerton tragedy,   180–181
warnings,   288
web designer,   10
web-based images,   171
Weber, Jean Hollis,   146
weblogs. *see* blogs
webpages
as communication type,   10
and copyright,   204–205
designing. *see* digital design
ethical issues,   188
intranet,   10

links to,   220

readers' view of,   128

technical marketing material,
    296, 297–298

well-organized,   105

websites. *see* internet research

white space,   72, 130–131, 343

whiteboards,   264

widows,   132

Wikipedia,   10, 85–86

wikis

as communication type,   9–10

for research,   85–86

for teamwork,   15

word memo,   225

wordless instructions,   168, 282

word-processing programs,   172

word-processing templates,   231

words

choice of,   33, 65, 315

commonly misused,   349

wordy phrases,   66

work experience,   241

workplace

blogs,   116

culture,   32

email,   220, 222, 223

hierarchy,   32

pressures,   186

research,   84

technical communication in,
    10–11

works cited entries, MLA style

for books,   364–365

for electronic sources,   369–373

index to sample entries,   364

medium of publication,   370–373

for other sources,   367–369

page numbering,   370

for periodicals,   365–367

publication dates,   370

uniform resource locators (URLs),
    370

works cited page,   373

works-for-hire doctrine,   202

World Wide Web consortium,   277

writing

see also mechanics

audience needs,   104–105

clear and concise,   330, 338

clearly and correctly,   50–51, 250

issues, in digital design,   103–105

outline, creation of,   51

paragraphs, writing clear,   52–57

point of view,   70, 294

sentences, building clear,   59–61

transitional devices,   54–59

for translation,   70–71

usability and,   43–45

written communication. *see* email;
    letters; memos